Rosemary and Fra
In appreciation
wonderful evening in
from
June and her family and all
members of Waltham Priory Probus.
March 18th 2006

Feeling Better, Doctor?

BILL INMAN

Feeling Better, Doctor?

ISBN 0-9552044-0-2

Published by
Highland Park Productions
Southcroft House
Winchester Road
Botley
Southampton
SO32 2BX

A CIP catalogue record of this book
can be obtained from the British Library.

Design & production co-ordinated by:
The Better Book Company Ltd
Havant
Hampshire
PO9 2XH

Printed in England by 4edge Ltd. www.4edge.co.uk

Cover design by MusicPrint, Chichester

Contents & Synopsis

FOREWORD

by Michael O'Donnell

This book tells the story of a far from ordinary man who has lived a far from ordinary life. It is also a story played out against the background of the most dramatic changes in recorded history in the medicinal treatment and prevention of disease. The most ironic of those changes came just a year before Bill – thanks to a piece of benevolent chicanery that today's straight-laced medical establishment would never countenance – qualified as a doctor. In 1955, a clinical trial in the United States confirmed the arrival of an effective vaccine against poliomyelitis, the disease that had hobbled Bill and threatened to hobble his medical ambition.

By then he had, with characteristic energy, started to fashion a career that would lead him to play a remarkable role, as monitor and restrainer, of the therapeutic revolution that accelerated through the next four decades. The scale of that revolution is taken for granted by a generation that assumes there is a pill for every ill. Yet in 1949 when, unlike Bill, I was able to leave Cambridge to "walk the wards" – we never used the phrase but our elders still did – at St Thomas' Hospital in London, medicines were just one ingredient of treatment, and not necessarily the most important.

Boils were lanced, carbuncles dressed with hot fomentations, painful joints splinted, and duodenal and gastric ulcers were treated with milk dripped down transfusion tubes inserted through patients' noses and threaded down their gullets to deliver the healing fluid to their stomachs. Tuberculosis was treated with aggressive exposure to fresh air on the balconies of sanatoria and, though some people left their GP's surgery with waxed boxes of pills scooped from the jars in the doctor's dispensary, most left with bottles of coloured fluid which, in posher practices, were wrapped in fine paper sealed with a dab of scarlet wax.

Like many of the complex pharmaceuticals that were to follow, those medicines had a powerful placebo effect and patients would often recommend a doctor to a friend because "he gives a good bottle". (In those days only a few GPs were "she"s.) The only effective drugs we could use in common ailments were the sulphonamides that had appeared in the 1930s, the recently discovered penicillin, and the ever reliable aspirin.

Fifty years later nearly all non-surgical treatment was pharmaceutical and patients collected prescriptions from surgeries, often without seeing their GPs, then took them to pharmacists who handed over drugs already packaged by the manufacturers. This "pharmaceutical revolution" offered great benefits but also introduced great hazards. Readers will discover the part Bill played in protecting us from the hazards – a role he sometimes played so heroically that he won the only honour really worth having in our hierarchical society: a warning from a cautious servant of the establishment that he had blown his chance of a knighthood. To which news Bill responded with a characteristic, "Well, bugger me".

The shelves of medical libraries are packed with books that record the long-legged strides taken by medical science and technology during the second half of the twentieth century and most readers will have a passing acquaintance with them. There are fewer guides to the cultural changes that took place in medicine over those fifty years. In this book they flicker shadow-like upon the backcloth while Bill lives his life downstage. Today's readers may need a guide to them.

To those who have yet to reach pensionable age the world that Bill and I entered in the 1950s would come as a nasty cultural shock. Today, when baby-boomers rule the world, the public face of medicine wears an earnest expression. Medicine's lingua franca is a strange tongue imposed by management and described by the journalist Michael Leapman as: "Verbal detritus bred from the half-digested nostrums of the business schools and the self-important hype of the public relations industry". Every NHS hospital has a Mission Statement incorporated in its title, every ward a platitudinous declaration posted at its entrance. A Sheffield paediatric ward boasts: *The philosophy of care in this ward aims to deliver holistic individualised family centred care meeting the needs of both the hospitalised child and their (sic) families.*

I suspect that Harold Shipman murmured similar platitudes to his patients before he killed them just as Prime Ministers and Health Ministers use them to persuade the populace that the NHS is in vigorous health. Unassuaged by platitude, patients have grown increasingly litigious and the most valued doctors in twenty-first century hospitals are spin doctors.

When Bill and I went up to Cambridge, the language doctors used to disguise paucity of thought was not ManagementSpeak but dog-eared Latin. The naming of parts in anatomy books was already being anglicised – in truth, Americanised – but we still used Latin to name diseases and to enclothe prescriptions with a mantle of placebo-enhancing mystery.

Wartime traditions still lingered and affected the way in which medicine was practised. Patients and their doctors took risks, and knew they took risks. People who had lived through a war had learned that survival is a matter of luck and that life is never perfect. When things went wrong people didn't see themselves as victims: they'd had bad luck, drawn the wrong card, or fallen foul of what insurance policies called an Act of God. Grown-ups didn't whinge, they shrugged their shoulders and did the best they could. Soldiering on, they called it.

Patients needed that resilience if only because medicine was still a sporting activity. Richard Gordon had yet to publish *Doctor in the House* but, when he did, we recognized our world. A Cambridge contemporary Bruce Hepburn who, like most of the medical students in my year was an ex-serviceman home from the war, later described how when his daughter went to medical school in the 1970s, the first thing she sent home for was a slide rule; the first thing he'd sent home for was a woolly cover for his number two wood.

Television repeats of old films offer regular reminders of what we looked like: our hair short, our clothes still wartime utility. Most of us wore grey flannels and tweed jackets, often with leather patches on the elbows. Idiosyncrasy in dress strayed no further than an occasional bow tie or a pair of corduroy trousers. I suspect our accents were pretty uniform too, the cut-glass sort we heard each day on the BBC. Working-class accents were acceptable in patients but not in doctors. Nor, as it happened on radio or cinema screen where comic underlings were played by cosy souls like Stanley Holloway or Joyce Grenfell using fractured cut-glass voices designed to let you know they could really talk proper off the screen.

Most medical teachers in 1950 would have been outraged by any suggestion that they should breach the conventions of the social class they were training us to join. So social convention took precedence over education. Sexual intercourse, for instance, was deemed an unsuitable subject for discussion in polite medical society, despite the fact that it was often the only active ingredient in the stories our teachers told one another in the pub. As a result we got no instruction in contraception. When Martin Bax, a student at Guy's, asked a consultant about family planning, as it was then called, he was told: "You'll know more about these things when you are married yourself." And when I asked an obstetrical registrar at St Thomas' if we were going to be taught how to fit a Dutch Cap he told me that, until attitudes in the hospital changed, we'd have to rely on our girlfriends for instruction.

The only information we got about venereal disease – since euphemised, for some tenuous reason, into sexually transmitted disease – came from bawdy stories exchanged in the bar at the students' club. At St Thomas' we had no teaching from the hospital's venereologist and the VD department was always referred to, even on hospital signs, as the "special department". Its unmarked entrance was tucked away so discreetly it's a wonder patients ever found their way there. The only information on offer to us, and indeed to everyone else, was a list of addresses of "VD clinics" posted inside public conveniences by the London County Council. An attempt to advertise them elsewhere had been condemned as an affront to public decency.

Yet, try as she may, Mrs Grundy can never wholly suppress the jauntiness of the human spirit. One evening a music hall performer, who earned his living as a *Siffleur*, entered the "special department" still wearing the clothes he used in his act: white tie, tails, top hat, and white gloves. Doffing his topper to the receptionist, he announced in carefully modulated tones: "I've come in answer to your advertisement in the gentlemen's lavatory in Leicester Square."

In those years medicine was also blighted by professional class distinction. Consultants regarded GPs as their intellectual and technical inferiors: doctors who had failed to cut the mustard in *real* – by which they meant hospital – medicine. A handful of enthusiasts were trying to establish general practice as a specialty of its own but won little more than patronising smiles from the medical establishment.

The prevailing attitude was that real medicine happened in hospitals; those who practised outside the hallowed institutions were ignorant barbarians. True, consultants speaking to GPs on the telephone or happening upon them in a hospital corridor would butter them up because each was a potential referrer of profitable private patients yet, in my student years at St Thomas', I never heard a hospital doctor commend an action taken by a patient's GP. Even when a GP's letter revealed an astute judgement or diagnosis this was read out to us as an entertaining oddity as if a dog trained to bring slippers had, just for once, brought the right pair. And when registrars described someone as a good GP what they meant was that he or she had the makings of a good hospital doctor.

Junior hospital doctors – and they were labelled juniors well into their forties – were so dispirited by low pay, poor prospects of promotion, and the reactionary antics of medicine's ruling elders, they were emigrating in large numbers to North America or Australasia. The hospital service countered the loss of its juniors by importing doctors from the Asian and African Commonwealth. Lured to Britain by the promise of specialist training, these overseas graduates were exploited as cheap pairs of hands. Many received no training. For those who did, the teaching was often perfunctory.

This was the world from which Bill, and his wheelchair, set out on the adventure chronicled in these pages. It was also the world that Bill, like others of his generation, helped to change. That change was fuelled by the honourable features of 1950s medical culture: the post-war altruism that had led to the creation of the NHS and would later fuel Bill's determination to thwart the efforts of the drug industry to influence medical practice and infiltrate medical institutions; the defiance of overweening bureaucracy that led Sir Lionel Whitby and his co-conspirators to "bend the rules" to help Bill graduate from a "one student" medical school; the burning sense of "natural justice" that drove Bill when he retired from the medical skirmishing fields, to take up his well-worn cudgels on behalf of Sally Clark, wrongly imprisoned for nearly four years for the alleged murders of two of her three children.

This rugged campaigner has displayed, in every aspect of his life, a quality we honoured in the 1950s but which is now not mentioned as often as it might be, as if we were ashamed to acknowledge its existence. In the South West of Ireland, where the most recent elements of my DNA were fashioned, the highest accolade a person can bestow upon another is that "he is a dacent man" or "she is a dacent woman".

As you will discover on your journey through this book, Bill is, above all, a decent man. Our 1950s concept of decency, like the Irish one, carried no overtones of compliance or complacency. Indeed, when you reach the final pages I suspect you will agree that their author has earned the accolade that J B Priestley awarded to Margaret McMillan when he described her as "one of those beastly people who are always bringing up awkward subjects and making respectable people feel uncomfortable".

Michael O'Donnell FRCGP
Writer and Broadcaster
Loxhill. April 2005

Acknowledgements

So many friends and colleagues have helped with the preparation of this book that I decided not to attempt to mention them all by name, in case one or two might be omitted by accident. Many are mentioned in the book and a collective 'thank you' to all.

Three, however, are outstanding. Two are professional authors, Betty Beaty and Dr. Michael O'Donnell and the third, my long-suffering wife, June. Betty read my first attempt and steered me towards major restructuring, and she commanded me on no account to 'lose my reader' in the maze of unconnected events that make up the sometimes bizarre and totally fascinating life I have enjoyed. After I had spent nearly half a century writing articles for medical journals, Michael taught me how to write English; how, for example, to avoid adjectives – 'important' is much more convincing than 'very important' – and the need to conduct a 'which hunt'. Michael kindly wrote the foreword to this book. June agonized through innumerable drafts with an eagle eye on my dyslexic spelling and inability (I hasten to say through defective refraction rather than ignorance) to distinguish commas from full stops.

My thanks are also due to Jude Garvey and his staff at The *Better Book* Company.

Finally I shall not miss this opportunity to thank innumerable friends, colleagues and carers who have supported me through rather a lot of adversity over many years and made it possible for me to pack so much enjoyment into my life; a heartfelt thanks to everybody.

Dedication

For June, our daughters Stella, Rosemary
and Charlotte and our grandchildren,
Anthony, Richard, Lara, Arran, Riley, Rufus, Nina,
Mathilda, Zeljka and Mia.

Prologue

Anatomy Viva

A small greyish-white triangular piece of bone about the size of a human hand floated up from the table in front of me. I was sweating and faint. I could not remember ever feeling as ill as this before and could not understand why. The examiner asked me if the human sacrum he was holding came from a male or a female. It was my anatomy viva in Cambridge on Wednesday the 4th of October 1950. He seemed to be moving in and out of focus and swaying slightly, or perhaps I was. He asked, "what sex?" The bone was rather short and quite wide: I knew my bones.

"Female," I replied.

"Good. What age?" He handed me the bone and I examined it carefully. I hesitated, fuddled, but the miasma was lifting slightly and I could see the horizontal lines where the fusion of the segments of the bone was not quite complete.

"Young adult, probably around eighteen." He nodded but said nothing. I had fudged the first couple of questions but I thought I was doing rather better.

We moved to a table where a laboratory technician was lying, stripped to his underpants. This was the test of one's knowledge of 'surface anatomy'. The examiner handed me a skin pencil and asked me to trace the outline of the spleen. There were more questions about the internal relations between the spleen and the other abdominal organs. We moved again past tanks and jars containing dissected human and animal heads, deformed foetuses, genitalia, livers, thick horizontal slices through complete human bodies and other human bric-a-brac, stopping from time to time to point to one of the 'pots' and ask questions about its contents.

"Not feeling too well?" he asked.

"Got a bad cold, I'm afraid."

"Bad luck in the middle of the exam. Thank you very much. Please go out that way." He pointed to a side door leading to a flight of stairs that avoided the queue of students still waiting for their vivas at the other end of the museum. I stumbled down the stairs into the sunshine and walked slowly back towards Caius College, calling first at Dr. Bevan's surgery in Trinity Street. It was still early and I was his first patient for evening surgery. I explained my problem; I thought I had 'flu and was in the middle of the exam. I told him that the previous day had been free and I had decided that exercise would help and had spent a day rough shooting with Jim Garson. In those early post-war days only older undergraduates, who were mostly ex-servicemen, were allowed to have cars; however, I had kept my mother's old Hillman Minx in the outskirts of Cambridge. Jim and I had driven to one of our favourite wildfowling haunts on the 'Washes', a mile-wide strip of marshland and rough grazing that lies between the two parallel man-made channels known as the 'Old Bedford' and the 'New Bedford' rivers. We had flushed a few snipe and teal in the autumn sunshine, normally an enormous pleasure but I had felt tired and weak and had great difficulty keeping up with Jim. The single woodpigeon in my bag hardly justified the effort.

Unfortunately, I did not give Dr. Bevan an important clue. On returning to the car I had found it unaccountably difficult to raise my left arm to insert the key in the ignition. This, I thought, might have been due to the effects of a minor accident some months earlier when I had fallen off a horse (that was stationary at the time). I had injured my left shoulder badly enough to consult a surgeon who had told me that I had damaged a nerve and temporarily weakened my deltoid muscle. More than half a century later, I was reminded by a former school friend, Francis Bullock, that I had met him by chance outside the college and had told him that I was feeling so ill that I would be grateful if he could park the car for me. This he did and presumably left the keys at the porter's lodge. He did not hear what subsequently happened for several days and I had forgotten this incident completely.

Dr. Bevan took my temperature. It was normal. He thought for a moment before pronouncing, "a typical case of 'examination nerves', nothing to be ashamed of, one of several this week." He gave me a couple of sleeping pills and an aspirin, advising me to forget the exams until the next day. I climbed slowly and painfully up several flights of stone stairs to my room on the top floor of the College, muttering "Examination nerves". I undressed and went to sleep.

I woke a couple hours later; the room was dark and the window shut, although I had not drawn the curtains. The College was totally silent apart from distant traffic sounds and as term had not yet started there were only a few people staying in the College. I was aching all over had a violent headache and needed a pee. I sat dizzily on the edge of the bed for a few moments and slid onto the floor. The diagnosis was obvious. My legs were paralysed; I was barely able to move my arms and hands — I had polio.

I cannot remember any panic, though I considered the possibility of being found dead by the bed-maker in the morning. I tried a few deep breaths and was not impressed; breathing was already difficult. I needed help, but how to summon it? There was no point shouting, because all the rooms on the staircase were unoccupied.

I managed to pull the reading lamp off the bedside locker and I arranged some bedclothes around myself. Could I reach my shotgun propped up against the wall some eight feet away and the cartridge belt in my game bag? Perhaps I could fire a shot through the window that would bring the police (another case of 'examination nerves' shoots himself?). I could not reach it and would have to wait until the bed-maker arrived in the morning. I had been staying in college for several days and the previous mornings she had woken me with a cup of tea.

I sat on the floor through the night, objective and detached. My bladder was distended and I tried to pee into a rolled up towel, but could not. Periodically I reviewed my dwindling stock of functioning muscles. Anatomy was a strong subject and this was revision for real. Both legs had gone except for some movement in the right ankle (tibialis anterior working). My right arm would not extend at the elbow (triceps gone) but it did flex strongly (biceps OK). I could not raise my left arm at the shoulder (deltoid out). The grip in both hands had gone. My neck muscles were weak. The paralysis had overtaken me with astonishing speed but at least I was still breathing. Fortunately I was propped against the bed; had I slipped onto my back I would have stayed that way. Sitting, I was in command of my situation; lying down my nerve might have cracked.

About eight o'clock the following morning I heard movements in the pantry next to the sitting room and tried unsuccessfully to call out. Fortunately, the bed-maker did come in with a cup of tea. From years of experience of hung-over young gentlemen she viewed me without emotion. "Stay close to the door," I wheezed, "I've got polio; I'm infectious, I don't want anybody to catch it."

Events moved rapidly; first to arrive was Dr. Bevan, apologetic for missing the diagnosis the previous evening and astonished by the speed of my total collapse. Next my Tutor, Hubert Tunnicliffe, and Norman, one of the college porters lifted me onto the bed. Two men with a stretcher-chair arrived and carried me down six flights of stairs with difficulty. I had yet to lose five stone that would melt away over the next three or four weeks. There was a brief journey to Brookfields Isolation Hospital in Mill Road. The 'ambulance' was a plain black van; infectious cases were not transported in normal ambulances.

The Medical Superintendent, Dr. Cameron, a charming Scot who I immediately identified as a source of confidence and hope, greeted me. Heads were shaken and tuts tutted when I recalled my physical activities during the previous two days. Vigorous exercise during the early stage of polio had virtually guaranteed paralysis of the most-used muscles and I had used all of mine. Dr. Cameron warned me that it would be some time before I could expect any improvement.

Memories of the next few days are of painful muscular spasms, splints and bandages on all four limbs (to prevent deformity caused by muscle spasm), intolerably long nights and breathing difficulties, injections, the indignity of an inflated rubber bed-pan and the need to be supported by two nurses during my attempts to use it. I tried to write a letter to my girlfriend, Pamela, with a stub of a pencil fixed to my index finger by a rubber band. My mother and father established a base at the University Arms Hotel. Four days later my father drove back to Cheshire, but I deteriorated during the day and he returned at midnight.

By that time I was installed in what I was soon to describe as 'Mr. Drinker's Ventilated Coffin' — the iron lung. My chest muscles and diaphragm were weak and I had developed pneumonia; I was not expected to survive. The penicillin caused a rash and I was given streptomycin. A day or two later, when I was taken out of the machine briefly for attention to pressure points, I surprised the pessimists with some shallow breathing and, most important, I was able to cough weakly when eased into a sitting position.

I was in a side ward that contained two Drinker machines, the other one occupied by Mrs Simpson. I was not encouraged when I learned that the poor woman had already been in it for several months (I believe she died in it a year or two later). The machine comprised a box about six feet in length, connected by a large pipe to a pump. It was extremely noisy as air was pumped out of the box at regular intervals, creating negative pressure that sucked air into my lungs. The patient (or as I began to feel, the victim) lay on a narrow foam-covered board on rollers. The top end of the box was split into upper and lower halves, bolted together by large chromium-plated wing nuts and there was a hole for the patient's neck. A rubber flange surrounded the neck-hole and produced an airtight seal during inspiration. Portholes in the sides and top of the box allowed access for nursing. A glass urinal that could be replaced through one of the portholes was stuck between my legs and a mirror on a bracket permitted a limited view of my surroundings.

The movement of the neck collar many times a minute became extremely uncomfortable and it seemed to be skinning my Adam's apple. More sinister were my bronchial secretions, noisily sucked up and down my windpipe; the ventilator prevented attempts to cough them up. In Drinker's apparatus I feared I was drowning in my own phlegm. Nowadays I might have had a temporary opening into my windpipe (tracheostomy) that would have allowed my secretions to be sucked out. I was able to speak only during the expiratory phase of each mechanical breath. I could see Mrs Simpson's serene and beautiful face through the mirror and I was able to apologize to her for the language I had used to describe the apparatus, the collar, the medical profession in general and Mr. Drinker in particular. I forgave him later for saving my life in the absence of more advanced technology.

After a stormy period in the machine, Dr. Cameron was sufficiently impressed by my requests to be removed from the lung, to call in Dr. Leslie Cole, the senior physician at Addenbrooke's Hospital. Dr. Cole was a small, balding, scholarly man, who was later to become my good friend and teacher. He was also the first doctor I had met who believed in involving the patient in discussions about his own management. I was taken out of the machine and a bedside conference was held in an adjoining room, out of earshot of Mrs Simpson, while they unobtrusively observed my ability to breathe for myself. Being a Yorkshire man by temperament, ancestry and length of domicile in that county, if not quite by birth, I argued politely and vigorously—if they didn't get me out of that bloody ventilated coffin, I was likely to bloody well die on them (in truth I used the 'F' word). Rather to my surprise they did agree that I seemed to be able to breathe by myself. The streptomycin injections were now working and it was decided that I could, provisionally, be allowed to stay out of the machine. A physiotherapist supervised postural drainage and thumped my chest while I lay in a head down position. From that time I never looked back.

By the end of the month I was fit to travel and on 2nd November I was driven by ambulance to the Robert Jones and Agnes Hunt Orthopaedic Hospital at Gobowen near Oswestry in Shropshire. Years later, when I was delivering babies as a medical student in a wheelchair at the Mill Road Maternity Hospital a few yards from the Isolation Hospital, I called on Dr. Cameron. He introduced me to his assistant as that "outspoken young laddie who talked himself out of the iron lung".

I shall gloss over many of the traumas of those four weeks and others need not suffer similarly now that polio vaccination, introduced in 1956, has largely eliminated the disease in Europe and many other parts of the developed world. I do not think I have ever moaned about my predicament; nevertheless, November 2, 1950, and the journey north marked the start, at the age of twenty-one, of a bit of a struggle.

Bill Inman died in October 2005 before this book was published. He was a brave and compassionate man who is greatly missed by his family and many friends.

1

DNA

Although our genes dictate *what* we are, Environment, physical and social, determines *who* we are. Genes handed down by our ancestors enable us to become ancestors ourselves. The events described in the prologue might have robbed me of my chance of becoming an ancestor, but I survived and became a link in an unbroken chain of thousands of ancestors and I have already passed these ancestral genes on to two further generations. Note that I say *these* genes, not *my* genes. The chance that any significant mutation has occurred during my period of tenure is remote. I may delude myself that my genes have some qualities that will make them especially useful to future generations, but all the effort I put into replicating them merely enables me to pass on ancestral instructions to which I have added little or nothing. We all hope that our descendants will resemble us, although this too is ephemeral because our genes are scrambled and our ancestor's contribution is halved in each successive generation. After four or five generations, the genes that lived inside us for a few years merge with the general gene pool as grains of sand in the desert. We compete for mates and fight for our families as long as we have strength, but we cannot hope to have much lasting influence beyond our grandchildren. We hope we will not pass on some weakness and we must make sure that we do not destroy the environment in which they will live.

'In the beginning was the word and the word was DNA'. Well it wasn't, quite, but DNA started to shape the forms of living creatures when it appeared for the first time in organisms no more advanced than bacteria. We are genetically engineered by evolutionary selection over which we have no control. The way DNA works was discovered in Cambridge in 1953 by two members of my college, Watson and Crick, while I was a medical student. We could at last begin to understand how we had evolved and could relegate many traditional beliefs and all religious myths to the storybooks. DNA instructs other molecules in our cells how to make protein, how to tell a monkey to produce another monkey and not a gorilla. We cannot change the chemistry of the genes living in our bodies, but our environment, our parents, our peers and our own efforts may modify their influence on the information-processing system living inside our skulls that we call *consciousness*. Once we have acquired our full complement of billions of brain cells, we cannot, within the limits of present technology, increase or replace cells that are lost through injury or old age. We may, however, switch or re-route some of the interconnecting 'wires' that connect our brain cells. I am uncomfortable with the metaphor that our brains are nothing more than sophisticated computers. I can, however, imagine billions of micro-processing cells embedded in a living, multidimensional and constantly changing network of wires connected to our data-gathering and transmitting systems, our eyes and ears and other senses. I can imagine a mechanism that thinks or reasons that is several orders of magnitude more complicated than that so far evolved by our nearest mammalian relatives. How we use this equipment depends partly on programmes we inherited and partly on alterations to the wiring that we may make ourselves in the light of experience. The programmes we write ourselves cannot be passed on to future generations in genetic code but we can use them to change the environment in which our children will live and their descendents will evolve. We may leave them a legacy in writing or music, or by discovering things or, if we are hungry or religiously inclined, by starting wars.

A fortunate combination of genetic material will probably give us a small advantage in competition with those around us, but the environment created by our parents or grandparents usually has a more profound and lasting influence on the way we grow up, think and behave. Some resemblance to our parents or grandparents is not merely physical. Similar psychological traits are too often found in immediate descendants to be coincidental, though they are unlikely to pass far down the line. Dormant traits that give our children particular skills may be unlocked. For example, it is recorded that fifty-three members of the Bach family earned their living as organists, cantors or town musicians.[1]

The greatest influence on children is not parents but peers. We usually do our own thing, or rather what our peer group does. The only way parents can exert any lasting influence is to create an environment that determines who their children's peers are likely to be. If I grow up in my father's carpentry shop, I have a more than an average chance of becoming a skilful carpenter, but not because there is a gene for carpentry. If a boy's mother is over-fussy about how he dresses and sends him to a ballet school, he will probably become homosexual. A gene for homosexuality seems unlikely. One would expect such a mutation to be a no-hope gene for the simple reason that it would not often be replicated.

While researching family records for this book, I learned how much the successes of my grandparents and parents had influenced my character. I appreciate the value of their investment in my education and how they had taught me to be a risk-taker and a survivor in a hostile and competitive environment, made all the more difficult by the illness that struck me at the age of twenty-one. We were relatively well off and privileged and I was taught to be responsible for others who were not so fortunate. I learned at an early age that rich people give employment to poor people and that this is good, but that to treat them as inferiors is bad.

The most recent ancestors on my mother's side were the Staffordshire families of Andrews, Ward, Lowe, Carter and Ashby. They were proudly and successfully 'in trade'. They were much respected for their piety and lack of ostentation, though one relative was said always to have drawn the curtains over the windows of his carriage so that he could not see or be seen by his poorer relatives walking on their way to church. An early maternal ancestor is believed to have been one of three Ward brothers who came to England from Normandy in the eleventh century and settled in Aston in Staffordshire. His descendants have lived in the Wolverhampton area for about nine hundred years. A father, a son and a grandson, all 'iron masters' and all named Abraham Ward (b.1681, 1712 and 1737) and their descendants married several times into the prolific Andrews family. In the eighteenth and early part of the nineteenth century, a daughter's and occasionally a son's name incorporated the surnames of both parents. For example, my great-grandmother, Zara Carter Andrews, was formerly Zara Carter Lowe, the daughter of Mary Carter and Thomas Lowe. This fashion seems to have died out in the latter half of the nineteenth century. None of the families indulged in the fiddle-faddle of hyphenation as a means of social advancement.

Some of the families became widely dispersed throughout the Empire; for example one document records the place of death of the ten sons and one daughter of John and Mary Lowe. Three, including one killed in the Mutiny, died in India, three in Canada, one in Burma, one in Tasmania, one in Greece and only two in England; seven of the eleven were outlived by their mother.

The first Andrews I identified, Joshua, was born in 1660. He had three sons. One of them, also called Joshua (1697-1777) had six sons and two daughters. His son, Randle Andrews of Tong Hall (1740-1791), married into the Webb family and had five sons and five daughters. Randle's fifth son, Richard (1774-1864), was one of my eight great-great-grandfathers. Richard married Mary Ward whose family owned the iron foundries of which nothing remains except the name of Ward Street running to nowhere through acres of dereliction to the south-east of the city. Richard and Mary produced eight boys and one girl, all but one of the boys surviving into adulthood. I identified thirty-seven of their grandchildren. Richard's seventh son, my great-grandfather Frederick Andrews (1820-1876), married Zara Carter Lowe (1817-1880) from another large Wolverhampton family prominent in pharmacy and insurance. They had a daughter, Jessie, and four sons, Frederick, Charles, Archibald and Howard, my grandfather.

From the early eighteenth century several branches of the Andrews clan became involved in the drapery, millinery and haberdashery trades in the Midlands and further afield. My great-great-grandfather, Richard, founded Andrews and Sons Ltd. in Wolverhampton. His uncle, William Andrews, had a drapery in Newport, Monmouthshire, and he in turn set up his son as a draper in Southampton. Richard's eldest son Thomas Randle Andrews had a drapery in Stafford; his fourth son Henry (b.1816) was apprenticed in the same trade to an uncle in Dublin.

William Ward (separated by three 'greats') the father of Richard's wife Mary, had offices in Queen Street and his foundries were connected by Ward Street to his private wharf on the River Severn by Bilston Street Bridge. He probably supplied raw materials to Thomas Clark, down the road at Horsley Fields, who advertised *'Fine Cast-iron Kitchen Furniture, Door Knockers and Humane Man Traps'*.

My wife June and I visited what remains of Frederick Andrews and Sons Ltd. in Dudley Street. Gone are the marble pillars and the frock-coated assistants shown in a contemporary lithograph; instead 'The Shop', as Zara always referred to it, now roofs a depressing combination of a discount superstore, a Body Shop, a Mcdonald's Restaurant, a dentist's surgery, and sundry other businesses. Only parts of the nineteenth century facade remain. One can nevertheless imagine the Victorian elegance that helped to make Dudley Street a focal point in what is now a sadly down-market Wolverhampton.

Frederick and Zara and their five children, the youngest

of whom was my grandfather Howard, lived at *Tor Lodge* in Tettenhall Wood. Malcolm Scott, who now owns *Tor Lodge East*, still poses family groups in exactly the same place as in the photos taken in the 1860s. Frederick made the journey to Dudley Road each day in his gig. For longer journeys, such as to Bristol docks to collect fine silks, hose and other imported materials, he used his coach and four. He had businesses in Glasgow and London and an interest in businesses in Dublin and Paris.

In 1876 life at *Tor Lodge* was shattered when Frederick was accidentally drowned. Jessie, Charles and Archie, all enjoyed careers in London. Fred junior was supposed to help with the family business but seems to have become a dropout and was frequently in debt. Their father's death left the youngest son, my grandfather Howard (1861-1944), at the age of only fifteen and still at school to help his mother with the drapery businesses, a task that he tackled with remarkable tenacity and skill.

In 1881 Zara was taken ill while on holiday in Oban. A local GP Dr. McKelvie wrote to Howard on September 6th.

> 'I have seen Mrs. Andrews today. She is troubled with her gums. At the roots of the teeth, the gum has got slightly ulcerated which annoys her much. I think this state has been caused by the acidity of her stomach. Her gums are better today and when I see her on Thursday I expect she will be much better. You need have no anxiety about Mrs. Andrews'.

On September 13th she died.

With Frederick and Zara dead the business was soon in serious trouble in spite of my grandfather's efforts to hold it together. The economy was in recession and the family decided to sell *Tor Lodge* and the rest of the estate together with numerous town properties, in the hope of saving the company. On May 9th 1882, at the *Star and Garter* Hotel, *Tor Lodge* was auctioned together with seven messuages (properties with outbuildings) in Tettenhall Wood, five acres of building land

and farm buildings in nearby Wightwick and fifteen houses in Charles Street, Wolverhampton, together with a quantity of stocks and shares. *Tor Lodge* was described as a 'desirable family residence' with four reception rooms and nine 'chambers' (but only one bathroom). There was a coach-house, stabling for the four coach horses and the gig pony, a piggery and a 'boot and knife' house.

After the sale of *Tor Lodge* the injection of capital enabled Howard now aged twenty-one, to advertise for additional staff for 'Woollens', 'Mantles', 'Fancy', 'Carpets' and several other departments and trade was brisk enough to require more than one shop-walker to control pilfering. Although I have not researched deeply, there seem to be few traces of the Andrews family apart from their graves and Frederick Street and Howard Street at a cross-roads to the south of the city, named after my great-grandfather and grandfather.

In another way 1882 also marked a turning point for Howard. To the horror of the Andrews family, who were staunch Protestants, Howard converted to Rome because he had fallen in love with Teresa Ashby who lived in Upper Vauxhall. Teresa was not the best looking girl in Wolverhampton, although Howard had plenty of rivals. They included a mysterious Don Julio de Leon, who wrote from Bilbao on the 11th of May 1883:

> 'My ever Darling Teresa,
>
> I know you will be surprised when you receive this letter because you will think that I have forgotten you since I left Wolverhampton, but that is not truth because I always everyday remember you. Teresa, are you married? Are you happy or are you in the convent? What are you? Will you please answer me telling me all about it. About me, I only tell you I am not very happy. I am not married. I shall not be married. NEVER because I can't be in love with any girl. I have been once and then it was with you my very dear Teresa.

Adieu my love

Yours sincerely
Julio de Leon

(PS) If you are married, tell your husband don't be alarmed because I live a little far away from you.'

The day before Howard's marriage a hasty note from his brothers insisted that, as he was marrying Teresa the next day, it really was time that he gave up seeing Miss Lewis. Miss Lewis had gone to some lengths to persuade Howard not to change his religion and I suspect that a relationship with Miss Lewis may have developed. The marriage to Teresa was a low-key affair, not attended by members of his family. Their first daughter May was born in 1887. Gladys was born two years later and my mother, Maude, in 1892.

In 1914 my mother volunteered to nurse troops at the St. John Hospital in Southport and in 1916 she was recruited by the War Office to help to run the postal censorship in Liverpool. In 1927 she met my father in Southport at a performance by Billy Cotton. They courted for a year and applied to the Archbishop of Liverpool for the dispensation required in those days for a 'mixed marriage'. This he refused to grant and she moved to London to establish residence there while Father continued working for ICI at Cunard House in Liverpool. The Cardinal Archbishop of Westminster was more accommodating and they were married at St. James, Spanish Place, on July 5th 1928.

My father's family is not as well documented as my mother's but seems to have shared their comfortable prosperity and to be involved in industry; a shipping line and a coal field are mentioned in various correspondence. The Inman family first appeared in the small Yorkshire town of Knaresborough in the fourteenth Century. My father, Wallace Mills Inman, was always called 'Bill'. His father, William Inman (1869-1935), was a journalist who left his native Yorkshire in 1891 to work for the *Earlstown Guardian* and later became a senior reporter on the *Liverpool Post and Echo* and a contributor to several other Lancashire papers. His mother, Anne Lupton (1873-1910) of Knaresborough who was always known as 'Polly', died many years before I was born. William died when I was six and I have only fragmentary memories of him during rather infrequent visits to his home in Lancashire. He lived in St. Helens where my father was born in 1894. William had a fine tenor voice and sang a solo at the laying of the foundation stone of Liverpool Cathedral by Edward VII. He was also a keen photographer and cyclist. When he died a full page of the newspaper recorded how he had attended every meeting of the St. Helens Council for forty years. The Mayor directed that a street should be named 'Inman Avenue' and that a letter of condolence should be sent to his widow. She had been dead for twenty-five years!

My father was an only child. He attended grammar school in St. Helens and later graduated in chemistry at Liverpool University. He was not one to shoot a line about his war service and only a few stories survive. He volunteered for the Artillery in 1914 and attained the rank of Sergeant. He was slightly wounded in France and after recovering he was commissioned in the Royal Engineers and served for much of the remainder of the war fighting the Turks in Palestine and Mesopotamia (Iraq), where he applied his scientific training to the clandestine blowing up of railways. Once he recalled becoming a slave-trader. When faced with the problem of burying a large number of rapidly putrefying Turkish dead, a fellow officer arrived at the camp in charge of forty Armenians who had been prisoners of the Turks and for whom he had no food. Father had plenty of food but few men. The Armenians had no love for the Turks and would have buried as many as they could find, alive or dead, and they set about their task with gusto. On another occasion, when his Company was short of food, father disappeared into the desert one night with an armoured car, a Lewis gun and a driver. The following morning a dust cloud was seen moving slowly across the desert towards the British lines. When it got closer it turned out to be my father sitting on top of the best part of a herd of 'antelope' (his story, or were they goats?). During one of his rail cutting excursions into Mesopotamia (Iraq) he captured a railway station and removed an elegant brass plaque that he presumed was the name of the station. Many years later I learnt from an Arabic-speaking visitor that he had captured a station called 'gents toilet'. It now hangs over the appropriate door in my front hall.

After demobilisation in 1918 father joined the Research Department of the United Alkali Company (UAC) in Widnes, Lancashire. UAC has been described as the 'Foundation stone of a thousand industries' [2]. In December 1926 with another company started in Northwich, Cheshire, by Alfred Brunner and Dr. Ludwig Mond, UAC merged with the British Dyestuffs Corporation and Nobel Industries to form Imperial Chemical Industries. Twenty years later my father became Chairman of ICI's Alkali Division based at the former Brunner Mond factories at Northwich and he was also Chairman of its Salt Division based at Winsford in Cheshire.

When I first knew them the Andrews had left Wolverhampton and lived in a house called *Knighthill* in Southport. It was small and over-furnished. The drawing room was crammed with objects that could be knocked over and was out of bounds except when Grandmother was presiding. The dining room at the rear opened into a long narrow garden comprising small lawns with dense shrub borders and a range of outhouses, ideal for hide-and-seek. I remember with shame the small square of loose carpet to the right of the dining-room fireplace that covered a large purple stain. I had been given a 'jelly-pad' duplicating set for Christmas and a whole bottle of the special ink had left indelible evidence of an otherwise blameless visit. No words were ever said but the small square of loose carpet was my last memory of that house when I glanced round after the contents had been sold.

My favourite room was a large kitchen presided over by

Florence, a rotund lady with an inexhaustible source of fudge, treacle-toffee, good humour and stories. She performed the functions of housekeeper and chauffeuse after Ferrier, the family chauffeur, retired. I was a 'bookworm' and spent many happy hours perched on the windowsill of a small sunny room overlooking the garden, browsing grandfather's extensive collection of books, especially those touching on natural history. Like many Victorians Grandfather had a wide interest in scientific subjects.

My great uncle Archie (1858-1943) now had a surgical practice in Liverpool. He never married and lived with my aunt May in Southport and was the guardian of May's two children after her husband had deserted her. He was an impressive figure dressed in 'plus-fours' and hand-made brogues (that fitted me perfectly and saw me through university after his death). Archie always kept a gold sovereign on the mantelpiece of his consulting room to give to a patient in need. He played a significant part in my choice of a career in medicine and I wish he had lived to give guidance when I started to plan it towards the end of the Second World War.

My mother's other sister, Gladys, was a nun. She was a Sister of Charity and Mother Superior of a convent in Birmingham that was run as an Approved School for wayward young ladies. She was a formidable character who died at the age of forty-four when I was quite small.

Thus I inherited a three-fold legacy from the Andrews. The first, from my grandfather, was an appetite for books about natural sciences, the second, from uncle Archie, a strong ambition to become a doctor, and the third, from granny Teresa, affiliation with the Catholic Church.

Andrews, Wolverhampton c1850

Mother, c.1920

*Father,
Mesopotamia 1917*

2

Peace and War

I was born in Banstead in Surrey on August 1st 1929. My brother Chris was born two years later and Hugh five years later. Although born in Surrey, I spent most of the first twenty years of my life in Yorkshire and prefer to be thought of as a Yorkshireman. We moved to Ilkley early in 1931. My father bought *Overdale,* a large house on the northern edge of Ilkley Moor. It was the first of ten house moves we were to make as my father climbed the promotional ladder during the next twenty years. When we left in 1935 it became a school, then a health farm and later still a nursing home. *Overdale* stood close to a track along the edge of the moor that led to the *Cow and Calf* rocks. The three-storey building had superb views especially from a small tower on the roof. It had a billiard room on the lower floor. We did not have a billiard table but the room was big enough to race tricycles and pedal-cars. We also had a spacious nursery on the first floor and sometimes fell for nurse's entreaties to tidy it up because she had heard that the Queen might be coming for tea that afternoon. I never met Queen Mary; perhaps the severe winters deterred her, but one day an elderly woman called Mrs. Kershaw was lost on the moor in a blizzard. Fortunately she saw our lights and sought shelter. She stayed the night and kept in touch for several years; we called her the 'Storm Lady'. In September 1934 I started my schooling at *Kingsbury* and earned a rather encouraging first term report from the Headmistress, Miss Barton:

> 'Billy listens with obvious appreciation and shows a marked sense of humour. He knows what he wants to say and expresses himself clearly'.

Subsequent reports were less flattering, commenting on my scruffy appearance and liberal use of ink on everything but the paper I was writing on and suggesting that I might be using Richmal Compton's 'William Brown' as a role model (Mother used to read her books to me at bedtime). I was musical and good at sums and drawing, but my spelling was reported to be 'as heard'.

In 1935 my father moved to ICI's Manchester headquarters for a short period and bought a house called *Rookwood* in Alderley Edge, Cheshire. Our next door neighbour was Sir Vincent de Ferranti, Head of the electronics business, and we used to play with his two boys, Sebastian and Basil. 'Duffer de Ferranti' (Sebastian) later went with me to boarding school in Yorkshire. The de Ferrantis had all the latest electrical devices including a radiogram and I was more fascinated by the way the machine swallowed and ejected our records than by the music it played. One summer afternoon there was an incredible noise of aircraft engines and the house was 'buzzed' at low level by two large autogyros. Unlike a helicopter, the rotor of an autogyro freewheels and is not attached to the engine that drives a conventional propeller. I think they were Italian Machi autogyros putting on a show for the Ferrantis next door.

In Alderley Edge I fell in love with a five-year-old, Anne Carey-Morgan. Returning from a children's party I was said to have described every minute detail of her party frock and repeated every word she had said. I wonder what happened to the first love in my life?

In 1937 father moved again to ICI's works at Billingham and he bought *Northrifts Hall* near the Italian Gardens in Saltburn. We were comparatively well off and in those days people were glad to have a roof over their head. Service with a family was much sought after. The staff at *Northrifts* included Gladys and her husband 'Evans' (Father always insisted we should address him as 'Mr. Evans') who were cook and butler, a succession of pairs of house-maids, a nanny, a full-time gardener-handyman, Mr. Carver, and his 'boy', a teenager who did a lot of the digging and stalked the maids. Our nannies, Margaret and Evelyn who succeeded her, in their blue uniforms and shining starched cuffs commanded our respect and affection. Our lives were well regulated and relaxed. Discipline, a strong sense of purpose and the need to respect and help others were instilled from an early age and we learned how far we could go and when to stop. We were encouraged to be creative and experimental. I was the self-appointed leader of the *Black Gang* comprising Douglas Blair, John Fardon and Lionel Crow, who met regularly in a den in the rhododendron bushes. Douglas was a farmer's son who won all his fights with other boys and was my lieutenant; the other two were loyal foot soldiers.

One day we lit a fire in a huge hollow oak tree at the entrance to the drive with the idea of cooking some sausages. The inside of the main trunk and the main branches were lined with rotting tinder-dry wood. The flames roared up the hollow trunk and outwards as separate jets from large holes in the trunk and smaller jets like candles on a Christmas tree. A crowd collected and the fire brigade arrived, followed later by men with enormous double-handled saws (chain saws had not been invented). No one was impressed by Lionel's observation that it must be unusual for a tree to be struck by lightning on a summer afternoon or John's suggestion that a jackdaw, noted for the habit of carrying unusual objects to a nest, must have flown in with a lighted cigarette.

One day a man in a wet and rather dirty raincoat rang the front door bell and said he had 'come for Father's money'. I didn't like the sound of that and went to Father's desk, collected his service revolver and returned to the front door. The man's feet hardly touched the ground as he zigzagged down the drive like a driven snipe. He telephoned to complain and it turned out that he was the Golf Club Steward collecting subscriptions. At this point I deemed it prudent to leave home and at dusk that evening, just as the family were beginning to worry, a small white face was seen lurking in the rhododendrons.

It was safe for children to cycle on the quiet roads of those days and as smoking was a beating offence the Black Gang used to share a packet of Woodbines in an old shed on the road to Marske. Pocket money was 6d (2.5p) per week with an extra 'milk penny' if we drank it. I hated milk and to this day can barely drink a glass without gagging. Sixpence was enough to purchase several 'Cow Bars' (a toffee bar with a picture of a cow on the cover), or packets of sherbet that you sucked through a liquorice straw, and there was a penny or two remaining for catapult elastic and other basic essentials. My father's banking system encouraged saving; any pennies saved and banked with him were recorded in a book and matched with an equal sum to supplement birthday or Christmas money and used to purchase lead soldiers or sports equipment. This was the last time I enjoyed 100% interest on an investment. We always hoped that relatives would give us money to put towards major items that we could not afford in any other way rather than send 'surprises'.

Father was a model railway enthusiast and a whole room at *Northrifts* was devoted to it. The track and fixtures such as transformers, signals, tunnels and stations were fixed to a massive wooden platform some eighteen inches from the floor and hinged to one wall so that the whole structure could be lifted with ropes and pulleys like a draw-bridge. The platform virtually filled the large room allowing perhaps a yard of space on three sides. Father made up the track himself. Lengths of rail up to a yard long were bolted together with miniature fishplates and fixed by tiny shoes and sprigs to individual sleepers; not for him the plug-in sections available in the shops. He had two large Hornby 'OO' electric locomotives and several smaller shunting engines running on many yards of track, with bridges, tunnels and points operated by levers in a signal box. Platoons of lead soldiers were drawn up on the platforms ready for shipment to the far-flung Empire (we were intensely patriotic and the Union flag always flew from the tall mast in the garden).

Father was also a keen supporter of Saltburn's *Little Theatre* on the upper promenade and was responsible for the operation of curtains, lighting and other apparatus required for amateur theatre productions. He was much in demand for school plays and concerts, at one of which my solo performance of '*Little Boy Blue Come Blow Your Horn*' received sufficient applause to stimulate the Black Gang to start its own rival show at *Northrifts*. Douglas Blair, who would fight to the last conker (horse chestnuts fired from a catapult) for the honour of the Gang, decided that acting was sissy. John Fardon and Lionel Crow were too shy to do more than collect money from parents who parked their cars in our drive. As the most extrovert and precocious member of the Gang, all the acting and singing roles were performed by me. Father was tone-deaf but encouraged any potential musical skills and always bought the best equipment for us. In sport he wanted us to win but expected us to do it 'sportingly'. If you won a point you should be humble; if you lost it — 'jolly good shot'. Father would have blown a fuse if he had to witness the fist punching gestures of today's football players after scoring a goal and would have muttered something about the behaviour of male frogs in the spawning season.

I had a piano accordion, a large professional mouth organ and a ukulele-banjo, with all of which I could produce recognisable tunes, and I developed a repertoire of cowboy and George Formby songs. '*The wheel of the wagon is broken*', and '*I've only got five bullets in my old six-shooter 'cause I had to say good-bye to Mona*' (a song about a cowboy whose horse broke its leg), usually produced applause. I could also handle the difficult '*Dot and Carry One Brown*', that was written in five beats to a bar and I occasionally risked a rendering of *The one-armed flautist*. Appearing on stage with one arm tucked inside my shirt and trousers and wearing a flat cap, I sang a verse or two of '*Phil the Fluter*' followed by a few toots on my tin whistle, held horizontally with one hand to simulate a flute. An index finger then appeared suggestively through my flies and gripped the whistle while I passed the hat round with my one arm.

We often went to professional repertory shows at the *Little Theatre* and several of the artists used to come to dinner and sometimes to stay at *Northrifts*. Cal MacCord was my hero, an American cowboy act with bullwhip and lariat who sang to a guitar in the style of Roy Rogers. Another house guest was the daughter of Charles Shadwell, the orchestra leader. During the war, Joan Shadwell played a small part in the BBC's popular radio series *Garrison Theatre,* as the girl who introduced herself with the catch phrase "*Programmes, Chocolates, Cigarettes*". Father was a member of the *Savage Club* and when we moved south during the war I met several of his regular lunching companions, including Tommy Handley, Arthur Askey, Richard Murdoch, Sydney Taffler and Kenneth Horne. My parents seldom missed a major London Show.

In 1936 my brother Chris severely burnt his buttock when he sat on a hot towel rail. He developed pneumonia, was hospitalised for two weeks, and may have been saved by the new sulphonamide drug known as M&B 693. He took a long time to convalesce and required a nurse for several months. Miss Rowlands wore huge horn-rimmed spectacles and became one of the family. We called her *'Nig-Nogs';* nowadays I suppose a politically incorrect likening to the gollywogs that were our favourite soft toys.

In May 1938 my father toured the I.G.Farben chemical works in Germany where he was followed everywhere by men in jackboots and brown shirts with swastika armbands. There was probably more to the visit than gathering sales figures because immediately before the outbreak of war he went to Norway with a colleague, to visit the Norsk Hydro plant that was producing 'heavy-water' (deuterium oxide) for nuclear research. They returned to England with a large bottle of the pure isotope. According to legend, his colleague, hung-over by a long night in the bar while crossing by sea to Harwich, forgot father's instructions to describe it as 'holy water', and declared it as 'heavy water'. Four years later, in November 1942, two gliders were towed from Scotland with soldiers and explosives. Both gliders and one of the tugs crashed and the survivors were shot. In February 1943 the Special Operations Executive (SOE) sent in a party of agents who blew up the deuterium concentration plant and halted production. Later, the Americans attempted to bomb the plant but only succeeded in hitting the nearby town. The Germans decided to abandon Norsk Hydro and moved their total stock of heavy water by rail and loaded the tankers on to a ferry but they failed to realise that a Norwegian agent had placed explosives in the bilge. The ferry sank while crossing a lake en route for Germany. This was probably the most important operation ever conducted by SOE and may have altered the course of the war.[3]

At the age of eight, before going to boarding school, I earned the privilege of dining with my parents when they were entertaining. On the first occasion it happened that the maids were ill and mother had hired a jolly woman to help at dinner with some guests from Billingham. She was enormously fat and red faced and, while bending down to get something from the sideboard, released a resounding carpet-creeping fart. She turned to the guests, beaming from ear to ear, "Oh, hark at me". I disgraced myself by laughing.

In September 1938 my parents drove me to Gilling in Yorkshire, the preparatory school for Ampleforth College. I was introduced to Fr. Maurus the Headmaster and Mother helped me unpack my things in the dormitory. As the dreaded moment approached I was teamed up with a boy called Cleaver, whose parents were leaving for America. We said goodbye and shook hands formally (it was deemed sissy to kiss). Cleaver and I turned our backs on the departing cars and, with quivering lips and no backward glances, walked slowly to the roller-skating rink. I cannot remember Cleaver's first name; the masters and boys never used them. Cleaver became a close friend and stayed with us during the holidays as he had no home to go to in England and travel by sea was too hazardous because of U-boats.

Immediately after we arrived we were issued with gas masks and we all had to walk through a smoke-filled room in the courtyard to test their fit. My main interests at Gilling centred round the carpentry shop that was presided over by the appropriately named Mr Skillbeck and my only achievement at Gilling was the first prize for carpentry for my combined bookcase and reading-lamp. Helped by my father and inspired by the *Little Theatre* in Saltburn, I built an elaborate model theatre. It had blue velvet curtains operated by an electric motor, footlights, a spotlight, a trap door (for the Genie in Aladdin) and a mechanism for raising and lowering scenery. The silver-painted proscenium was about thirty inches wide and was set in a wide folding screen of blackout material that concealed the operators. The characters were operated by strips of wood and we made some string puppets. I produced plays that I had scripted myself and I copied pantomimes that I had seen in Middlesborough during the Christmas holidays. I spent three happy years at Gilling and then moved across the valley to Ampleforth College.

In June 1939 father was moved to London and bought a house called *Sunnymead* in Higher Drive, Banstead, Surrey, in the same road in which I had been born. He made another 'business trip' to Germany and then returned to help Mother with the move from Saltburn. Like our previous house in Ilkley, *Northrifts* also became a school when father sold it to Mrs. Harrison, the Headmistress of the school that we used to attend. This was a sad time for Mother who was fond of the house and the staff. Evans was turned down by the army because of flat feet and a weak back and became an air-raid warden. Our much loved nanny, Evelyn, left to marry a soldier (whom I believe was later killed). We moved south on August 8th with 'Nig Nogs'. The 'Crisis' started on August 22nd and, having unpacked at *Sunnymead*, we were told that Father's department was to be evacuated to Northwich in Cheshire. He decided to move the family rather than leave us in Banstead for an uncertain period. And so on August 31st we locked up *Sunnymead* and trekked north in two cars with roof racks loaded with as many of our belongings as we could carry and with our Airedale dog, 'Piper', and 'Clarence' the canary. We reached my grandparents' home in Southport next day and on September 3rd, we stopped for lunch at a hotel on our way to a rented house in Northwich. During lunch we listened to Neville Chamberlain's announcement that we were at war with Germany.

For three months we lived in a cold, dark, terraced house, No 40 Winnington Hill, of which I have few memories except that a stray cat I had befriended killed Clarence the canary. Then we heard that Father's headquarters was to move again – back to London. On December 30th 1939 we returned to Banstead and *Sunnymead.* At school in Yorkshire I was hardly aware of the phoney war or the early fighting in Europe until the British Expeditionary Force was evacuated from Dunkirk at the end of May 1940. At home in the holidays, life in the South was rather more exciting. Shortly after Dunkirk a mysterious Free French Army Major, Maurice Saint-Jacques, became a frequent house guest. He had been evacuated from Dunkirk and was attached to de Gaulle's staff in London. I believe his real name was Du Clos and he had been an employee of ICI in Paris before the war. Maurice was involved with the Resistance and frequently disappeared for several weeks, to be dropped by parachute into France and picked up by Lysander or submarine. He soon became one of the family and taught me to play his musical saw. He had lost most of his belongings when he was evacuated but the first thing he saw on disembarking, propped against a wall in Folkestone harbour, was the canvas and leather case containing his musical saw and violin bow. After the war Father tried unsuccessfully to locate Maurice in Paris, where it was thought that he had gone to South America; it seemed that he might have been unable to adjust to post-war life after five years of clandestine activity. Father returned from Paris with a professional musical saw that, like Maurice's, was much longer than a carpenter's saw and had no teeth. It was played with a metal clamp fixed to the free end of the saw. It was a genuine musical instrument which, provided the performer has a good ear, is not difficult to play once several essential movements are co-ordinated. The free hand controls the pitch by varying the amount of primary bend and the tension that imparts a secondary or 'S'-bend and also produces 'vibrato'. For the higher notes, sliding the knee towards the free end reduces the length of the saw and, finally, each note has its own bowing position. Later in life as an undergraduate, my ability to play almost any melody, providing I had an accompanist, supplemented travelling expenses and drinks in bars on the Continent.

The first daylight air raid heralding the Blitz was on July 2nd 1940. Father had taped all the windows to reduce the danger from shards of glass penetrating the layers of blackout material and heavy curtains, and on July 7th he erected an Anderson shelter in what had been our playroom on the ground floor. Unlike the Morrison shelter that was nothing more than a heavy steel table with wire-mesh sides, the Anderson shelter was constructed from heavy corrugated iron and easily accommodated four bunks for Mother and the three boys. He reinforced the ceiling with large beams of timber that would support the wreckage if the house collapsed. We were much more comfortable with an indoor shelter than in the more customary position half underground (and probably half under water) in the garden and covered in soil. He also built a substantial wall of cement blocks faced with sandbags to protect the playroom window.

Father was 'Controller of Purchases' for ICI and his work involved constant travelling to arrange for supplies of raw materials required for the production of explosives, aircraft alloys, incendiaries, artificial fibres, and thousands of other items. His travels to the various branches of the company such as the Nobel Explosives Division in Ardeer in Scotland and the

Kynoch works of the Metals Division in Birmingham, kept him away for long periods. My mother had the burden of looking after the family during the almost nightly air raids. We lived five miles from Croydon and seven from Biggin Hill, both of which were attacked repeatedly during the hot dry months of July and August 1940. We had magnificent views of the air battles and frequently found spent cartridge-cases in the garden or on the adjoining golf course. On return to school in Yorkshire we traded them for sweets or postage stamps with boys from the north who were not lucky enough to be spectators at the Battle of Britain.

When daylight raids ceased and night bombing commenced we had several near misses within a few hundred yards of *Sunnymead* and I still recall the sound of tiles sliding off the roof and breaking on the path. One night we counted twice as many 'whooshes' as explosions and had to evacuate the house while the engineers defused several unexploded bombs. Most fell along the railway cutting about five hundred yards from the house; our damage was minor, but our next door neighbour's house was uninhabitable and she came to stay with us for a while. The guns disturbed sleep more than the bombs. During the raids many of the houses in Higher Drive were damaged and *Braehead*, where I was born, was almost destroyed. A young couple down the road returned to their bedroom after an All Clear and found a length of railway line lying across their bed.

On Sunday November 15th it was claimed that one hundred and eighty-five German aircraft had been shot down for the loss of only twenty-six RAF planes. To maintain morale nothing was done to refute this story, although the figure for German aircraft lost has since been revised to fifty-six. Churchill announced that civilian casualties during the first two weeks of September had been two thousand killed and eight thousand injured, while service lives lost during the same period numbered only two hundred and fifty. Mother concealed from us that there were some casualties among our neighbours and friends. A colleague of Father's, Colin ('Bags') Bagnell, the Managing Director of British Nylon Spinners, lost his wife and his leg in one of the raids. Much later, when 'Bags' was staying with us in Sevenoaks, Mother had to cope with an ashen-faced housemaid who had taken his breakfast into his room and attempted to collect his shoes for cleaning. 'Oh Ma'am, I took his shoe from under the bed and his leg came out with it.'

In February 1941 Father suffered a retinal detachment and was referred to a distinguished ophthalmic surgeon who fortunately was on leave from the Middle East. He was Henry Stallard, one of the athletes who had paced Harold Abrahams in the pre-war Olympic Games. Father was admitted to St.John and Elizabeth's Hospital in London. After the operation his head was fixed by sandbags and movement restricted for three weeks. Meanwhile, the bombs rained down around the hospital. Mother visited him every day in spite of the raids and took us to see him several times. The operation was successful in as much as the upper half of the field of vision in the eye was preserved, together with the all-important central vision. In 1943 he detached the opposite retina. Stallard had returned to North Africa and another surgeon was unable to salvage any of the vision in that eye. Father's fortitude during these operations and his adaptation to partial blindness the rest of his life was an inspiration to us all. His lack of stereoscopic vision prevented night driving and increased his golf handicap, but seemed not to have had any other dramatic affect on his life-style. He was, however, advised never to fly in case the pressure changes damaged his remaining eye.

Father soon resumed his normal work, but was forbidden to continue his night duties with the 'Higher Drive Fire Brigade'. The 'Brigade' had comprised Father and two or three friends who had removed the doors from an ancient London Taxi and adapted it to carry 40-gallon drums of water, buckets of carefully dried sand, stirrup pumps and dustbin lids. Incendiary bombs were a more frequent threat to property than high explosives because a single aircraft could overwhelm the fire-fighting services by starting hundreds of fires. Several neighbouring houses were burnt out and there were numerous fires in the gorse on the adjoining golf course and in the gardens that backed on to it. The incendiary bomb was approached by a fireman carrying a bucket of sand or a sandbag in one hand and protected from spitting fragments of burning magnesium by the dustbin lid held in the other. The sand had to be completely dry. If water was sprayed directly on the bomb or the sand was damp, there would be a spectacular display of pyrotechnics as the steam projected pellets of burning magnesium, spreading rather than extinguishing the fire. The water and stirrup-pumps were used only on the woodwork or furniture after the bomb itself had been smothered. In anticipation of a bomb in the house while he was away, I was allowed to deal with one that landed in the garden, although at twelve years of age, I was not old enough to join the 'Brigade' and stay up at night. My war service during the school holidays was limited to patrolling the golf course with my air rifle and Piper our Airdale dog looking for parachutists skulking among the gorse bushes.

Mother kept up our morale in spite of endless sleepless nights during the raids. The bombing was always at night and it was reasonably safe to cycle to the cinema in Sutton or Epsom in daytime. On one occasion her new Sunbeam bicycle was stolen; it had been chained to my old bike that had not been taken. She had made a note of the number (VG 895) in her diary and the police visited a local cycle dealer who had filed the numbers off several bikes and re-sprayed them. They treated the bikes with acid that revealed the numbers and he got eighteen months. I can still remember his name — Curtis Amos Wilber Edmund C... half a century later; this is a genuine feat of memory because there is no written record of his name in Mother's papers. I wish my memory of events of ten years ago was as sharp.

In 1942 I became depressed for a few weeks because of the fear that, when I went away to school, I might never see my parents again. It passed when the raids became fewer and after several months in a rented house in St. Albans we moved to Sevenoaks in Kent. By coincidence our new house, *Sevenholm*, was the seventh house I had lived in. My bedroom opened onto a balcony overlooking a small formal garden and three acres of woods. There was a hard tennis court that had been cratered by a bomb. As none of us was interested in tennis the crater was roughly filled in but the playing surface was never properly repaired. German bombing raids had ceased but the V-I flying bombs and V-II rockets were still to come.

My interest in birds was aroused by the famous bird photographer Eric Hoskins, who had lectured at school within weeks of losing an eye after an attack by a tawny owl. Hoskins had been erecting a hide to photograph its nest when the owl dived and struck him in the face, a talon penetrating his eyeball. He had returned to photograph the owl a few days after the eye had been removed and we were shown pictures of the bird and the claws that had caused this accident. [4] I made several new friends in Sevenoaks, especially Charles Knight, the 'Eagle Man', and our GP, Dr. James Harrison and his sons Jeff and David.

Captain Charles Knight brought his golden eagle, 'Capt. Ramshaw', to Ampleforth during the war. His act included flying the eagle over our heads in the auditorium of the school theatre. On the command "Attention", the eagle on his gauntlet responded instantly by spreading its wings. Knight subsequently confessed to me that this was faked by twisting his forearm slightly so that the bird was thrown off balance and forced momentarily to open its wings to regain it. He was a veteran of World War I and lived with his hawks and his daughter Jean, who was in the Land Army, in a ramshackle farmhouse called Quebec Cottage in Montreal Park to the north of Sevenoaks. The 'Two Captains' toured widely during the war in America, Canada and South Africa to raise funds for war charities and to entertain the troops in France. Shortly after Dunkirk he was torpedoed three hundred miles from Scotland while on his way to America. Knight found himself in a lifeboat, bemoaning the fate of Ramshaw, still in the hold of the sinking ship. A few days later, the shipping agent telephoned and said that the ship had not sunk; it had been towed to Scotland and beached. Knight hurried over from Glasgow and climbed aboard the half-submerged ship where he found Ramshaw alive and well in the hold, sitting on his crate. Presumably somebody had released him in the hope that he might fly home, but he had preferred to stay by his crate. [5]

Father was able to obtain an inexhaustible supply of 12-bore cartridges from ICI's Kynoch works in Birmingham; they were known as 'Jobs' (job lots) because of slight manufacturing defects. Often the defect was nothing more than an imperfectly printed label. 'Jobs' were identified with black bands painted round the case. They were supplied to the RAF, supposedly to teach air-gunners the art of aiming off when shooting at moving targets. I suspect, however, that for every cartridge used for its official purpose, a dozen had been fired at hares and partridges destined for the mess. Only Ramshaw and a buzzard remained of Knight's collection of raptors. Several eagles and hawks had been sent to various zoos when the shortage of cartridges and chicken heads made it difficult to feed them. When we mentioned that we kept ferrets, the Captain's eyes lit up and we hatched a plot to exploit the combined skills of ferret and eagle. There were several rabbit warrens in Montreal Park and we selected one in a long narrow copse on a ridge that was particularly suitable because it ran along the side of a gently sloping field of about two acres. The plan was to cover most of the burrows in the copse with purse-nets, leaving one or two holes on the lower edge uncovered. Knight stood with the eagle on his gauntlet or perched on a fence post and I released the ferrets at the top of the warren. On a good day the eagle might catch one or two rabbits and I would trap a few more in the nets. We used our 'jobs' to shoot pigeons at dusk to feed the birds. Ramshaw was at least fourteen and Knight was in his sixties. When I tried to find Montreal Park several years after the war, the fields and woods had disappeared under a blanket of modern urban housing development. Many years later I was pleased to meet Knight's grandniece, Jemima Parry-Jones, who manages a fascinating and comprehensive collection of raptors in the Cotswolds.

Each school term six ferrets travelled in the school train from King's Cross, an old polecat called 'Ferdinand', four young male ferrets named after the halogen elements 'Fluorine', 'Chlorine', 'Bromine' and 'Iodine' and a female called 'Betty'. During the term they lived by the powerhouse at the back of the school. Ferdinand, my 'line ferret', was used to locate other ferrets that had killed and eaten and then gone to sleep. His line, marked with knots at two-yard intervals, indicated the length of the burrow that had to be followed. A flexible willow wand, ten feet long, was used to find the direction of the burrow. Retrieving a lost ferret could be a lengthy process involving digging at intervals with a special spade that had a long narrow deeply curved blade. The willow wand had the tip broken off to leave a ragged end. I pushed it up the hole until it met an obstruction and twisted it several times before withdrawing it. A tuft of brown fur in the broken end showed when I had located a rabbit or white fur, the ferret. One spring day in a beech wood near Gilling Castle, Ferdinand's line became trapped under tree roots. I dug as far as I could but had to cut the line and abandon him. The next day the cut end of the line was no longer visible and I hoped that he had escaped. Incredibly, the following autumn in 1943 I returned to the same wood on a warm autumn afternoon and there was a fat Ferdinand, ambling towards me through the dry beech leaves. If ferrets could wag their tails in pleasure I am sure he would have done. He was soon in his box with two of the halogens.

Our GP, Dr. Jimmy Harrison, was a distinguished ornithologist and artist. Part of the upper floor of his house was used as a museum with hundreds of elegantly mounted birds from many parts of the world and thousands of 'skins' collected for scientific study in large specimen cabinets. His watercolours were painted in a somewhat oriental style. Many of them were published in his monograph on the *Birds of Sevenoaks and Western Kent.*[6] Both his sons became doctors and joined him in the practice. The elder, Jeffrey, who sadly died from a stroke at an early age, was also a leading ornithologist and conservationist and David was a world authority on bats. They preceded me to Cambridge and introduced me to wildfowling. In addition to the art of taxidermy, the Harrisons also taught me basic scientific skills. They showed me the importance of systematic classification, careful measurement, note-taking and drawing. My collection of stuffed birds grew rapidly and included my most treasured possession, a bittern that had been found dead in Norfolk.

I enjoyed rugby, hunting with the college beagles, athletics and cross-country running and broke the junior mile record, but I was weak at cricket. Since the cricket team was better off without me, I spent the summer afternoons roaming the countryside. I joined a group of nest watchers that included Peter McBarnet, who taught me a lot of ornithology, and three other enthusiasts —David Slattery, Peter Harvest and Vernon Lowe. I kept extensive notebooks and in the spring of 1943 observed and recorded the hatching and fledging of twenty-one species of birds in sixty nests. By the time I was fifteen I could recall the Latin names of all the birds on the British list. I was Secretary to the school Natural History Society, organized the meetings and frequently gave talks myself.

Ferdinand died of old age in 1944 and I sold the other ferrets because ornithology was competing for my time. I also started a lucrative business in exotic mice that were much in fashion at the time. My father built a four-storey mouse condominium with four 'rooms' on each floor, each room fitted with sliding glass doors and partitions. The floors and ceilings were protected with perforated zinc to prevent escapes and cross breeding. I had several multicoloured piebald mice and some most attractive lilac-and-tan and black-and-tan animals that commanded high prices. My mice bred in great numbers and at the end of each school holiday I kept a nucleus of stock for next term's breeding and sold the majority of the crop to a local dealer in Sevenoaks, making a respectable profit.

The headmaster, Fr. Paul ('Posh') Neville, always read the latest list of old boys killed in action during assembly in the 'long passage' each morning. One day he told us that we would be proud but sad to learn that one of them, Michael Allmand, had been posthumously awarded the Victoria Cross. I think we all secretly hoped that the war would continue long enough for us to get into it. The Junior Training Corps (that had replaced the Officers Training Corps) was compulsory and parades and training replaced sport for a whole afternoon each week. The Ampleforth Battalion comprised three companies each with three platoons and each platoon had a Bren gun, managed by two men, one of whom had to wave a gas-rattle to simulate firing when on manoeuvres. At a Polish army camp near Helmsley I was allowed to fire one round from a PIAT (Projector-Infantry-Anti-Tank) weapon. The projectile from these weapons contained a hollow charge that focused the explosion in such a way that a hole, barely wider than the thickness of a pencil, was driven through the armour, causing a shower of lethal fragments to spray around the inside of the tank. I managed to hit the tank, an old wreck perforated like a Swiss cheese. The PIAT had been manufactured in large numbers by ICI under the management of Father's colleague and life-long friend from the days when both families lived in Saltburn, F.E. Smith. I was the Battalion Signals Sergeant in charge of a Section (a third of a platoon) that was well equipped with No.18 sets. These were heavy and were carried on the back of one man and operated by a second. We also had a few smaller and lighter No.38 sets and a selection of telephone equipment, including a portable plug-board exchange and drums of wire all loaded on the truck that also carried refreshments for the battalion. Both my brothers subsequently did their National Service as officers in the Royal Signals.

Two months after D-Day Father bought a three-ton Bermuda sloop called *Dart*, and we started a series of family sailing holidays in Chichester harbour, renting a cottage on the sea front at Bosham. When the tide was up the road in front of the cottage flooded and we rowed Dart's dingy to the back door. Wartime restriction on sailing at sea kept us within the harbour but I was able to grasp the rudiments of boat handling.

I spent many autumn and winter days with the Harrisons on their rough shoot near Ightham in Kent, walking up partridge, pheasant and hares. One afternoon with the three Harrisons and one of Father's ICI colleagues, Raymond Pennock, I shot a Land Girl. She was much too far away to have been more than rained on by falling shot while doing something private behind a corn-stook. She jumped up with one hand on her rump shouting "I'm shot, I'm shot" and all three doctors Harrison rushed eagerly to the scene to attend to her injuries, but she refused to show them. I was shot a few years later at much closer range by my friend Chris Cummins (of whom more later) while duck shooting at night in my wheelchair; it did sting.

Listening to the radio in my den in the loft at Sevenholm, I heard that an atomic bomb had been dropped on Hiroshima. The significance of this news took a few seconds to sink in and I charged downstairs shouting "Benny Goodman was right, Benny Goodman was right". The man behind this outburst was Richard Goodman, the Head of Chemistry at Ampleforth, whom we always called 'Benny' after the famous American bandleader. Benny had introduced us to Einstein's equation, $E=mc^2$, and had explained how huge amounts of energy could be released from a tiny amount of matter and how radioactive materials might be made into a bomb. When I read the papers a day or two after Hiroshima, I was surprised to see the names of several wartime visitors to our house. One was Sir James Chadwick whom I would meet again in Cambridge as Master of Gonville & Caius College. Others included Prof. John Cockroft also of Cambridge and members of the 'Tube Alloys' team (the cover word for the bomb project), including Frank Ewart Smith and Wallace Ackers who was in charge of the ICI work. F.E. Smith and his family, who used to live close to us in Yorkshire, were now living near us again in Sevenoaks. After leaving Banstead we had rented a house near St Albans. The reason for this was never explained and it didn't occur to me that it might have been because it was close to the Atomic Research Establishment in Amersham. Even after the war my father fended off questions about ICI's role in the atom bomb; possibly he was disturbed by the way the Americans had used it. Several wartime meetings had been held in our dining room in Sevenoaks, while taciturn men in raincoats sauntered around the garden. ICI's contribution to the development of the bomb was significant because they knew how to separate the isotopes of Uranium.

To make a bomb it was first necessary to separate the lighter isotope of uranium— U235 — amounting to less than 1% of the uranium metal, from the heavier U238. This could be done by turning the metal into uranium hexafluoride gas and then passing the gas repeatedly through membranes perforated with tiny holes. At each passage a small fraction of the heavier isotope tended to be held back while the lighter one passed through the pores in the membrane. One of ICI's tasks was to manufacture metal sheets perforated at a density of 160,000 holes to the square inch. One of my father's golfing friends, Michael Clapham, Manager of ICI Metals Group's Kynoch Press, who later became Deputy Chairman of ICI, had the idea that a photographic printing technique using micro-dots might be adapted to enable thin metal membranes to be perforated by etching with acid. This failed, but he then had another idea that an electro-diffusion technique used in offset lithography might be used instead. It enabled filtration membranes to be manufactured in huge numbers.

Another memory of Michael Clapham was the new sports car (I think an Aston Martin) that he brought to our house to show my father. As he leaned over the engine the bonnet snapped shut, leaving him trapped by his voluminous sports jacket. Characteristically, Father muttered "most impressive Michael" and sauntered off for a few moments.

Towards the end of the war Father's ICI title changed from 'Controller of Purchases' to 'Sales Controller'. Had he not been barred from flying, because it was thought that his eye problems could be affected by pressure changes in aircraft, I am sure he would have been appointed to ICI's main board and remained in London. In October 1945, however, he was moved to a job that was much more 'hands on', a style that he greatly preferred. He was appointed Chairman of ICI's Alkali and Salt Divisions in Cheshire. He became a weekend commuter staying at Winnington Hall Club, a Victorian mansion around which the ICI chemical factories had been built early in the century. In the nineteenth century Winnington Hall had accommodated *Miss Bell's Academy for Young Ladies*. It was now the venue for social occasions including my twenty-first birthday party in the famous Octagon Room, a few weeks before I was disabled by polio. Father was also on the Board of the subsidiary Magadi Soda Company in Kenya and made a prolonged tour of that country and South Africa before taking up his new appointment. Later, as a member of the Wilton Council, responsible for the development of the huge complex of factories near Billingham he had a car adapted so that he could sleep in the back while his chauffeur drove him overnight across the country from Northwich to Billingham.

We moved to Hartford in Cheshire in April 1946. Our boat, *Dart,* that we had sailed in Chichester harbour after the invasion landings in Normandy, was taken out of the water at Bosham jetty and shipped overland to the Conway Estuary in North Wales. My birthday in August always followed the summer examinations and I had completed my Higher Certificate requirements (physics, chemistry, organic chemistry, botany, zoology and maths) while still sixteen. Cambridge would not accept me until I was eighteen so I had a spare year without serious commitments other than to enjoy my various pursuits and attend a few courses of my own choice. With no exams to pass I dabbled in what was known as 'Scientific German' with one-to-one tuition from Paul Hayward and attended classes in Political Philosophy and Economics. I had time to read and think about subjects of my own choosing, unfettered by the need to follow a curriculum. Nowadays I would probably have left a year early and travelled abroad but in 1946 this was not easy.

Life at Ampleforth was inextricably linked with the monastic life of the Benedictine community. The high academic standards and achievements of the school could be attributed to the total dedication of the teachers, most of whom were monks. Teaching was their vocation rather than a mere means of earning a living. They worked us hard without driving us. Great emphasis was placed on 'learning how to learn' and most of the teachers seemed to have the knack of making learning fun. Passing exams was not merely a question of what you knew but of how you presented what you knew.

In one respect I was always out of line. I was a bad Catholic; in fact I am sure I had never been a Catholic. I suffered silently from the beliefs that everybody around me seemed to take for granted and had not long reached my teens before I realised that cherished 'mysteries' such as transubstantiation or virgin birth that I had been taught in prep school were quite potty and that the sun had not moved from west to east at Fatima, but I went along with them passively while I was at school, resenting time wasted in church which would have been better spent in the open air or the library. Why should a mere accident of birth bind a human mind to any particular set of beliefs, Catholic, Jewish, Moslem or any other? There were more interesting ideas that I could talk about. I had begun to dabble in astronomy and physics and found it difficult to accept the idea that space and time had to have a beginning and a boundary. My chemistry master, Richard ('Benny') Goodman, had shown me how energy and mass were interchangeable. It seemed to me that somewhere in timeless and infinite space a minute disturbance in a sea of energy had caused a speck of matter to appear. Since energy itself had mass, more energy would be attracted to it by gravity, causing it to turn into more matter. Why should time have a beginning or space a boundary? I found it easier to believe in an infinity of space and time in all dimensions, past and future. I could accept a 'big bang' as the start of *our* universe but it still seems probable that there is an infinity of universes, banging and crunching in infinite space and infinite time. It follows that there is almost certainly an infinite number of sentient beings, marvelling at what they see through their telescopes or the windows of their spacecraft — wishing they could travel faster than light, or through 'worm holes', and communicate with each other. I have wondered if the expansion of our universe and the acceleration of distant galaxies to speeds approaching the speed of light (where clocks stop and time stands still) might be due to the gravitational pull of surrounding universes. My perception is substantially unchanged sixty years later.

By 1946 my interest in the natural sciences had already revealed a world of greater beauty and interest than anything I had read in books on religion, but I was far too shy to voice my thoughts. I believed that once man had evolved language and the ability to communicate abstractions, he experienced the need to create gods to account for all the things that could not otherwise be explained. Religions depend on belief in an after-life. This has enormous emotional and psychological appeal, but belief in an after-life has also made many humans treat each other as if they are expendable. The senior boys had been shown the newsreels of Belsen, and the majority of Germans were Catholics. Surely it was time to wake up, grow up, and push aside the mythology and dogma that had caused most of the wars, persecutions and atrocities throughout the ages. In the mid-40s, although opposed to abortion, I was also opposed to the Catholic attitude to birth control. War, starvation and pestilence are still the main factors retarding population increase. In spite of them the world population has tripled in my lifetime. I had begun to understand that the only way to prevent famine, flood and war was to keep populations to a level that the resources of each country could sustain by its own efforts. There were only two choices — birth control or conflict. The spare year at school allowed time for thought and reading that I might not have otherwise enjoyed and it probably helped to equip me for the struggle that lay ahead.

Writing at a time when the Catholic Church seems to be disintegrating, with exodus priests and allegations of homosexuality and paedophilia, I have been asked to what extent these problems were a problem at Ampleforth when I was there sixty years ago. I am not sure if they are a significant problem at this particular school today — reading the school journal, things seem much as they were in the 1940s — but I can honestly say that at no time during my eight years there did I encounter a single instance or remember any discussion among the boys that was not strongly heterosexually orientated. My education in this respect was limited to the lurid anecdotes of Sgt. Kelly, who ran the school armoury and regaled us with stories of 'poofter-bashing' on Clapham Common after the pubs closed on Saturday nights when he was in the army.

I shall not mention religion again in this book and will close this chapter with the few thoughts that remain, although chronologically out of sequence. Many human beings would sink into hopelessness and misery if they lost their belief that their souls have a potential for immortality. In the books by Richard Dawkins, I have been fascinated by the concept of a self-replicating '*meme*', defined as a 'unit of cultural inheritance'.[7] Whether or not the original idea was his does not matter, the concept is brilliant. Unlike the self-replicating *gene* that is a link in a chemical chain within a chromosome, the meme may be an idea, a story, a musical phrase, a concept or a belief, that lives in a brain. It may remain personal to that brain or it may infect other brains. The 'God meme', or the memes for ethnic purity, circumcision, racial hatred, male superiority, vegetarian diet and survival after death have powerful psychological appeal for some people. Perhaps the most potty, the 'creation' meme, the proposition that the universe is only about six thousand years old and that all living organisms were created over a period of six days, is the most outrageous of all insults to our intelligence. Unlike genes that mutate perhaps only once or twice in hundreds of generations, a few seconds of exposure to a meme may have profound consequences. For example, a particular musical phrase may cause brains to hum it occasionally for the remainder of their lives. The memes for religious fundamentalism or political dogma can rapidly infect thousands of brains, especially when presented with persuasive rhetoric by an evangelist. The consequences in my lifetime have included Auschwitz, Kosova, East Timor, Northern Ireland and the World Trade Center in New York.

Memes have almost limitless potential for mutation in the process of jumping from brain to brain. Once infected by a fundamentalist meme and convinced that our belief is the only correct one, we may see those who are not similarly infected as infidels who must be converted or slaughtered. It may be that some religious persons are happier because they are not constantly seeking answers to the unanswerable. Possibly only a minority of us are content to make the best use we can of our talents for our own fulfilment and to improve the lot of others. If we want to impress future generations we must be sure to broadcast our memes. Indeed, we can forget *our* genes because they disappear into the gene pool in two or three generations. They were not our genes in the first place, since we are merely a link in an unbroken ancestral chain and we cannot change them.

Alderley Edge, Cheshire, about 1935.

(Standing, left to right), May ('Donna') d'Oliveira, Father, Mother. (Seated) Howard ('Bobby') Andrews with Hugh, Theresa ('Tree') Andrews, Dr. Archibald Andrews, (on ground) Basil d'Olivera, Chris, Olivia ('Dinkie') d'Olivera with Piper, our Airedale, Author.

With my brothers about 1937
Chris (right) and Hugh (centre)

Junior Mile Record, Ampleforth, 1945

3

The End of the Beginning

I 'went up' to Gonville and Caius College, Cambridge, in October 1947 and shared rooms on 'Q' staircase with an old school friend, Ernest Kirwan, who was also a medical student. Although well prepared academically, we were schoolboys competing with war heroes five to ten years older and a lot richer than we were. In some ways we settled to the new life more easily. We were less irritated by the inconvenience of having to return to college before midnight, the exclusion of female visitors or having to obtain an 'exeat' (permit) to leave the environs of the University from our tutor.

The first day in an anatomy school leaves lasting impressions. Wearing a new and, almost for the last time, clean white coat, I walked through the double doors of the dissecting room. About twenty naked and uncovered corpses lay in neat rows on white ceramic slabs, some intact and others in various stages of dissection. We worked in pairs, taking turns to dissect or to read the instructions aloud from Cunningham's Manual on dissection. We referred to this as 'Little Cunningham' to distinguish it from 'Big Cunningham', a tome too large and heavy to be carried around that we couldn't afford to buy anyhow. The pages of Little Cunningham darkened while our hands became soft and smooth from daily contact with human fat and embalming fluid. Five terms were spent dissecting five 'parts' – arm, leg, abdomen and pelvis, head and neck and thorax. For our first term, Ernest and I found that we had been allocated a leg. We asked the attendant which body the leg might be attached to and he pointed in the direction of several large tanks at the end of the room saying that we must search for one of the 'spare parts' that bore a numbered label. Ernest lifted the lid of the first tank and we were greeted by at least twenty human heads bobbing about in the pickling solution. After rummaging in the logjam of floating limbs in the next tank, we found one with our number on a label attached to the big toe. Ernest carried it to a vacant table and I opened Little Cunningham.

In those days less than one in ten of the medical students was a female and I can only remember two in our year, Judith Fitzsimons and a girl called Rosemary. They were both beautiful and quite beyond the reach of two schoolboys competing with war veterans. Both of them were unperturbed by their first introduction to death, but several white-faced young men left the room hurriedly and another sat on a stool by the door with his head between his legs. Ernest and I were made of sterner stuff and I had seen bodies and parts of bodies during the Blitz. The 'subjects', as the textbook referred to them, were preserved with embalming fluid that had been injected under pressure through the vessels in the neck. A red paste was also injected into the arteries. As the dissection progressed, our knowledge was tested in short, informal, viva voce discussions with one of the demonstrators, whose signature was written in a logbook (the 'Grey Book') that recorded our progress throughout our time at the University. Post-war students will remember with affection the Head of the anatomy department, Professor H. A. Harris. He was a Welshman who enjoyed tormenting the know-alls who usually sat in the first row in the lecture theatre, or entertaining disciples who gathered round him in the *Blue Boar*. Two teachers, known as 'Big Davies' and 'Little Davies', were remarkable for their ability to make drawings on the blackboard 'move'. With coloured chalk in one hand and a duster in the other, adding a few strokes with the flat side of the chalk and obliterating earlier ones, we were shown how, for example, the heart of the embryo turned from a simple tube into a four-chambered pump.

Although competing for time that might have been spent on subjects directly relevant to my medical career, I had decided to take an extra 'half subject' in vertebrate zoology and I especially enjoyed one-to-one tutorials with Michael Swann. Michael was a large untidy man embarking on an extraordinary career. He was a Fellow of Caius College who had been appointed in 1946 as a demonstrator in zoology. In the early fifties, after I caught polio, he left Cambridge to take the Chair in natural history at Edinburgh. Having excelled as a scientist Michael became increasingly involved in public affairs. Eventually, as Lord Swann, he was appointed Chairman of the BBC. By an odd coincidence in 1947, the year I started to work under Michael's supervision, a distant relative, Phillip Inman (Lord Inman of Knaresborough) from my father's home town, was appointed Chairman of the BBC and Lord Privy Seal in Clement Attlee's Cabinet.[8]

The Professor of Physiology, Edgar Adrian (1st Baron Adrian), was a gentle scholarly man who was always at great pains to treat students as individuals. He became Master of Trinity College and Chancellor of the University. His son, the late Professor Richard Adrian (2nd Baron), was a member of our exclusive wildfowlers' dining club, the Guttersnipes. Other memorable teachers included H.F. (Bill) Grundy for pharmacology, Professor H.R. ('Daddy') Dean, Granville Naylor, Michael Stoker and Basil Herbertson for pathology and immunology. Most of our teachers were distinguished scientists in their own right and I cannot remember one of them whose presentation was less than excellent. We owe an immense debt of gratitude for something for which there is no substitute — enthusiasm. None was ever guilty of reading a lecture, referring to notes or failing to enhance his talk with clear and appropriate illustrations.

Physiology lectures were often illustrated with demonstrations using 'live' patients and tended to focus on the circulatory and nervous systems. Syphilis, a disease we rarely see nowadays, produced a variety of striking symptoms or physical characteristics that were especially dramatic for teaching purposes. A retired policeman enjoyed showing us the 'slapping gait' of people with syphilitic damage to the spinal cord. He had lost his 'sense of position' and was unable to judge how close his foot was to the ground when he walked. At every step, he slapped his foot hard on the floor before committing his weight to it. When asked to light a cigarette, another patient with brain damage, rubbed the end of a cigarette on a matchbox in an attempt to light it. Care was taken to avoid words such as 'syphilis' or 'VD' being mentioned in the hearing of patients. Patients with 'specific' disease were seen in the 'Special Clinic'. Syphilis was a taboo topic in polite society; how different today after the epidemic of AIDS.

Living close to the Fens and encouraged by the Harrisons, my main outside activity in the winter was duck shooting. Two or three times each month I shot duck during their evening flight from the coast to the inland marshes. This was difficult during my first year in college because I either had to return by midnight or stay out all night. In my second year I lived in a dilapidated house full of cats with an outside toilet that had no electric light. My landlady, Mrs. Mollineux, was an obese widow of boundless good humour who had no qualms about my irregular hours, especially when they produced a fat mallard or a partridge for her supper or a rabbit for the cats. Once or twice a week she cooked a beefsteak for my breakfast. She strongly approved of the moustache that I grew to hide the age gap from my ex-service peers. "As I used to tell my Albert, kissing a man without a moustache is like eating an egg without salt".

I breakfasted in my digs and dined most evenings in College. I could afford an active social life after visits to the rear entrance of MacFisheries shop near the market square, where pheasants, partridges, duck and snipe changed hands at very respectable prices in times of post-war food shortages. I played rugby occasionally but resisted invitations to take up rowing, although I was over six foot four, fourteen stone and extremely strong. I was not interested in politics and, although invited several times to dine at the Pitt Club, I could not afford to be a member. I preferred to lunch with a few cronies at the Union or in one of the pubs such as the *Blue Boar* or the *Volunteer*. The members of the *Guttersnipes* included its founders at Clare College, Jeffrey and David Harrison, Tim Tatham, Richard Adrian and a number of other dedicated wildfowlers. We invited Winston Churchill to become the honorary President of the Club as he had been called a 'Guttersnipe' by one of his political opponents, but in a hand-written letter he declined gracefully because of pressure of other commitments.

Wildfowling often involved a cycle ride of some fifteen miles to Earith where two man-made rivers known as the 100-foot drain or 'New Bedford River' and the 30-foot drain or 'Old Bedford River' start their parallel courses towards the coast. The fields between the two drains, known as 'washes', are flooded in the winter. Most duck were shot in the evening or late at night, especially when the moon was full and they were clearly silhouetted against the clouds. Sometimes I took my bicycle in the train to Ely and rode to a point where the main road to Wisbech crosses the washes at Welney. I had three regular companions—Ric Prestwich, Nigel Laing and Mike Weaving. Mike had a heavy 10-bore gun and loaded his own cartridges. Each discharge was followed by a vivid orange flash that tended to blind him (and any others who might be standing nearby), making it difficult to fix the position of a falling bird. We used to borrow a punt used by the osier cutters that we called the 'Flak Ship'. It enabled us to cross stretches of deep water and to retrieve birds that had fallen in the water.

Back in Cheshire, Caleb Walker, who looked after the garden at our house in Cheshire and lived with his family in a cottage in the grounds, taught me how to catch rabbits using long nets. Caleb had learned this skill when unemployed during the Depression. Working alone in the dark I could manage two fifty-yard nets, set end-to-end; they had drawstrings running along the top and bottom and strong wooden pegs at each end. Netting was possible only on a moderately windy moonless night when the ground was soft enough to allow the supporting canes to be pushed in noiselessly at intervals of a few yards. The nets were set along the downwind side of the field between the feeding rabbits and their warren. I then walked up the side of the field and drove the rabbits towards the net, traversing the field several times in a series of zigzags. The rabbits bolted into the net and it formed a 'purse' around each captive animal. A 'set' could take over an hour and might produce up to twenty rabbits. Wildfowl helped to pay my bills in Cambridge and rabbits kept me solvent during the vacations. I was also becoming quite a reasonable golfer and had an arrangement at Sandiway Golf Club to pay a greatly reduced membership fee in exchange for rabbit control. I often did a solo practice round at first light, carrying a 4.10 shotgun and a small selection of clubs in my golf bag. Shooting when and where I liked and making a fair profit from it was infinitely preferable to a regular holiday job.

The highlights of the Cambridge social calendar were the May Balls that started in June. To polish up my dancing technique, I found a couple of equally inept friends during the Easter vacation and sheepishly paraded for lessons with Kitty Oakes who taught ballroom dancing over a shop in Northwich. We gyrated in a circle around Kitty to the sound of an ancient gramophone and scratched '78s' while she clapped her hands, shouted instructions, and occasionally grabbed one of us for a more intimate demonstration of how a man should hold a woman. After half a dozen lessons our self-conscious group rapidly became surprisingly proficient in the waltz, the slow foxtrot, quickstep, and a few more exotic dances such as the tango and polka. I had a good sense of timing and felt confident enough to test my skills on the more attractive wallflowers at the Dorothy Café in Cambridge on Saturday evenings in preparation for the Caius May Ball of 1948. My father's tuxedo and tails had become too tight for him so I had both jackets rendered down and had one new pair of trousers made that almost matched both outfits.

In the spring of 1949 I consulted the Rev. Lancelot Flemming at the Scott Polar Institute in Cambridge who advised university expeditions and arranged funding for them. One interesting project was an expedition into Lapland. An expedition had been planned that was to set out from Abisko, some two hundred kilometres north of the Arctic Circle in Sweden. Peter Scott was eager to acquire some lesser white-fronted geese for his wildfowl collection at Slimbridge and I thought this might be an opportunity to capture some lesser whitefronts while they were flightless during the annual moult, but I had only a sketchy idea of the location of their breeding grounds and it was imperative that I talk to Peter Scott. I tracked him down after he had given a lecture in Cambridge. Our meeting had a slightly traumatic outcome. While talking to me he was preoccupied signing copies of his latest book at the rate of perhaps one every ten seconds. He tried to explain the problems that were involved in shipping goslings by land and sea to England. When I asked him the location of the breeding area he inadvertently wrote the location — Vassijaure — in the fly sheet of the book he was signing, ruining it. He was not amused. The expedition was cancelled after a fire had destroyed the hostel we had planned to use as a base at Abisko.

Instead, I joined another group to sail a small boat to the Faeroe Islands. *Ellen Louise* was a twelve-ton wooden fishing smack built in Brixham in 1913. She was a two-masted ketch powered by a single-cylinder Bollander diesel engine and owned by Harry Leney, who was a master at Gordonstoun School. I was to assist John Miles, a virus specialist who hoped to study fulmar petrels and puffins that were a significant part of the islanders' diet. They had recently been responsible for a serious epidemic of pneumonia in the islands. John Miles, Sam Essame and I joined the boat in Aberdeen while Harry Leney, Jerry Thomas and John Collison-Morley, sailed the boat up from Rye. An hour out of Rye the banjo bearing on the flywheel broke and for the next thirty-six hours they had carried on under sail to

Harwich for repairs. This delayed their arrival in Aberdeen by several days. Much of the work that should have been done to equip her properly for the North Atlantic was skimped.

We cleaned the boat and loaded diesel oil and coal for the stove, a large quantity of salted and tinned meat, paraffin for the lamps and forty gallons of drinking water. Ellen Louise was ill-equipped for deep-sea voyaging. The engine filled much of the main cabin. There were no 'heads'; essential functions were conducted by 'friggin in the riggin'; in other words, hanging from the shrouds over the lee side, undignified and wet but preferable to risking fundamental injuries from a bucket in the chain locker. We carried spare diesel in two forty-gallon drums on the deck and a small dinghy was lashed upside down over the drums. There was no deckhouse or protection for the helmsman who steered with a tiller and took bearings from a portable compass that was not screwed to the deck. We had a domestic radio receiver but no transmitter.

We sailed from Aberdeen at 1.30 p.m. on July 28th 1949 and almost immediately ran into bad weather. During the morning watch we briefly sighted Orkney to the north-west and, to avoid being swept into the tide-race of Pentland Firth, we turned south, sighting land again in the afternoon and found Wick harbour at midnight. The following morning we brought *Ellen* into the inner harbour and tied up alongside an Aberdeen coal-boat, the *SS Deedon,* while waiting for calmer weather.

In spite of a falling barometer Harry decided it was safe to leave Wick and we sailed again at 2.00 p.m. on August 1st, my twentieth birthday. With a moderate easterly breeze and the tide in our favour we raced through Pentland Firth, passing the southern entrance to Scapa Flow and the Old Man of Hoy at 9.00 p.m. The Faeroes are a ninety-mile chain of volcanic islands roughly half way between Cape Wrath and Iceland. We should have reached the capital, Torshavn, in about forty hours. Tuesday August 2nd, however, brought a full gale from the north. We were being driven south-west with only the mizzen to keep our head to wind and the engine providing steerageway. At midday the log line parted and we carried no spare. For the rest of the voyage we had no means of estimating our speed. Although Harry had a sextant there was no horizon and no sun or stars. I have never been seasick but I had an attack of migraine. I had suffered from it in the past but thought I had grown out of it. For several hours at a time I lost some of my vision and was not an effective member of the crew.

By the 3rd of August we were in trouble and our survival depended on whether or not the engine kept running. The boat had no engine-operated pump and the bilge had to be pumped by hand every half-hour. In the evening the pump failed. Although the hull was reasonably sound, a lot of water seeped through the deck planks. We formed a bucket chain; one of us had to open and close the hatch each time a bucket was passed up to be emptied on the deck. We lashed the tiller and stayed below because the risk of being run down was smaller than the risk of losing someone overboard. The engine proved to be the most reliable piece of equipment on the boat and kept going. We had no idea how far we were being blown off our planned course or how likely we were to miss the Faeroes completely and possibly Iceland as well. On Thursday the 4th the storm abated slightly and the sun showed briefly. Early in the morning we sighted a large wooden Norwegian fishing boat and managed to get within hailing distance. A man on deck understood from our sign language that we had no radio and had lost our log and he disappeared into the wheelhouse, emerging with a piece of board that he heaved on to our deck. Chalked on it was the message, '0730 hrs. Suderoy 40 miles 333°.' Suderoy is the southernmost of the islands and we had not drifted as far West as we had feared. Later I learned that the Norwegian had radioed Faeroe coastguards that a small English boat was on course for Suderoy and making water. When we eventually stripped down the bilge-pump we found it blocked by a plastic bag of prunes and a sock.

We reached Suderoy on the 5th of August after one more crisis. The fuel in the main tank had nearly run out and it was necessary to transfer diesel from one of the drums on deck before the engine stopped. There was no fuel line and the tap was too close to the deck to fill a can. With one of the others on lifelines, I filled lime-juice bottles with diesel, a cupful at a time, one of us opening and closing the tap and the other keeping a thumb over the mouth of the bottle each time a wave came over our heads. We managed to top up the tank sufficiently to make a landfall before the engine stopped. To restart it would have meant lighting a hand-held blowtorch and using this to heat up a series of burners round the cylinder head. Two people would then have to swing the flywheel until the engine fired.

We anchored in Vaag Fjord at 3.00 a.m. on August the 6th. My bunk was full of water and I fell asleep on the floor. The following morning, soaked but slightly warmer, we were feeling more cheerful and decided to cook our first hot meal for five days. As we were about to eat it we heard a thumping sound and thought something had broken loose on deck. One of us went on deck and we heard the klaxon going and the sound of flares. Although we had used the heavy anchor and tied a weight further up the chain, the strong northerly wind had blown us across the fjord onto the lee shore. Fortunately it amounted to little more than large shingle and there was little risk of being holed but we could not start the engine for fear of damaging the propeller or launch the dinghy to take out the kedge anchor because of the swell. Within fifteen minutes a small Norwegian trawler put out from the harbour on the other side of the fjord and stood off about twenty yards from us. A light line landed amidships at the first attempt and we hauled over a heavy rope, fastened it to the mast and were towed to the harbour. To our surprise, several hundred inhabitants of Vaag lined the quay, cheering and clapping. I learned later that the news had got around that a "British ship has gone aground. A big ship? No, we think quite a little ship. The one from Cambridge University that was going to Torshavn to help with the pneumonia epidemic." The applause as we rounded the harbour wall was because they saw how small was the boat that had survived a storm that had forced a fleet of large trawlers and a whaler to run for shelter several days earlier.

We were taken to a large Faeroese ship loading salted fish, where we recovered rapidly, sitting naked in blankets while the clothes we had worn for six days were dunked in buckets of fresh water and then dried on the ship's boiler. We were offered a local delicacy — thin strips of crisp, salted, whale blubber from the small pilot whales known as 'grind', washed down with aquavit and Pilsener and were soon very happy. In the afternoon we were invited on board one of three Peterhead steam drifters, the *SD Rossard*, sheltering with her sister ships *Fertility* and *Lunar Bow* and enjoyed an enormous high tea. The local doctor came on board with the good news that the pneumonia epidemic was subsiding but the sad news that the Chief Medical Officer in Torshavn had died – from pneumonia.

Ellen Louise was a shambles and half the bunks were unusable. Harry and John Miles stayed with Mr Johanssen, the Headmaster of the local school, who was also the Mayor of Vaag. I stayed with Pauli and Alfrida Thomassen, the Harbour Master and his wife. Most Faeroese spoke good English, a legacy of the British garrison that had saved the islands that belong to Denmark from occupation by the Germans.

John Miles and I had planned to help the local doctors with the pneumonia epidemic, catch sea birds and collect blood samples for his virus studies. With no new human cases, there was now less urgency for John to continue his project. 'Puffinosis' was a virus infection of sea birds such as fulmars and puffins similar to parrot disease or psittacosis that had jumped the species barrier and produced an occasionally fatal human pneumonia. It bore a striking similarity to today's epidemic of 'SARS' or Severe Acute Respiratory Syndrome, but had not spread beyond one or two of the islands because they were so isolated. I had come to the Faeroe Islands with a secondary objective to collect some whale pituitary glands for the Physiology Department at Cambridge. Periodically, schools of small whales, called grind, are driven into the fjords and slaughtered by the islanders. There was only a small chance of a whale killing during my stay, even assuming I could reach one of the ninety-mile long chain of islands in time to dissect the heads of the whales. I was advised to abandon this idea as well. *Ellen Louise* was too cramped for six people, so John Miles decided to return to Scotland in the *Barjama*, the regular mail-boat from Torshavn to Leith. I asked if I could join *Rossard*. Robert Duthie, the skipper, seemed delighted to have an extra hand and refused the equivalent of the mail-boat fare (£11.11s). On the morning tide at 5.00 a.m. on the 8th of August, *Rossard* sailed for the Faeroe Bank eighty miles to the east of the archipelago for a week of halibut fishing. *Ellen Louise* was later sailed back to Scotland without incident.

The *SD Rossard* was a steam drifter of some ninety tons, equipped in the appropriate season to drift for herring or for long-lining. She had been built in 1913, the same year as *Ellen Louise*, and had a crew of ten. The owners, Robert Duthie and his younger brother Peter, were Captain and Mate. Sandy Jack was the Engineer, Bill Buchan the 'Gear Man' who owned the lines and other deck equipment, Jimmy Jabby the cook, Tommy Buchan (Tucker) the fireman and Jock Strachan, Arthur Pirie and two more Buchans, James and Joe, were deck-hands. None of the four Buchans failed to tell me that of course he was quite unrelated to any of the other three. I was given a spare bunk at the rear of the saloon across the propeller shaft, uncomfortable if the ship was rolling but warm and dry. Sandy Jack showed me the engine room with its gleaming brass wheels and dials, the fish hold and ice store and the deck layout and warned me about some of the areas on deck that were particularly dangerous during fishing.

The lines were carefully coiled in round wicker baskets each containing half a mile of line to which lengths of thinner line called *sneads* bearing the hooks were attached. About three hundred hooks were arranged in order around the cork-lined rim of the basket so that they left it in sequence without becoming snagged. The lines were 'shot' with Rossard travelling at perhaps two knots. Each hook was baited with a whole herring, half a mackerel or 'dollops' of white fish, as it left the basket. Four men were needed to join the half-mile lengths of line, bait the hooks and throw them clear. Each man had a sharp knife immediately to hand so that he could cut the snead instantly if anyone got hooked. It was said that some skippers had shot as many as thirty-six baskets (eighteen miles) of line. *Rossard's* usual shoot was about twenty-eight baskets extending for some fourteen miles. We shot the lines in daylight, but pulling often continued well into the night. As the last of the line was shot a weight carried it down to the seabed together with a pulling line of about three hundred fathoms (1,800 feet) attached to a dan buoy. The dan comprised nothing more elaborate than a bamboo and a small flag stuck into a large cork. The shoot took three to four hours and after an interval of two hours pulling started, last-hook-in-first-hook-out, because it would be impossible to locate the other dan at the far end of the line fourteen miles away. The main commercial catch was halibut, but a variety of other saleable fish were hooked including ling, conger eels, dogfish, skate, tope and cod.

One of my jobs was to keep the ship up to the dan while the crew got some sleep between shooting and pulling. It was easy to drift back half a mile before the engine-room telegraph took effect and it was vital not to overshoot the dan. In heavy weather it would be difficult to make a 360° turn to recover position without losing sight of the dan and losing thousands of pounds worth of gear and fish. At these times the engineer, Sandy Jack, or the fireman, Tommy Tucker, was in the engine room and I was alone in the deckhouse. In addition to the telegraph I could communicate through a speaking tube. By enabling a man to sleep while I kept the ship up to the dan I was doing something useful in return for my passage to Scotland.

Pulling was slower but equally skilful and dangerous as shooting. A small steam winch was fixed to the port side in front of the wheelhouse and operated by the winch-man who instructed Peter or Robert in the wheelhouse with hand signals. Too fast and the ship could foul the line; too slow and the line could break if the wind or tide caused the ship to drift. Snagging an underwater obstruction such as a wreck was a hazard because we were fishing in waters where dozens of ships had been torpedoed. The line broke on one occasion and there were several anxious hours of trolling slowly backwards and forwards with a grapnel until the line was snagged and brought to the surface.

Immediately behind the winch-man stood the unhooker who pulled the fish onto the deck using a short gaff. Behind the unhooker were two 'readers' who separated the half-mile lengths of line and coiled them loosely into empty baskets and then carefully re-coiled them into another basket and arranged the hooks round the rim ready for the next shoot. A 'cleaner' gutted the fish, throwing the liver into a tin marked 'Halibut' for medicinal liver oil or 'other' for making into paint, and the guts were thrown to the seagulls and fulmars. A 'dolloper' cut baitfish into suitable sized pieces for the next shoot. Periodically everybody changed jobs, the winch-man became an unhooker, the unhooker a reader, a reader a cleaner or a dolloper and so on. The biggest prize, halibut, was worth a guinea a stone at the dockside. In 1949 large fish were still caught, sometimes weighing six to eight stone and requiring four men with gaffs to bring them over the side.

My jobs also included hosing down, gutting and dolloping and any other unskilled deck jobs that were going, as well as doing my dan-watching stint in the wheelhouse. There were several minor accidents which, although not yet a clinical medical student, I was expected to deal with. I removed a four-inch fishhook from the face of one of the Buchans and treated an abscess in the cavity in Jimmy Jabby's skull that normally accommodated his glass eye. Whenever the cry of 'Buttie' went up everybody, including Jimmy the cook, rushed on deck and grabbed long-handled gaffs. During one tussle Jimmy's glass eye went overboard. He carried no spare and soon developed an abscess in the socket that I treated with great success with frequent rinses of the only readily available antiseptic – strained boiled and diluted sea water. Abscesses were troublesome, particularly on the wrists where the sleeves of the oilskins chaffed and where the hands were constantly exposed to the stings from fragments of jellyfish torn apart by the lines.

As soon as the fish-hold was full, a race began to catch the top of the Peterhead market. With Plymouth Brethren and Exclusives among the crew, *Rossard* was a 'dry ship' (our contraband was stowed in the lifeboat), but, judging by the songs sung by both their skippers on the ship-to-ship radio, both sister ships, *Fertility* and *Lunar Bow,* were far from dry. On my last day at sea, while the crew slept, I was given the wheel and a compass bearing on a glorious summer evening and a few hours later I woke the crew as we entered Pentland Firth, abeam of Hoy.

On docking in the dark at Peterhead, the customs man came on board and we sat with him in the cabin with a cup of tea and presented a few token bottles of gin and packs of cigarettes. "I expect you've got the rest in the life-boat as usual," he said wearily, but he didn't look.

The week with the crew of *Rossard* was one of the happiest I can remember. They were exposed to danger every minute of their working day and they survived by constant vigilance and care for each other. The rewards were meagre. They were at sea for all but a few days each month, sometimes sailing as far as Spitzbergen or across the Denmark Strait to the Greenland Sea. Each took a share of the money depending on the size of their investment in the boat or gear or their special expertise and all of them worked flat out to make each voyage as profitable as possible. There were occasional arguments about football but I heard no backchat about individuals on board, no display of temper or sulking. I was with friends and shipmates.

Forty years later I telephoned the harbour office at the fishing port in Peterhead and was put in touch with Walter Milne, a nephew of Robert and Peter Duthie, both of whom, together with all but two of the crew (Jimmy the cook and Tommy the fireman) were dead. Walter reminded me of an incident that he had been told about as a child. It had happened while I was sailing with *Rossard*. The excitement of landing a particularly large fish could lead to momentary lapses of concentration and one man had gone down with a blow from the end of a six-foot gaff-handle. Minutes later the innocent perpetrator of the blow was also sitting in the scuppers next to his mate, laughing their heads off and nursing rapidly blackening eyes. Walter told me that *Rossard* had been "turned into razor blades" in 1954.

My last year at Cambridge was to end dramatically in the events described in the prologue, but there were happier developments. I fell in love. Pamela Cooper lived in Hartford not far from our home in Cheshire and was my partner at Saturday night dances in Chester and at the '49 May Ball in Cambridge. She was much approved of by my parents and I think I did not go down too badly with hers. Had disaster not struck in the autumn of 1950, I might have been looking forward to a long engagement until I had finished my training and junior appointments.

In the autumn, while my parents were in France, I was frequently invited to dine at the home of one of my father's colleagues. Several months later, in hospital, a researcher from the health authority who was following up my case interviewed me. I had been the only polio victim in the area for several months. She wanted to identify possible contacts. I knew who was most likely to have passed the virus on to me but I lied.

My kind hosts had both been unwell after a holiday on the Isle of Wight where there had been a severe epidemic. They had probably had mild attacks of non-paralytic polio. The truth could have destroyed them and they never thought of the connection themselves. My family avoided the danger and Pam, thankfully, was spared.

On a bright afternoon in October 1950, I walked along Trumpington Street to my rooms at Caius. Except in my dreams I would never walk again.

The 'Flak Ship' on the Washes near Ely in 1948, Mike Weaving (centre) and Ric Prestwick (right)

Waiting in the osiers for the evening duck flight

Father with Lord MacGowan
at Winnington Hall, about 1950

Philip Inman, from Father's hometown of Knaresborough, Lord Privy Seal in the Atlee Government and Governor General of the BBC

Cambridge Rag Week. Author with Ukelele, John Brockman in cart, Ernest Kirwan pushing

4

"I was wondering where you'd got to, Doctor."

The Robert Jones and Agnes Hunt Hospital at Gobowen near Oswestry in Shropshire was forbidding from the outside and worse inside. My first sight, as the ambulance turned into the hospital on November 2nd, 1950, was a row of beds with blue waterproof covers and almost invisible patients lying in a row under a glass-roofed, but otherwise open, verandah. I was glad to learn that they were tuberculosis rather than polio cases. It was still believed that the fresh cold mountain air of the Alps aided recovery from tuberculosis. Those who could afford to lingered in Switzerland; some of those who could not had a good view of the boiler house and mortuary in Gobowen. I was wheeled into a long single-storey hut that did have four walls and no verandah. Seven or eight young men lay in beds with their legs suspended from wooden frames known as 'Balkan beams'. They had heavy weights hanging from pulleys attached to pins through their leg bones. All of them had crashed a motor cycle. There were a few elderly or demented patients, constrained by cot-sides, who had survived a hip fracture. A small group of men and boys in pullovers, gloves and scarves huddled round one of the two small coke stoves that were the only source of warmth. The scene resembled a prisoner of war film, except for the uncovered glass urinals on the locker tops. Was it possible that paralysed patients, who above all needed warmth, were expected to rehabilitate in such conditions? The huts were wartime Emergency Medical Service (EMS) buildings, separated from the main hospital. When I visited Gobowen forty-four years later, although no longer used for patients, my 'ward' and one of the glass-roofed verandahs still stood unchanged at the rear of a more modern complex of buildings.

Nobody resembling a nurse was in sight when I arrived, but a stocky cheerful man in a brown storekeeper's coat introduced himself as George the ward orderly. George told me that until recently he had been a greengrocer and I was surprised that he was the sole person in charge of the ward and about twenty-five patients. Those who, like me, were immobile were totally dependent on him for all our needs. George did much to maintain a high level of morale. He fed and washed and shaved us, wiped our bottoms, laid out the dead, did the bottle rounds and, to roars of applause, stoked the stoves. He organised the walking wounded to run errands and place the bets with the hospital bookie.

I asked George when I could expect to see Mr Roaf, the orthopaedic surgeon. He told me that he only came over from Liverpool once every five weeks and would not see me for another three. Meanwhile they would replace the arm and leg splints that I had to wear most of the time. This was to prevent deformities as my muscles contracted. The splints made for me in Cambridge when I weighed two hundred pounds were too large to fit a body that was now about sixty pounds lighter. The sight of my naked legs and skeletal pelvis attached to a few disproportionately normal softer parts, evoked thoughts of the newsreels of Belsen and the Burma-Siam railway. I had been reduced to little more than a pile of bones and balls.

There were two other polio patients. Tom was a schoolmaster and music teacher; he could walk normally but had to wear a metal frame projecting at right angles to his body and supporting one arm. His fingers, like mine, were incapable of fine movements and it seemed unlikely that he would play the piano again. In the next bed to mine was Harry Back, a barber. Harry had been badly nursed in another hospital and had deep life-threatening bedsores on his hips and back. Unkind inmates used to ask him "How's your back today, Back?" He was being nursed in a plaster bed and his whole body, except his face, had been encased in plaster of Paris, the cast had then been split down the sides so that the front and back halves could be separated. It resembled a sarcophagus. When lying face down, only his face was visible through a hole that had been cut out of the plaster. Other holes had been made for bodily functions and the whole contraption rested on a wooden frame several inches above his bed. Harry had to alternate between lying on his back or his front for an hour or two at a time, day and night. To turn him, the two halves of the cast were strapped together and two porters had to be called in to roll him over on his frame. When lying on his back, the front half of the casing was removed so that the physiotherapist could exercise his arms and legs. When lying on his front, the rear half of the casing was removed so that his pressure sores could be dressed.

Although nobody had discussed my future with me I had rapidly come to terms with the probability that I would not walk again and would spend the rest of my life in a wheelchair. I had broken the bad news to myself. I could see difficulties ahead but my immediate thoughts were focused on getting away from these awful surroundings. I was not prepared to accept that my problems should be considered only at five-week intervals by the consultant's travelling circus.

It was obvious that, like me, Harry would never walk again either. It was equally obvious that he had no inkling of this probable outcome and he talked enthusiastically about what he would do when he got out of hospital. I shall never forget the way the news was broken to him. A few days after I arrived, he plucked up courage to ask the Registrar how long before he would be able to walk again? At first, it seemed that the man might not even stop to answer as he walked past Harry's bed; but he paused, half turned, and said with his strong Australian accent, "You don't seriously think you'll ever walk again do you?" and moved on, leaving me to comfort a shocked and weeping Harry. I could just reach across between our beds to grab his hand as we talked it through.

After a month of stagnation my spirits revived when I was driven home for Christmas. George took the day off to accompany me. Pamela made numerous visits to my home and I returned to Oswestry on the 2nd of January with renewed hope that positive treatment, whatever that might be, would start soon; Mr Roaf's next visit, however, produced nothing more than a note, dictated to the secretary who accompanied him on his round — "see again in five weeks". This was crushing. At least I had expected to have hydrotherapy exercises in a warm bath. Some strength was returning in my arms and hands but delicate movements required for writing or manipulating small objects were still severely restricted. My biceps muscles had regained quite a lot of strength and I had started to sit up with the help of a length of rope attached to the foot of the bed. I could not support myself on a conventional bedpan and had to recline on an inflatable rubber one and be cleaned by George. Crapping like a baby, while reclining nearly horizontally, is both difficult and degrading.

I have no doubt that the conditions in the main part of the hospital were greatly superior to those in the huts and I had no complaints about the valiant efforts by George and Sister Brogan to maintain morale. The infrequent visits by the Roaf circus, however, convinced me that I could make only slow progress at Oswestry and my father, who always got his own way, arranged for me to be moved to Clatterbridge Hospital in the Wirral of Cheshire.

I guessed that my mother and Pam's mother had discussed our future, but I had already decided not to allow my feelings to overwhelm common sense. It would be several years before I could reasonably expect to rehabilitate to the point of earning enough to support a family. I let the relationship wane from April 1951 with great sadness. There were no dramatics and the grief was well concealed.

Clatterbridge Hospital was a great improvement. The orthopaedic patients were housed in a row of single-storey buildings some distance from the main hospital. They were freshly painted and warm; the windows were unbroken and clean and staff were plentiful. I was a patient of George Partridge, the surgeon whom I had consulted the previous year after falling off Pamela's horse and damaging my shoulder. Clatterbridge had a Hubbard hydrotherapy tank in which I spent a comfortable forty-five minutes each day, exercising with much of the weight of my legs and arms supported by warm water. Paul, the physiotherapist, worked hard to develop any useful movement using an electric stimulator on any residual shreds of muscle fibre that could be made to contract. He concentrated on my quadriceps, the large muscles at the front of the thigh that are essential to extend (straighten) the leg and give stability to the knee. There was a barely perceptible flicker of movement on both sides but we never succeeded in developing them enough even to tighten my kneecaps. Paul and I worked as a team and it was not always easy to decide which of us got the greatest pleasure out of any small improvement that might be noticeable at the end of a hard week's work. I soon recovered enough strength in my arms to qualify for a self-propelled wheelchair and I was able to write slowly. From the earliest days in the isolation hospital in Cambridge I had written letters with a stub of pencil fixed to my index finger by an elastic band. Now I could write by steadying the upper end of a pen or pencil between thumb and index finger, gripping the lower end between my fourth and fifth fingers. My brain soon switched writing instructions from my thumb and forefinger to my fourth and fifth fingers and I have written like this ever since. To have any chance of useful employment it was obvious that I must learn to type. I bought an Imperial Good Companion portable typewriter and soon reached an acceptable speed and accuracy using three fingers of my left-hand and two on the right. I would have broken the heart of any typewriting teacher.

I was fitted with full-length callipers and started a determined attempt to walk. The first pair comprised leather-covered metal rings fitting round the upper thighs; each had two long metal rods, bent at the lower end to fit into sockets drilled into the heel of my boots. Leather straps encircled my legs above and below the knees and round the ankles. The equipment was excruciatingly uncomfortable. During ward-rounds the 'Orthopods' floated bright ideas such as cutting my hamstring tendons and moving them round to the front to do the job of the quadriceps, but my hamstrings never recovered enough strength. One keen young registrar suggested permanently fusing one knee and the opposite hip joint. I could see difficulties getting into a car with one permanently extended leg and one stiff hip and it would probably preclude use of a wheelchair.

Although the outlook for walking looked bad and I had accepted that I would probably fail, I was fitted with more sophisticated callipers by Hangers of Roehampton in London. They were beautifully made in leather and stainless steel, hinged at the knees and attached to a pelvic band encircling the hips. The whole contraption could be made rigid with sliding locks at the knees and hips. I was never able to move either leg individually and could only make progress on crutches by swinging both legs and the lower half of my body in one piece. By the end of the following year, using elbow crutches, I could cover a hundred yards on the flat in about thirty minutes.

When people fall, the body tends to fold at the natural hinge-points, the hips and knees. Whenever I fell, with my hips and knees locked in iron and leather, six foot four of bone and metal crashed down like a telegraph pole. The 'drill' for falling was to get rid of the crutches as soon as possible, leaving the arms free and flexed to 'fend off' the floor. I broke several ribs and suffered wrist sprains and bruises, although I avoided major fractures. Getting in and out of my car restricted by the pelvic band and callipers was extremely difficult.

By 1952 when I had become expert with my wheelchair I decided that the risk of injury, inconvenience and fatigue involved in achieving no more than a pretence at walking, was unacceptable. There could be no second chance if I gave up the attempt because after a few months in a wheelchair my hamstrings would start to contract, leaving my legs permanently flexed. Regular physiotherapy to prevent this would have seriously interfered with employment and I had a life to get on with.

My decision to abandon futile attempts to walk came as a relief. I had seen patients become acutely depressed about their failure to walk. For many of them, life in a wheelchair was unthinkable. How could one earn a living? What chance would one have with the girls? My solution was to cut my losses, set aside the callipers and crutches, get a fast car and see if that impressed the ladies. I started to experiment with various kinds of wheelchair. Setting aside minor variations in seat and backrest design, the choice was between the most popular design that has the castors in front and one with trailing castors. The latter is quite rare but it is a choice that I commend to anybody with weak arms. A chair with trailing castors is significantly shorter, sometimes by as much as fifteen percent compared with one with castors in the front and it can turn in a more confined space such as a right-angle bend in a narrow passage. When self-propelled over rough surfaces the front castors are more liable to sink into a rut than the trailing ones. However, the front-castor chair should always be chosen if the disabled person is normally pushed by a helper, as it can be tipped more safely when negotiating curbs.

In Clatterbridge I made two friendships, one long lasting and the other, sadly, short. One was with Gordon Cowie, a Wirral farmer whose spine had been fractured by his prize bull, fortunately with no permanent ill effects. After leaving hospital I was frequently entertained by Gordon and his wife, Wyn, at *Goldstraw Farm* at Ness-in-Wirral. The other patient was a young man in the next bed to me. He was a painter and decorator working for ICI. Frank had an osteosarcoma, a form of bone cancer, in his thigh from which few recovered even with dramatic surgery. He agreed to a mutilating 'hindquarter' amputation, involving the removal of the whole of his leg and half his pelvis. We became close friends during the run up to the operation. He was highly intelligent and faced it with incredible bravery. After the operation I spent several days sitting with him in a sideward as he adjusted to the loss of a quarter of his body. When he had recovered somewhat, Frank and I organized some serious beer-drinking parties in the bathroom block with the help of one or two stalwarts, an attractive nurse called Jean Hirst, and a 'lookout'. Frank could soon stand and move about the ward on crutches, but only a few weeks after the operation, a new swelling appeared at the base of his spine. "Bill," he said, "I've had my chips." He was discharged before I left Clatterbridge and I was able to make only one journey to see him at his home before he died. I heard subsequently that some people had worried about the effect on me when the inevitable happened. They need not have worried; every minute I spent with Frank was enriching.

Throughout the summer my strength increased impressively, though almost entirely in my arms. I learned to overcome a problem with my right arm where the triceps muscle, that normally holds the arm straight at the elbow, was completely and permanently out of action. My knowledge of anatomy was useful; I knew that some muscles in the forearm that enable it to be rotated, for example when using a screwdriver, were attached to the humerus in the upper arm. By rotating my forearm so that my thumb pointed away from my body, I was able to use these muscles to lock the arm straight. This enabled me to lift myself from my wheelchair to the bath, loo, bed or car. It was probably my most important physical achievement; had I failed to find a way of holding my right arm straight and rigid, life might have been different and I would have been dependent on help from others.

In September 1951, a year after my illness had started, my parents borrowed a caravan and I spent two weeks fishing for bass near Aberdovey in Wales. I slept in the caravan and my parents in a nearby hotel. I caught very few bass but coped well in the caravan, sliding over the floor on my bottom and lifting myself onto the seats without help. This marked the start of an acrobatic period that lasted for many years. I learned how to get back into my chair, unaided, after falling out of it. I could climb stairs on my bottom and transfer easily from chair to car, pulling the folded chair after me.

The example of two of my father's disabled employees was inspiring. Bill Robinson, a Canadian, was a walking demonstration of raw courage rather than a technical adviser in my particular situation. Bill was blind and had never seen his wife Monica or his numerous children. He walked everywhere at normal speed — fast. I watched him one day, bowling down Walnut Lane and crashing face first into a lamppost. He recoiled and set off again at the same speed dabbing his nose with a bloody handkerchief. Until their family became too numerous, the Robinsons exercised on a tandem bicycle; Bill was seen riding the tandem from the front, taking steering instructions from Monica. The other was a Scottish Baronet, Jimmy Stuart-Menteth, who had lost both legs above the knee when his tank 'brewed up' while serving in the Scots Guards. When I first called on him I found him weeding his garden. He was sitting, naked and without his artificial legs, in an old school satchel that served as a 'body boot'. He propelled himself around his garden on his hands and boot. Jimmy loved fast sports cars and gave me many useful tips about various kinds of hand controls.

Father's chauffeur, Bill Tench, drove us to Birmingham for lunch with one of Father's many 'chums', who turned out to be the Chairman of Austins. I was shown a bright blue *A90 Atlantic* sports convertible that had been used as a demonstration car for overseas dealers. It had less than three thousand miles on the clock and was thought to be especially suitable for me because it had only two large doors that opened almost to a right angle, allowing easy access from a wheelchair. Seated in the driving seat I was not strong enough to lift the chair over my head into the back of the car, so I developed a technique that I used subsequently in about a dozen cars over more than forty years. I got into the car from the passenger side, collapsed the wheel chair and lifted the rear castors onto the sill. I then moved across to the driving seat and folded the back of the passenger seat forwards. Finally I hauled the chair into the rear of the car. In several successive cars I replaced the passenger seat with a folding seat from a wrecked *Scimitar* sports car. An alternative strategy was to make the seat squab detachable so that it could be stowed on the rear seat and then haul the wheelchair into the front beside me holding it in place with the seatbelt. With either solution a passenger could lift the chair in for me and sit beside me; this was important if the passenger happened to be female.

The *A90* was taken to Altrincham to be fitted with Feeney and Johnson hand-controls. A lever attached to the steering column operated the servo brakes. The clutch was operated by a pistol-grip attachment on the gearshift. A cable connected directly to the foot pedal operated the throttle. Although extremely powerful this system proved to have serious flaws. The cables that operated the servo valves tended to wear rapidly and snap, and the two vacuum bellows that powered the clutch and brakes were slung below the chassis a few inches above the ground. They were damaged several times by obstructions such as the gate-stop in the middle of a neighbour's driveway. My next vehicle was a long-wheel base *Land Rover* fitted with a vacuum-hydraulic system made by Clayton-Dewandre. This was powered by pistons placed in less vulnerable positions within the engine compartment. Subsequently, automatic transmissions made disabled driving much easier.

Having acquired a car I next had to tackle the problem of insurance. The representative for the *Alliance* insisted, quite reasonably, that before the company could underwrite the venture he had to be convinced that I could drive with hand controls. He turned up at the garage in Altrincham on the day that I was due to collect the A90 from the fitters and before I had ever driven any car with hand controls. The fitter explained how the controls were operated and warned me that the brakes were fierce. We tied on L-plates and shot off, with the hood down, my mother in the passenger seat and the insurance man perched nervously on the rudimentary rear seat, clutching his hat with one hand and the back of my seat with the other. During the next ten minutes I learned how to drive a powerful sports car without the use of my legs. I could see in my mirror that he regarded the whole exercise with modified rapture, verging at times on terror. Fortunately he seemed satisfied that I could drive the car but turned down my offer to drive him back to his office in central Manchester.

I had booked a driving test before delivery of the car and had only one week to practise. I felt confident enough to drive my parents to Scarborough for the weekend and passed the test for disabled drivers the following Monday. One week later I started my first job, exactly thirteen months after going down with polio.

I have been asked how I got back on course so soon. I had three advantages; the first was my tendency to ignore the advice of anybody who suggested that my objectives were unrealistic; the second was education and discipline; the third was money. My home life, schooling and the war had all contributed to self-reliance and we were comparatively affluent. Support in the form of disabled equipment, cars and living expenses, was instantly available. I did not have to wait for supply of a wheelchair. I always had two chairs and was never immobilised while one was repaired. I made no demands on the State for physiotherapy, occupational therapy, or any other kind of therapy; I was far too busy shifting for myself. With a car and somewhere to live, a couple of wheelchairs and sundry other equipment, I was ready to start a new life, whatever that might be.

My father's career in ICI had steered me towards science. He had never missed an opportunity to explain how chemicals worked or how they were made and we had many visits together to see the factories. ICI had played a leading role in the history of organic chemistry and the production of drugs was a natural development of its interest in dyestuffs. It seemed that polio had put a stop to my ambitions to be a doctor and he encouraged me to apply for a job in the new pharmaceuticals division of the Company. Imperial Chemical Pharmaceuticals Ltd. was an offshoot of ICI's Dyestuffs Division at Blackley, near Manchester. It had acquired *Fulshaw Hall* and *Harefield Hall*, two large adjacent houses in Wilmslow, Cheshire. I had an office in a prefabricated building at the rear of Harefield. In *Reviews and Abstracts*, my job was to write précis of articles that had been published in medical and veterinary journals that might be of interest to the research departments. I learned how to select the essential facts to include in the review and I began to recognise why scientific writing is often unpalatable or misleading because of non-essential details, pedantic language, neologisms and inappropriate statistics. I was advised always to find out as much as possible about the authors of articles and to be particularly cautious about writers who invented new words to create an illusion that they were developing new methods of research and analysis. I was taught that papers must always be written in such a way that they can be understood by an intelligent lay person. The techniques I learned in *Reviews and Abstracts* were to prove useful throughout my career.

Reviews and Abstracts worked in tandem with an *Intelligence Section* set up by a former King's Messenger, Sir John Chichester, who scanned newspapers and trade journals with an eye for information that could be useful to the commercial side of the management. The two sections provided a service that resembled, on a small scale, the one provided for the pharmaceutical industry by the Philip Brown organisation through its journal *Scrip*. John Chichester and his wife Anne, a sister of Lord Montague of Beaulieu, entertained me at their home several times during my early days with the company.

Reviews and Abstracts was part of a medical department headed by an anaesthetist, Dr. Ben Wevill, assisted by two doctors — Alex Stewart and Kenneth Green. After I had been working for the company for only about nine months Dr Wevill called me into his office and suggested that I should return to medicine. I was in a secure but dead-end job and he believed it would be possible to qualify in medicine in a wheelchair. I was told to think it over and see him again in a week or two.

My life-style was surprisingly normal; I was independent, physically and financially. I could travel anywhere. Much of my upper-body strength had been regained and I had resumed my main sport – shooting – and thought little of wheeling my chair for several hundred yards over rough ground. I fished for trout from boats that I could row myself. Although access to many public buildings and private houses was difficult for wheelchairs, all hospitals had lifts. I had already completed my preliminary studies as a pre-clinical student and needed only to retake the anatomy examination that I had not been able to finish when I collapsed. I could see no reason why I could not practise in any medical speciality where mobility was not a prime consideration. I drove to St. Thomas' Hospital in London where I had already been offered a place before developing polio. I told the receptionist that I had an appointment to see the Dean, Dr. MacSweeney, and was asked to wait near the desk. After several minutes I asked again and was directed to the outpatients department. I could not convince anybody that I was a prospective medical student and not a psychiatric patient, so I sought out a porter who was prepared to accept my story that I was looking for the Dean's office. Arriving ten minutes late I knocked on the door and a high-pitched voice shouted "Come in you bloody fool". I gathered this was his standard response to a diffident knock on his door. MacSweeny wasted no time on pleasantries; there was no chance that I could cope with the architecture of St. Thomas'. He believed, however, that the Secretary of the Medical School, Dr. A.L. Crockford, had some helpful ideas and took me through to his office. Crockford, ('Crock' as he was affectionately known to medical students), had obviously done some homework on my behalf and had been in touch with John Woodcock, the Secretary of the Postgraduate Centre in Cambridge. After three years pre-clinical instruction in Anatomy, Physiology and allied subjects, Cambridge graduates completed their training at a teaching hospital in London or the provinces and then returned to the University to take their final examinations three or four years later. Cambridge did not have an undergraduate clinical school, but the Regius Professor of Physic, Sir Lionel Whitby, wanted to start one to compete with the school in Oxford. Crockford told me that I had presented Cambridge with a serendipitous opportunity to fulfil Lionel Whitby's dream. Unfortunately Whitby died from cancer before I qualified and further development of the Cambridge medical school was delayed for several years. In 1956 I had the distinction of being the first student to qualify at the Cambridge medical school and did so several years before it actually became one.

Dr. Wevill had promised that if the plan did not work and I failed to qualify, ICI would keep a job open for me and suggested that I might eventually consider a job as a doctor in the Medical Department. I left ICI in August 1952 and found rooms at Madingley Hall about three miles from Cambridge. It was a large country house used by the University as a hall of residence for extra-mural students. Albert the Prince Consort had stayed in the Hall from time to time to supervise the education of his wayward son, the future Edward VII. The Hall accommodated about forty post-graduate students, mostly in a new two-storey building at the rear of the main building. It was organised somewhat in the style of a Cambridge College presided over by the Warden, Canon Charles Raven, and administered by the Bursar, Anne Young and her assistant,

Marjorie Price. Some of the students were attending courses for overseas administrators and others were working for their PhD. I kept in touch with several of them for many years. My close circle of friends included Brian and Rosemary McEwen from New Zealand who stayed with my family several times during the vacations. Brian had worked in Samoa where he was in charge of Maori Affairs for the New Zealand Government. After leaving Madingley, Rosemary tragically succumbed to a slowly progressive degenerative disease of the nervous system, probably caused by a virus contracted while they were living in the tropics. Patrick and Anita Bolshaw occupied the 'Prince Consort's Room'. Patrick had been a colonial civil servant in Malaysia, and later became a Crown Commissioner in England before retiring to Sussex. Professor Howard Fry, an historian and ex-RAF pilot, took me for my first ever flight from Marshall's Airport. David Nickol was a District Commissioner in Southern Highlands Province of Tanganyika. Professor Duane Evans was a statistician from Washington and a pioneer in the use of computers. He had played a prominent part in the development of the Anglo-American Productivity Council. Duane succeeded in removing two doors and a wing of a passing taxi, in addition to one door of my A90 in Trinity Street when he forgot that in England we drive on the left. Sheila Stenning, one of the nurses who had looked after me in Brookfields Hospital when I was admitted with polio in 1950, and her husband Derrick who was an anthropologist, had worked in West Africa with the nomadic Fulani tribe. Derrick lectured in Cambridge for a few years and they then returned to Africa where some ten years later he died from leukaemia.

I had returned to Cambridge during a period of intense socio-political change. The country was still suffering from the overthrow of Churchill and the Tories and the new administration had slowed recovery of the post-war economy and damaged many of our major industries such as steel, shipbuilding and mining and we endured food rationing until

1953. Although highly desirable as an objective, I was uncertain about the impact of the new National Health Service on freedom to practise medicine as we had known it. The seeds of another World War had been sown in the Middle East as a result of the worst political decision of the century. Instead of supporting and protecting the shattered survivors of the holocaust while they rebuilt their communities in their own countries, the politicians succumbed to biblical mythology about a 'Promised land' and permitted annexation and colonization of Palestine that had been the homeland of the Palestinians for centuries. Young Jewish friends, including doctors and medical students, were moving from Britain and many other countries to work in communes or Kibbutzim in the so-called 'settlements' on the Arab side of the borders of Israel. Queen Elizabeth II was crowned and Everest climbed in the same year.

Having spent a relaxed six months at Madingley revising for the anatomy exam that I had failed to complete when I went down with polio, I typed my papers in a side room and passed quite easily and then became a full-time student at Addenbrooke's Hospital in the same year. Almost immediately I became a patient again. Playing table tennis at Madingley one evening I felt a ripping sensation in my chest. I found that my windpipe had shifted to the left side of my neck and that tapping the right side of my chest produced a drum-like sound, confirming that I had suffered a pneumothorax. Air had escaped through a hole in the surface of my lung into the space under my ribs, causing my lung to collapse. It re-expanded quite rapidly but three months later collapsed again. This time I was treated with injections of sterile olive oil into my chest cavity. The idea was that the mild irritation it caused (pleurisy) would stick the lung back to my chest wall. A long rubber tube was inserted into my chest and the open end placed in a bottle of water on the floor. Each gentle cough forced some air into the water that acted as a non-return valve. Over a period of several uncomfortable days the lung re-expanded. A year or two later, I had to perform this operation as a ward emergency on one of my old friends from Madingley, Tim Glover, a veterinary surgeon.

I was the only medical student at Addenbrooke's and I depended on ward-rounds and informal teaching sessions with the registrars as a substitute for lectures. I had nearly three hundred beds to myself and this was an enormous advantage over a conventional teaching hospital where there are several students to each bed. I soon found that the wheelchair put me at little disadvantage, indeed it often helped rapport with patients. Their greatest cause of anguish stemmed from 'they never tell you anything'. As an experienced patient myself, communication was not a problem.

My first attachment was as a *clinical clerk* to one of the three medical firms. Dr. Leslie Cole, a general physician with a special interest in diseases of the heart, was the same Dr. Cole who had made the decision to release me from the iron lung three years earlier. Knowing that the patient is often overawed by the 'circus' that gathers round the bed during a teaching round, Leslie always held the case-conference out of the patient's hearing. He then returned, often with only the sister and the house physician or his clinical clerk, to inform and reassure the patient with a gentle hand on forearm or shoulder. He showed me what doctoring was all about. The three medical firms, headed by Dr. Cole, Dr. Martin and Dr. Dick, each admitted patients for one week in every three and by working with one firm I was able to follow up about one third of the general medical admissions to the hospital. I was encouraged to follow individual patients throughout their whole stay in hospital from admission to discharge, including post-mortem, and to perform nearly all the procedures carried out by the junior doctors. I was soon trusted to set up transfusions and perform lumbar punctures and other diagnostic procedures without supervision. Three ward sisters taught me how to care for patients rather than merely diagnose and treat them; they were Joyce Jones of Griffith medical ward for men, Pat Mountford of Hatton medical ward for women and Sue Godley of Bowtell and Goode wards for patients from the haematology and other specialised departments. I spent time with dying patients and became familiar with problems that most medical students do not encounter before they qualify. The richness of this experience more than compensated for the lack of formal teaching during the three years it took me to qualify. The camaraderie of fellow students was missing but the professional and social relationships with doctors were a more than adequate substitute.

The first six months as a clinical clerk on Leslie Cole's firm passed enjoyably and in the summer of 1954 I started to tackle what seemed likely to be a more physically demanding task. I became a *surgical dresser* to one of the three general surgical firms. The Chief was John Withycombe who specialised in urology. Surgical admissions alternated between three firms headed by Mr. Phillip Ghey, Mr Brian Truscott and Mr Withycombe. I followed up the most interesting patients from about a third of the general surgical admissions and this gave me ample time to attend surgical outpatients and to work in the casualty department. The hospital joiner solved the problem of raising me to operating table height. He built a wooden extension to my wheelchair that raised the seat height to about thirty inches. To avoid the risk of pitching headfirst onto (or into) the patient, it had a webbing belt attached to the rear frame of the chair. I scrubbed up, was gowned and gloved and wheeled to the table by a nurse who applied the brakes and I was ready to hold retractors and clamps or swab the wound while the surgeon operated. The casualty department was also a rich source of practical experience. I spent many hours stitching wounds, applying plaster bandages and learning the techniques for resuscitation. One evening a Yorkshireman was brought into casualty with a broken wrist and rather the worse for drink. I was given the job of reducing the fracture and applying the plaster while the duty anaesthetist subdued him. Afterwards I learned that I had set the arm of the Astronomer Royal — Fred Hoyle!

John Withycombe's Australian registrar, Des Cooper, taught me most of my surgery and I assisted him at major operations such as partial gastrectomy for ulcers. With fewer sophisticated diagnostic aides available in those days, surgical diagnosis depended on the patient's history and on one's own hands and eyes. Des taught me how to distinguish the causes of various lumps and bumps: had injury, infection, a new growth or something odd such as a congenital cyst caused them? Was a lump mobile or fixed, hard or soft? Was it warmer than the surrounding tissues? Was it painful? How did the patient first notice it and how long ago? All these were clues to the most likely cause. I spent a lot of my spare time with Des Cooper's family, his wife Leslie and two small boys, Nicky and Timmy, and also with his House Surgeon, John Lewis and his wife, Margaret, who also contracted polio and told me later that she had been greatly helped by my example. Fortunately she recovered almost completely.

Late one night, much to my surprise, I saved a patient's life. John Davis, the Resident Senior Surgical Registrar, had removed a huge gallstone measuring about two inches long and more than an inch thick, that had worked its way through the wall of an old lady's gallbladder into her gut, causing obstruction of her small intestine. He had dropped the stone into a kidney dish, complete with the length of bowel that it had obstructed. While he was repairing the bowel I had a good look at the stone. It was roughly cylindrical with a rough surface. One end was rounded but the other had a flat, bright surface resembling a broken flint. With as much diffidence as I could muster, I suggested that it looked as though part of the stone had broken off. Lower down the small intestine John found another stone almost as large, with a similar broken surface that could have caused a further obstruction, and almost certainly the death of this very frail old lady.

One night I attended a beautiful young woman who had been brought into casualty by the police. She had been talking to her boyfriend in Trumpington Street when a drunken driver had struck her with the near side of his car causing a severe laceration of her buttock. While the nurse was undressing her I thought I could hear tinkling bells. We found that she had a number of tiny bells sewn into the hem of her underskirt. I examined the wound in her bottom and felt a hard lump to one side of it. On gently pressing it, the end of a chromium-plated car door-handle became visible and was removed without difficulty.

Another unusual case was a woman from the local Pye Radio factory who arrived in casualty with her hand riveted to the chassis of a television set. After injecting local anaesthetic, the heads of the rivets on the under surface of the TV chassis were removed with a small grindstone and electric drill borrowed from the engineering department.

I was taught pathology by Basil Herbertson and immunology by Granville Naylor and Michael Stoker, and for four months I made daily visits to the post-mortem room where A. M. Barrett and Austin Gresham (who later became Godfather to one of my daughters) gave brilliant demonstrations.

Only obstetrics remained as a potential problem for me. Students were normally expected to deliver five babies under supervision in a teaching hospital and then, accompanied by a midwife, to attend fifteen more in the district hospitals or the patients' own homes. Home midwifery was impossible for me so I was given a room at the Mill Road Maternity Hospital where I spent an enjoyable two months, encouraged by the two consultants Janet Bottomley and Oswald Lloyd. I delivered fifty-six infants from fifty-five confinements (one set of twins). In those days women were usually delivered lying on their left side with the right leg supported by an assistant and this suited me well. One night I delivered an Irishwoman's seventh infant. All was going splendidly until the critical moment of crowning, when she caught me firmly in the midriff with her right leg and propelled me backwards through an archway into the sluice-room. I had neglected to make sure that the nurse had put my brakes on after scrubbing up. I wheeled back in time to catch the baby and

Mrs. O'R. rolled over with a grin that stretched all the way from Bantry Bay to Sligo. "I was wondering where you'd got to Doctor?"

Each autumn and winter my renewed mobility and strength were put to good use shooting woodpigeon and hares on farms around Cambridge. Friends from the hospital or Madingley often joined me, but I enjoyed afternoons after the corn had been cut decoying pigeon on my own. I developed a technique that occasionally produced as many as fifty birds in an afternoon. Having found where the pigeon were feeding I drove into the field in the A90 and laid a pattern of painted metal pigeon decoys or dead birds about twenty yards from the hedge without getting out of the car. I dropped off my gun, cartridges, camouflage netting and a small canvas folding seat and drove out of the field to park the car; then I wheeled back in my chair to build a hide. Sometimes I distributed strings of firecrackers at strategic places downwind of my decoying position. The firecrackers were sold for bird scaring by Gallyon's gun shop in Trinity Street; they were made up in strings of twelve. The touch-paper of each cracker was twisted into a length of rope that smouldered slowly, touching off the crackers at twenty to thirty-minute intervals. With several strings positioned up to a mile away, it was often possible to move distant flocks of birds towards my decoys. Pigeon flying into the woods at dusk also provided some fine sport and a test of skill equal to that required for driven pheasants. When shooting in woods I had to ensure that the birds fell into a clearing or onto an adjacent field; if they dropped into cover I could not retrieve them in my wheelchair. I learned to shoot off either shoulder, thus doubling my arc of fire and my rapid reactions made me a fair shot. On one winter afternoon near Newmarket I spent several hours with a gamekeeper at the edge of a thin belt of firs lining a farm track. It was snowing heavily and the birds were flying along the edge of the trees into a field of kale. I shot about two hundred and fifty pigeon that afternoon using both of my guns, from time to time laying them in the snow to cool. The keeper who was watching this performance and retrieving the birds told me that he had counted eleven consecutive 'right and left' kills (one with each barrel). He remarked that it would have been good if some of his Lordship's guests had been watching. I sold the birds to MacFisheries in Cambridge. As a student my income from this source greatly exceeded the salary I was later to earn as a newly qualified doctor. Woodpigeon were a serious pest and George Paul and his neighbours, who farmed at Bottisham near Newmarket, allowed me the run of several thousand acres of arable land.

One evening I arranged a pigeon shoot at Six-Mile-Bottom near Newmarket for Dr. Laurence Martin (who later became my Boss). I placed him at the best end of the wood where he was directly in the flight line and his House Physician and I waited at the other end to turn the birds towards him. All evening a barrage of shots from Laurence's end of the wood suggested that he was having a good time. The other gun and I picked up about half a dozen birds each. After at least thirty shots from Laurence's end of the wood, the light had gone and he sauntered up the path towards us carrying a pigeon by one leg. "You seem to have had a great time Dr. Martin? I'll take the car down to pick up your birds. How many did you get?"

"Just the one," said Laurence; he seemed pleased nevertheless.

Early in 1954 I first met the senior surgical registrar at Papworth Hospital, Chris Cummins. He took me to see some work that he and Martin Greenberg, the Chest Physician (whose house officer I would later become), were doing with pumps that were later used in open-heart surgery in humans and eventually in heart transplant operations. Pigs were being used for these experiments at the Cambridge Veterinary Hospital on the Madingley Road. None of the pigs was intended to survive, most leaving in the boots of cars to become sides of bacon or pork chops.

Chris was exceptionally strong and used to carry me on his back for hundreds of yards. He was a good shot; when I missed a bird he often pulled it out of the sky shouting "Separating the men from the boys, what." He lived near the hospital in Papworth with his wife Cynthia and two children Bob and Penny. Chris worked at Papworth Hospital for nine years. He had expected to get the second consultant post that was created about 1956 but the job went to an outsider and Chris and his family settled in Australia. He became a Flying Surgeon, a parallel development of the Australian Flying Doctor Service. He operated in outback hospitals that were not large enough to have their own resident surgeon. Based in Longreach in Queensland and serving twenty-one towns, he had a twin-engine *Cesna 310* and a surgical team of three, one of whom was the pilot and anaesthetist. They flew, on average, about 19,000 miles per month.[9.] Chris performed a far wider range of surgical procedures than he would have done if he had stayed in England. In one operating list he might open a skull to tie off a bleeding artery, remove a cancer of the large bowel or a breast and insert a pin in a fractured femur. Only four of the hospitals on his circuit had air-conditioned operating theatres, so when possible, operating lists were started at 4.00 a.m., while the outside temperature was still under 100° F.

The senior orthopaedic surgeon at Addenbrooke's, Bill Butler, introduced me to a Norfolk wildfowling guide, MacKenzie (Kenzie) Thorpe. Kenzie was a former middleweight boxing champion and a professional poacher with a long string of convictions. He had looked after Peter Scott's collection of ducks and geese at the East Lighthouse at Sutton Bridge. Peter describes how Kenzie "fed the birds, painted pictures in the basement and was ready to be taken for me by casual visitors when I was away". The Sutton wildfowl collection formed the nucleus of Peter Scott's enterprise at Slimbridge. In Colin Willock's biography, Kenzie describes how I arrived at his house at 4.30 one morning with Dr. Ronnie Gibbs and how we drove in my Land Rover to Terrington Marsh, a mile or two south of the lighthouse. It was snowing hard and he (in fact for most of the way it was Ronnie) carried me over the sea wall and across a long stretch of soft mud known as the Slaw Pits. He dug a shallow pit for my legs by the side of a creek and I sat on a game bag while the others walked further out on the saltings. Kenzie claimed that he and Ronnie picked fourteen ducks apiece and then returned for me at daybreak, by which time the tide was running up my creek and I was sitting in several inches of water, covered in snow.

> 'Of course he couldn't feel nothing in his legs but his lips were blue with cold. He hadn't done too bad. We found four dead ducks and a curlew. Though he could hardly speak with the cold he seemed pretty happy. I reckon that man had really got guts.' [10]

Kenzie's memory of the size of the bag that he put at thirty-two duck and a curlew is somewhat at variance with my game book which recorded six duck and a curlew for the three of us and I didn't shoot the curlew. In those days wading birds such as knots and curlew were legitimate quarry and were sold in the shops. One night shortly after the end of the war, I had found a flight line for curlew on the river Conway in Wales and, with one of the local wildfowlers, I shot more than twenty of them and sold them to hotels where they probably appeared on the menu as 'woodcock'.

Our flamboyant life-style at Madingley is reflected in the following anecdote. One evening in November I drove to St. Ives with one of the residents, Dr. David Surrey Dane. There were few duck about and I could see David crouching in the reeds a hundred yards down river. A swan was flying slowly upstream towards him. Surely he couldn't? Could he? He did. The swan landed in the river and I saw a naked Dane jump in and tow the dead swan to the bank. It was smuggled into Madingley and up to his room. Helpers were recruited to pluck the bird, an operation that lasted well into the night and produced two suitcases full of feathers, a bag of entrails and about two feet of head and neck. These were disposed of in a ditch five miles away for recycling by foxes (we had visions of the spaniel owned by Mary Raven, the Warden's daughter, returning to the Hall with the head and neck in its jaws). We invented an 'Auntie' for another of the residents, David Nicol. She lived near Cambridge and had offered to let him have one of her ganders for a celebration dinner at the Hall. One of the conspirators went to see the cook and asked her if she could manage a dinner party in the library. She agreed and was told that we would be collecting the goose next day. We prepared the bird for the table, concerned about the length of the wing bones, and carefully picking out pellets. She eyed it professionally and asked, "Is it a wild goose?" No, we understood it was one of Auntie's ganders. "Has it been shot?" she said perceptively. We didn't think so, unless Auntie was so fond of it that she couldn't bring herself to wring its neck and had got somebody to shoot it. We put on our dinner jackets and dined in style on roast 'goose' with four of the best-looking lady residents.

In 1956 my father retired from ICI, and the following year a member of father's staff, Alex ('Ivy') Irvine, moved to *Wilsbury*, the house near Northwich. Alex was a younger brother of Andrew Irvine the climber who had been lost with George Mallory on Everest in 1924. Mallory's almost intact body was recently discovered on the mountain more than seventy years after his death and another of many bodies scattered round the mountain is thought to be that of Irvine. We moved to Cooden on the Sussex coast near Bexhill. Father had devoted all his energies to the company for three decades and was determined to enjoy retirement without taking on new commitments. Politely but firmly he turned down two telephoned invitations that interrupted our family dinner on the day he retired. One was to chair a Royal Commission on the white fish industry and the other a United Nations appointment that would have involved extensive travel in the Far East. I was concerned that he might 'switch off' when he moved away from Cheshire and his friends. I had seen several of his colleagues deteriorate in health and spirits and die within a few months of retirement. I need not have worried; almost every week for twenty years my parents entertained guests and father kept active with golf and gardening and making things in his 'playroom'. He installed a huge metal-turning lathe and several workbenches. The lathe turned out to be a source of frustration because his eyesight was inadequate for much of the fine work he attempted. When he dropped a tool in the growing pile of iron and brass swarf that littered the floor, he drove to his favourite ironmonger to buy another one rather than rummage blindly around in the litter. Mother was not allowed to clean the playroom and when we cleared it after Father's death I inherited several almost complete sets of drill-bits, spanners, stocks and dies, files, screwdrivers and unopened packets of nuts and bolts.

By the summer of 1956 I was on the last lap before the finals. I had worried that I would have to type for the three hours it would take to complete each exam paper so I typed model answers to all the questions that had been set during the previous ten years. Similar questions were likely to have been set repeatedly and some of them did come up. I was in good physical and mental shape and decided that last minute swatting would be counter-productive so I spent several days with my parents on the south coast. The papers presented no serious problems. The vivas involved examining patients and discussing them with an examiner. I had taken the trouble to find out who the examiners would be and what special interests might influence their questions. I had heard that one of the examiners fancied himself as a bit of a brain surgeon. When he steered me round to the subject of craniotomy (opening the skull) he asked me how I would stop persistent oozing of blood from between the two layers of bone. I nodded gravely and said "Bone-wax, Sir."

"Very good", he said, "you are the first one today who has heard of bone wax."

The examiners were kind to me and on December 18th 1956 I qualified as a Bachelor of Medicine and Surgery. Polio had delayed my medical career by three years. My Tutor at Caius, Hubert Tunnicliffe, called to congratulate me and relayed the comments of the examiners who had remarked that it was about time Cambridge did have a clinical school and that they wished all students typed their papers; he also told me that I had been among the top half dozen in every subject. Laurence Martin immediately invited me to be his house physician and the General Medical Council agreed that, instead of doing one medical and one surgical job during my first year of provisional registration, I could do two consecutive medical jobs.

After celebrating with my friends at the hospital and at Madingley, I packed my belongings and drove to Bexhill to spend Christmas with my parents. The route to the Blackwall Tunnel was busy and I drove along the Bow Road with the intention of crossing the Thames further to the West. Stopping at a pedestrian crossing controlled by traffic lights, not far from the London Hospital, I noticed a large articulated lorry facing in the opposite direction, also stationary. The lights changed and as the lorry started to move an elderly man stepped off the pavement, well below the driver's field of vision. By the time onlookers had shouted to the driver and hammered on the cab door, the old man was lost from view. I threw my chair out of the car and raced over to the truck. The old man was still alive and I was able to reach him by forcing my chair between the tractor and the rig. One of the front wheels and then the double traction wheels had passed completely over his lower abdomen, pelvis and thighs, reducing them to less than three inches in thickness and virtually cutting him in half. None of my newly acquired skills was required. He was conscious and seemed to be in no pain. I held his hand as we talked quietly until the light went out of his eyes. An ambulance arrived and the ambulance man pulled my chair roughly backwards from under the truck muttering — "Interfering bugger". I took the driver and a police sergeant aside and told them that I had witnessed the tragedy from the start and that there was no question that the driver could have done anything to prevent it. The old man was my first patient as a qualified doctor.

My 'Ward' at the Robert Jones & Agnes Hunt Orthopaedic Hospital, Gobowen near Oswestry. Now used for other purposes, the 'Huts', as I knew them in 1950, were used for polio patients.

5

Feeling Better, Doctor?

The old house in Trumpington Street that was used as the doctors' residence at Addenbrooke's Hospital was inaccessible in a wheelchair, so a small room and adjacent bathroom were found for me on the ground floor at the rear of the hospital, next door to a small room where radio-isotopes were prepared. Occasionally I bumped into patients on my way to the bathroom, but I could give a fairly convincing imitation of being a patient myself. My first medical post was house physician to Laurence Martin. Because I was already familiar with all the routine procedures such as writing case-notes, transfusions, lumbar punctures and minor surgery, the only really significant change was that I now had much greater responsibility. In those days we had a more limited choice of treatments to offer than we have today. Patients with stomach ulcers who bled more than once usually had part of their stomachs removed (partial gastrectomy) and the operation had a significant mortality. Ulcer symptoms are often controlled nowadays by drugs bought in the chemist's shop without a prescription. Tuberculosis and rheumatic fever were still common. I was authorised to prescribe penicillin but had to get a consultant's counter-signature for newer and more expensive antibiotics such as tetracycline. Even though their use was strictly controlled, we were already beginning to see infections that were resistant to several antibiotics and I myself became a victim of the 'hospital staphylococcus' when I developed multiple boils that kept me off the wards for a month. A locum had to be found and my first appointment was extended to seven months so that I could complete the six-month minimum required for registration (licence to practise). In winter it was common to admit five or six extremely ill and elderly patients during one night and to lose two or three from heart failure or pneumonia before the morning. Many could now be successfully treated at home by their general practitioners. Fluid retention in heart or kidney disease was treated with painful injections of a highly toxic mercurial compound called mersalyl and we experimented with one of the earliest blood-pressure lowering agents called hexamethonium. Acute asthma attacks that would now respond to a simple inhaler often had to be stopped with large slow intravenous injections of aminophylline.

Heart bypass operations had to wait for heart pumps to be invented but we referred many patients with mitral stenosis, a common legacy of childhood rheumatic fever, to the surgeons at Papworth. I watched my shooting companion, Chris Cummins, operate on several of our mitral cases. In this condition the valve between two chambers of the heart becomes narrowed because the flaps or 'cusps' that should open and shut during each heartbeat are thickened and stuck together. The operation was called mitral valvotomy. It could be done without stopping the heart or using an artificial heart-lung machine. Chris operated sitting down (an advantage for me because I could watch over his shoulder). A portion of one of the chambers of the heart was temporarily clamped and opened to allow him to insert his index finger. A 'purse-stitch' inserted round the incision was then drawn firmly round his finger to make a blood-tight seal and the clamp released. Chris then split the valve with his fingertip or sometimes with a small knife called a valvulotome attached to his finger. This was done on a beating heart and any slight leak produced a jet of blood half way across the operating theatre. Today, operating with the heart stopped, the valves may be replaced with a man-made valve or one from a pig. Chris had enormous hands, more like those of our local blacksmith, but I have watched him perform open-heart surgery on a newborn infant, with instruments normally used for delicate operations on the eye.

I soon confirmed what I already hoped would be true before I qualified — my wheelchair presented remarkably few problems.

Perched on the armrest, my great height and long arms enabled me to examine patients easily. When performing any procedure requiring a sterile technique, I had to be wheeled to the patient by a nurse after scrubbing up. On one occasion a demented patient knocked me out of my chair with a well-aimed kick to my head. Perhaps he thought another patient was attacking him. Many patients thought I had been involved in an accident and was only temporarily disabled. Frequently they greeted me with the phrase that I chose for the title of this book — 'Feeling better, Doctor?'

The greatest source of frustration was the delay in moving between floors caused by lifts breaking down or by lift doors left open, accidentally or deliberately by porters collecting laundry from the wards. A lift problem was potentially dangerous when there was no one around to retrieve it for me. When called out at night I made sure that the telephonist told the night porter to have the appropriate lift (there was a choice of three) waiting for me while I pulled a pair of trousers over my pyjamas and wheeled at maximum speed to meet him. There were no portable phones or 'bleepers' and the loudspeaker system was switched off at night. The hospital depended on one telephonist working a manual plug board. I used to enjoy night work because it was physically much easier to move around the hospital and there was a smaller chance of being needed in three places at once and the night nurses brewed a better class of coffee. For a few weeks in the vacations I was assisted by a 'runner', Chris Nourse, the son of a local GP. Chris qualified two years after I did and became a paediatrician.

Complaints about the hours worked by junior doctors these days annoy me. During my week 'on take', I was available on call for one hundred and sixty-eight hours. It was rare to get more than two hours of unbroken sleep and the phone usually interrupted meals. I had to arrange cover from a registrar or another house physician before taking a bath and, even when not on call, we might still be actively involved for one hundred and twenty hours. At weekends the consultants or senior registrar always did a round to deal with seriously ill patients. When not 'on take' we were able to cover each other so that one of us could occasionally get a whole day off and this could be extended to two days if one was prepared to work for two weeks with no time off at all. I exploited this arrangement in the winter so that I could go wildfowling, which meant that many weeks passed while I paid my debts and took no time off. For this we were paid a wage of £350 per year, less nearly half in accommodation and mess fees. During five years at Addenbrooke's I can remember very few junior doctors on a first appointment who were married. Residence within the hospital was mandatory and marriage was for non-resident registrars or consultants. If a registrar was single they could usually be counted on to provide additional cover for the juniors. When on take, one registrar always remained in the hospital to provide more experienced cover but the houseman was always first to be called and it was up to him or her to decide if more help was needed. There was no question of leave. If lucky, and if the necessity to secure the next job permitted it, one might take a holiday (without pay) at the end of the first six-month appointment. We considered it a privilege to be able to work our apprenticeship in a first class hospital with first class colleagues and receive a modest salary for it. With the exception of one doctor with an acute psychiatric problem, I do not recall any of us breaking down under the strain, becoming generally pathetic and in need of tranquillisers, counselling or treatment for 'post-traumatic stress disorder'. We felt no need to complain to a Union or the Department of Health about the hours that we had to work.

I had been exempted from a pre-registration surgical appointment provided I did a second medical appointment and it was decided that after I had completed my first appointment with Laurence Martin I could fill a newly created post originally intended for a more senior doctor. This involved looking after patients admitted by several specialized departments with a handful of beds in many different wards rather than concentrated in two or three. Care for these groups of patients was unpopular with the junior doctors on the three main firms because of the difficulty of complying with the schedules of several consultants, each of whom had fewer than a dozen beds. There was often a problem when more than one consultant wanted to do ward rounds at the same time. In my new job I looked after patients for Martin Greenberg, the chest physician, and a few belonging to the world famous nutrition expert, Professor R. A. McCance, Head of the Department of Experimental Medicine. A larger group of patients with leukaemia or other malignant conditions such as Hodgkin's disease requiring chemotherapy were admitted by the University Department of Haematology, headed by Frank Hayhoe. I was responsible for about thirty beds and the pace of the work was slower than in my first job because fewer patients were admitted as emergencies. The exceptions were mostly old friends who I had already admitted several times for chemotherapy and who had to be re-admitted for urgent transfusion or when they were dying.

Syringes were made of glass and metal. There were almost no disposables; rubber tubing, connectors and needles were sterilized by heating. Intravenous infusions of drugs were often given through small metal tubes inserted a short distance into a vein. The tubes had flat lugs attached to them that enabled them to be held in place with tape. Blockages were common and corrosive drugs sometimes leaked into the tissues around the insertion point. Long polythene tubes or 'lines' that could deliver drugs safely into larger blood vessels and portable drug-delivery systems that could be worn by the patient had yet to be invented.

Memories of individual patients remain vivid fifty years later. One man dying from leukaemia told me that during the war he had worked on the maintenance of radar towers on the south coast. Because German raids were almost continuous, routine work was done with the equipment switched on. He told me that the engineers were only able to work on the radar dish for a few minutes at a time because their bodies heated up. They were literally cooking in the microwaves. He believed that this was the cause of his leukaemia, but the experts were dubious and he felt aggrieved that no compensation would be given to his family when he died. We would probably now agree that he could have been right about the cause of his illness.

Another patient was a man of about seventy-five who had been involved in the design and installation of the engines for the first *Queen Mary*. During one admission I had to transfuse him with twenty-five pints of blood before his stomach haemorrhage stopped. He had a form of haemophilia called Christmas Disease, named after the patient in whom it had first been diagnosed. He was lucky to have survived to such an age.

One night I admitted a demented patient from the Fulbourn psychiatric hospital diagnosed as having advanced lung cancer. He had severe obstruction to his breathing and was coughing up blood. Fortunately, as it turned out, I thought of the possibility that the diagnosis was wrong. Could he have inhaled or swallowed a foreign body? Almost right first time — we could find only the top half of a set of false teeth when I asked the nurse to search his belongings and I rang Fulbourn Hospital to request a search for the bottom set. This cannot have pleased them in the small hours. They rang back an hour later to say that the teeth could not be found, but advised me that it would not be unusual to find them in the mouth of a fellow patient. I had already got the duty radiographer out of bed, and although a lung was badly collapsed, she could find no evidence of a foreign body in the chest. There was a large mass that tended to confirm the original diagnosis of advanced lung cancer. The patient was moribund and there was no question of doing more than trying to make him comfortable until he died early the following morning. At post-mortem his lower plate was found. He had swallowed and not inhaled it. It had lodged in his oesophagus and ulcerated through into the windpipe, causing a huge abscess around the root of the lungs. The plate may have been there for several weeks and was completely translucent to the X-rays taken by the portable machine in the ward. I wondered what the Coroner and the lawyers might have said if I had failed to think of the possibility of swallowed teeth.

One day I was called to see a very sick Irishman on Griffith Ward. As I approached his eyes sparkled and he sat up with a great effort and excitedly shook my hand. He was the husband of the lady who had propelled me out of the labour room during the delivery of her seventh infant a few years previously. He was a heavy smoker and had developed blockages of the arteries of both legs, leading to gangrene in one and incipient gangrene in the other. The condition was called *thromboangiitis obliterans*, one of two smoking-induced diseases suffered by King George VI (the other being the lung cancer from which he died). Paddy was extremely shocked and required frequent adjustments to the rate of flow of a drip containing drugs needed to maintain his blood pressure. Today he would have been nursed in an intensive-care unit. After several calls to the ward during his first night and many more throughout the following day as his condition worsened, I decided to sleep on the adjacent bed until he was fit enough to be transferred to the surgeons. I was able to reach over and measure his blood pressure and adjust the rate of his drip without getting into my chair. Paddy eventually left the hospital with two below-knee amputations, cheerful and smoking as usual, to rejoin his wife and seven children.

When Chris and Cynthia Cummins moved to Australia they gave me their cocker spaniel, 'Jock'. I had trained him to my special needs when shooting, using a 'silent' whistle that emitted sounds above the frequency of human hearing. One exercise was to 'sit' him on the small grass lawn in front of the children's ward. I took the lift up to the flat roof two floors up and peeped over the parapet to see if he was distracted by calls from the children or nurses who had been briefed to tempt him away. He was exceptionally well house-trained and I had no difficulty arranging for off-duty nurses to put their names on Jock's exercise list, pinned up outside my room, booking him for walks along 'The Backs'. I was heartbroken when, returning from a shooting trip one night, Jock saw a dog on the other side of the main road, jumped out of the open window of the car and was run over. He was replaced by 'Peggy', a yellow Labrador.

I exchanged my A90 for a Land Rover that was more suitable for my shooting expeditions. My brother Chris, who was farming near Bury St. Edmunds, sold the Austin A90 for me for £150 (equivalent to nearly six months' salary). This was a bad decision, because as a rare vintage car in excellent condition the A90 would now be valuable (I have seen only one working example at the Motor Museum at Beaulieu in Hampshire).

In the back of the Land Rover I kept a fibreglass boat that had been built for me by a gunsmith in Wisbech, to an American design known as a 'Barnegat Bay Sneak Boat'. I have been to Barnegat Bay, situated to the east of Philadelphia and north of Atlantic City, a strip of water about thirty-five miles long separated from the mainland by a sand bar. It is a haven for wildfowl and a favoured venue for duck hunters. The sneak boat was about seven feet in length and three in the beam and was stable in choppy water, although difficult to steer. The hospital carpenter fitted wooden bilge keels to make it easier to paddle and to protect the hull and I added some buoyancy bags. I used it mostly on the shallow water of the flooded washes near Welney where I had developed a somewhat hazardous although extremely effective technique for wildfowling. I rang up the AA before leaving Cambridge to check that the Washes were flooded and the road between Ely and Wisbech closed to traffic where it crosses the two Bedford Rivers at Welney. This is now the site of the *Wildfowl and Wetlands Trust* centre, close to *Kent Cottage* where George Kent and his brother had lived and worked with their punt guns. I drove the Land Rover along the flooded road from Welney until it was up to its axles in water. I had removed the passenger seat to make room for my folded wheelchair and when I lowered the chair into the water the seat was just above water level. Wearing rubber thigh-boots I was able to remain dry. I wheeled round to the back of the Land Rover, dropped the tailboard and pulled out the sneak boat, jammed it between the truck and the wheelchair and climbed into it. This was the most difficult part of the process. It involved lifting my legs in first while still sitting on the armrest of the chair and carefully sliding into the boat without capsizing it. It was essential that all the equipment I needed – guns, food and clothing – was within reach without getting back into the vehicle. Peggy my Labrador was always last out of the Land Rover to keep her dry until needed and she sat between my knees with her front paws on the deck. Finally, I loaded my old *magnum* hammer gun with heavy shot for use in case I got near to a goose and a second gun for duck and paddled down the road until I found a gap through the fence onto the flooded washes. With a dog and a boat I had an advantage over walking gunners because I could reach parts of the washes inaccessible to them and was able to retrieve birds landing in deep water or flowing too fast to risk my dog.

One evening John Norman, the head of a large vegetable marketing organization, took me to an inland feeding ground of the Pink-footed Geese near Guyhirn. John had the ideal job for locating where the geese were feeding as his work wholesaling vegetables kept him in daily touch with the farmers in the area. Although widgeon and other species of duck such as mallard, teal and pintail, fly inland at dusk as the tide covers the coastal mudflats, geese are unpredictable because their feeding areas change constantly as the crops are cleared from the fields. Often they spend the whole day flying from field to field, especially when the potato and beet harvest has left tons of edible scraps rotting on the ground. With help from John Norman, Fred Pearson, a farmer from Waterbeach, and John Carron Brown, a Norwich gynaecologist, I was installed in a ditch. There was a strong wind behind us and it was snowing — ideal conditions. We were wearing white sheets over our waterproofs. John Norman was expert at calling geese and succeeded in turning a small skein towards us. They approached at a height of about thirty feet and were obviously going to be in range. I knew that success depended on keeping totally still, squinting through the small gap between the brim of my hat and the top of my specs. I waited until they were almost overhead, aimed well ahead and fired both barrels. Two geese fell — my first (and last) 'right and left'. The skein climbed rapidly behind us but John continued calling them. A group broke away and flew in a wide circle about half a mile away before turning again in our direction. I kept my head down until they were overhead and shot the leading bird; the other three guns killed several more. Two of my birds had been ringed. The Wildfowl trust reported that one had been caught in rocket nets two seasons previously in Lincolnshire, the other had been ringed in Kinross in Scotland four years earlier. I was sad that the oldest of these birds had made the long return journey to the Arctic at least four times, only to be shot by me. I have not shot at a goose or duck since.

Forty years later I revisited Norfolk in February to chase the pink-footed geese with binoculars. My wife and I stayed at Park House on the Sandringham estate where Princess Diana spent most of her childhood; it has been adapted as a hotel for the disabled. We found one huge flock of at least five thousand pink-feet feeding on a sugar beet field near Sandringham and another huge gathering at Holkham, ten times as many as I had ever seen at any time during my wildfowling days. I was reunited with John Norman for the first time since the memorable sortie after the pink-feet thirty-five years earlier and we reminisced about the old shooting days before we both, like Peter Scott, became conservationists rather than shooters.

Apart from the shooting season from September to the end of January I did not travel far from the hospital on my occasional days off and I was co-opted as secretary for the residents' mess.

My first task was to do battle with the administrators over the arrangements for parking registrars' cars. The true story about the rather curious way in which I found a solution may now be told. At the Trumpington Street entrance to Addenbrooke's there was a forecourt with a large hut that housed the orthopaedic outpatients department. There were a number of parking places for consultants and administrators, but none for the registrars. We felt that at least four spaces were needed for junior members of the staff who frequently had to visit other hospitals in the area and might be called back at short notice to attend to an emergency. Repeated requests and discussions with Mr. Payne, the senior administrator, made no progress for many weeks. Meanwhile at the back of the hospital, an entirely unconnected series of events had been taking place. The Chief of the Physical Medicine department, Dr Fell, had noted that many patients with walking problems found it particularly difficult to get on and off a bus. Why not get hold of a double-decker bus and park it near the entrance to his department for patients to practise on? He acquired the rear end of an Eastern Counties double-decker bus from a local scrap yard. It had a platform and staircase but no wheels or roof. The bus had been delivered to Addenbrooke's on a low loader and a mobile crane had then lifted it off. It was approaching its permanent location when it broke through a drain and tipped over, depositing the load untidily several yards from its intended destination. More equipment was brought in and removed the crane but attempts to lift the bus were abandoned.

I saw this as an opportunity to further the cause of the residents' car parking problem. I borrowed a heavy-duty trolley from the engineers' workshop, four car jacks and sundry blocks of wood and recruited a dozen residents, including the senior surgical registrar, Oscar Stewart. After a briefing meeting at the *Little Rose* after dark we jacked up the bus and eased it onto the trolley. We then wheeled it down Tennis Court Road and up Trumpington Street to the front of the hospital and parked it neatly across two parking spaces. The following morning the administrators gathered round the bus scratching their heads. The *Cambridge Daily News* came round and photographed it and I explained to the press that some jokers had parked half a bus on the exact place that had been thoughtfully earmarked by the administration for the residents' cars. I then went round to see Mr. Payne and suggested a deal. I was sure I could persuade the residents to remove the bus if he agreed that at least two car-parking spaces could be reserved for them. He was gifted with humour and conceded defeat. The following night we trundled the bus back to the Tennis Court Road site and set it up neatly on concrete blocks at exactly the correct height (having measured a passing bus) in the place originally assigned to it and we painted it in the nursing school colours. Mr Payne honoured his half of the bargain.

Another contribution to the residents' quality of life was my invention of a *'Cremation Fund'*. Modest fees could be charged for signing death and cremation certificates, although few doctors in the hospital were in a position to claim them. I argued that many doctors such as radiologists, pathologists or anaesthetists should share in this supplementary income and a small sacrifice by the few could greatly improve the facilities in the mess as a whole. The residents agreed that the fees for issuing death certificates or for 'viewing' bodies and supplying a second signature on cremation certificates should be placed in a central fund. We started to make considerable improvements to the amenities in the residents' lounge such as new furniture and a coffee machine. After a few months, when the fund had reached several hundred pounds, I proposed that we should hold the first *Addenbrooke's Hospital May Ball* on midsummer night. I have always enjoyed organizing parties and all seventeen residents joined in. We used both the nurses' and doctors' dining rooms that had wood-block floors suitable for dancing. I hired two excellent bands, one specializing in Latin-American music and a singer called Lita Rosa, and free invitations were sent to the consultants and senior nursing staff and general practitioners in the area. Three hundred guests turned up including about twenty GPs and nearly all the consultants. My partner at supper was the attractive new Matron, Miss Puddicombe, and together we played host to Mr Parker, the Lord Lieutenant, his wife, and the new Regius Professor of Physic, Joe Mitchell, who had replaced Sir Lionel Whitby.

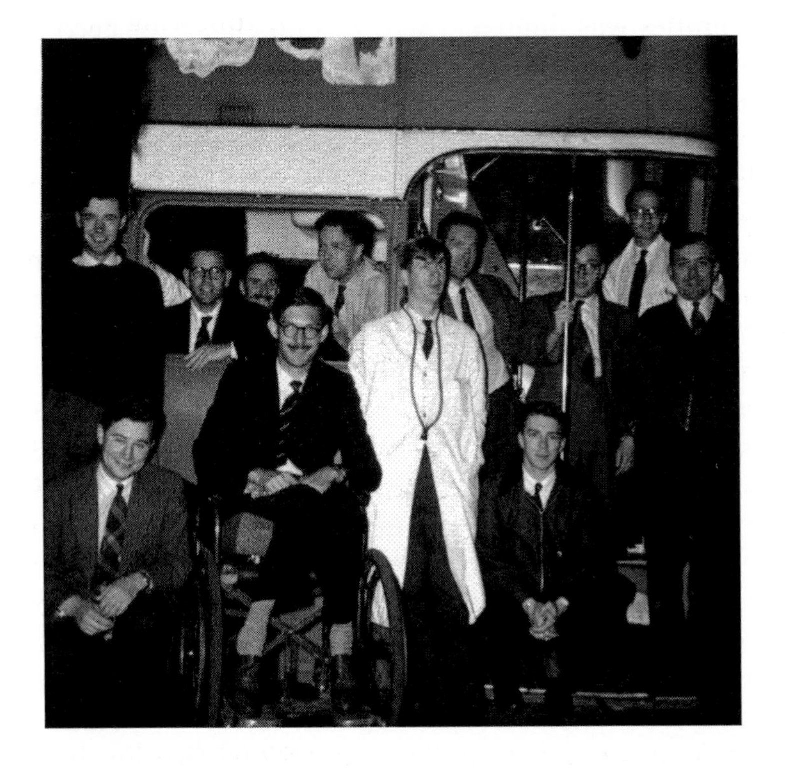

The strange case of half a bus that moved during the night

6

New Challenges

Having completed my 'house jobs' and the more senior appointment, I had to make a decision that would irrevocably change the course of my career. I loved hospital medicine and had coped well despite my disabilities, but the range of career opportunities was limited. There was no chance of becoming a consultant in general medicine or a GP. My dreams of life as a country GP were long discarded and I did not fancy a more sedentary clinical job such as psychiatry or dermatology, but a wide range of laboratory specialities were definitely open to me. Some form of research seemed likely to suit me best and I discussed various options with colleagues. The more I pondered, the more attractive was the original proposal by Ben Wevill that a useful career could be made in pharmaceutical medicine. Having grown up in an ICI family I had great respect for the company's traditions and standards and I appreciated the deep sense of loyalty of my father's colleagues over the years. I decided to return to ICI and make a career in their Medical Department. I found lodgings in a farmhouse in Ollerton, a few miles from Wilmslow, owned by Geoffrey Heap who had a florist's business in Manchester. He had kept the family home after both of his parents had died from cancer. The third resident was Ron Rutherford who worked in the electronics industry. An elderly retainer, Mrs Watson ('Watty'), cleaned the house and prepared our evening meals. One of my wildfowling friends from Cambridge, Ric Prestwich, lived nearby and both he and Ron were gliding enthusiasts, so it was not surprising that I would soon become one.

Ben Wevill had been promoted to the board of the Company and the head of the Medical Department was now Alex Stewart, with Kenneth Green as his deputy. The third member of the department was a huge amiable man weighing more than twenty stone, Michael Mungavin, with whom I shared an office at Harefield Hall until the department was moved to its permanent site in Alderley Park. Michael had worked for some time in the Far East and specialized in tropical medicine. Shortly afterwards there were three more recruits: Cecil Marsden, a dermatologist, Colin Downie, formerly a medical officer to the Bristol University students' health service, and Jimmy Langtry, who was half Spanish and handled the company's medical interests in Latin-America. Each of us was responsible for several new products under development. Mine included drugs for epilepsy, anaemia and cancer chemotherapy.

I became particularly interested in new methods for studying the circulation, using various dyes injected into the blood stream. A spectacular application was in trauma surgery. In the treatment of burns, for example, it is not always easy to decide whether a particular area of skin is viable. Two plastic surgeons in Chepstow, Emlyn Lewis and Michael Tempest, were injecting a green dye into burnt patients to determine the extent of non-viable tissue that had to be removed before grafting. The dye could not pass into dead skin where the blood supply had been cut off, but the surrounding living skin was stained green. For several days each of the *'Green Men of Chepstow'* remained a rich shade of bluish-green all over and relatives had to be warned before visiting. The dye injections also helped the surgeons to assess the success or failure of grafts. If the graft had acquired a good blood supply it rapidly took up the colour.

The *Green Men of Chepstow* inspired me to look for other possible applications of dye-injection techniques and I experimented with fluorescent dyes. White mice or rats were viewed in ultra-violet light after injecting the dye. They were quite unaffected by it and were an impressive sight, running around with brightly fluorescent eyes, ears and tail. I also injected the dye into monkeys and examined their retinas with the idea that this might be useful in the study of human eye problems. The teeth of a rhesus monkey snapping within an inch of one's nose while it was held by an assistant convinced me that these experiments would not be popular.

I was in charge of the clinical trials of a novel treatment for iron-deficiency anaemia that had been discovered shortly before I joined the company. A compound had been developed by one of the ICI pharmacologists, James Madinaveitia. 'Madina' as he was always called, had tested a number of chemicals called ferrocenes. They were organic iron-containing substances found as contaminants in mineral oils and petrol. He had tested several of them in animals and found one that could be given safely in quantities that were many times the relative dose that would need to be given to humans. Mice absorbed so much iron from a single dose, given by stomach tube, that their total body iron content could be doubled without harming them and we joked that Madina handled his animals with a magnet to avoid being bitten.

In my first study, a single dose given by mouth corrected severe anaemia in five of nine volunteers suffering from cancer and the remaining four were considerably improved. Such a response was unheard of with a single oral dose of any other product, so I set up a large clinical trial in Cambridge in collaboration with Donald Chalmers, the consultant haematologist at Addenbrooke's. Observed by myself or a nurse to ensure that they really had taken it, the volunteers drank a single dose of ferrocene washed down with a glass of orange juice. They had agreed to the collection of their stools in special receptacles so that our laboratory in Cheshire could measure how much of the dose they had absorbed. For many weeks I ran an 'express stool service'. Some colleagues did make other suggestions about its title and Oscar Stewart, the Resident Surgical Officer who had been one of the conspirators in the bus-moving operation, dubbed me the 'Iron Doctor'. Each Monday I drove to Cambridge with large biscuit tins containing waxed containers, labels and aluminium brackets that fitted inside a lavatory pan. Every Friday I returned with fifty to a hundred containers for Madina to assay.

The absorption study had its problems. At one point it was found that some patients seemed to be excreting more iron than they had been given. This was traced to flakes of rust falling into the test material from the fume cupboard in which the specimens were processed. In hot weather specimens collected in the early part of the week could not wait for my return to Cheshire each Friday. Don Chalmer's laboratory had no place to store them; the mortuary had refrigerated accommodation that was ideal for the purpose but it was nearly always fully booked. There was nothing for it but to dispatch samples by post. The waxed containers were packed in sawdust in cardboard boxes and then in tins with more sawdust and sent by parcel post as 'biological specimens' by special arrangement with the Post Office. Fortunately, none was lost or burst.

In these early trials, at least eighty per cent of the iron was absorbed and no patient had side effects. Permission was therefore obtained from the ethical committee to begin trials in pregnant women. The 'Iron Doctor' moved to Mill Road Maternity Hospital and recruited two hundred and fifty-two pregnant volunteers over a period of several months. Half were randomly allocated to a 'control' group who received the routine antenatal clinic treatment that frequently involved a course of iron injections and half received a single dose of the ferrocene by mouth. There were one or two complaints about the rather bland chalky texture of the mixture but no side effects. At the end of the trial the response in the two groups was identical and we concluded that a single treatment with ferrocene was equivalent to daily dosing with iron salts or a course of injections spread over several weeks. We had a new treatment with enormous potential particularly for anaemia in pregnancy, but after three years of intensive research costing several million pounds the project was shelved. An accident had occurred that was to have profound repercussions throughout the world — the thalidomide disaster — and I suspect that messages had come from the main company headquarters in London instructing the higher management to stop any new projects that would involve experiments with pregnant women. Madina and the 'Iron Doctor' drifted unobtrusively into history. Forty years later I still wonder if this was a lost opportunity.

I also became interested in a drug developed by Arthur Walpole and Michael Williams of ICI Dyestuffs that had shown promise in the treatment of cancer. Michael was killed in a car crash and I took over his clinical trials and organized a conference in October 1961 to review the results. The drug had a long name, triethyleneglycoldiglycidyl ether (TEG); it was eventually sold for several years as 'Epodyl'. It was extremely toxic to cancer cells but was destroyed within seconds in the general circulation. It was injected into the artery supplying blood to the tumour. We hoped it would kill the malignant cells as it passed through the tumour and would be destroyed so rapidly after returning to the general circulation that it would cause little damage to the healthy tissues in other parts of the body, especially the bone marrow. During the trials of 'TEG' I travelled to surgical centres in several parts of England and Scotland. Henry Maslowski, a Manchester neurosurgeon, treated patients with advanced brain tumours by infusing TEG directly into the brain arteries. Prof. Ian Donald in Glasgow treated women with advanced cancer of the uterus using the arteries in the pelvis; Donald Harrison in London treated patients with advanced cancer of the mouth and larynx. Some of the patients benefited with few of the side effects such as loss of hair or anaemia normally associated with chemotherapy, but there were no 'cures' or long-term responses. This was hardly surprising because only the most advanced and hopeless cases volunteered for these studies.

From the commercial point of view the most important ICI drug that I worked on was clofibrate. It was used to lower the cholesterol level in the blood and reduce the risk of heart attacks or stroke. Laboratory animals had responded best to a mixture of clofibrate with a hormone called androsterone and this mixture was used in the early human trials and for some time was marketed as 'Atromid'. It was soon discovered that patients responded just as well to clofibrate when given by itself without the androsterone. This presented the Sales Department with a dilemma — how to remove the unnecessary and expensive androsterone without damaging the product's 'image'? They solved the problem brilliantly by renaming the product 'Atromid-S', perhaps hinting that the 'S' would suggest 'Super' or 'Special'. In truth the 'S' stood for 'sine', the Latin for 'without' – without androsterone. This was my first exposure to the world of advertising where the truth is 'flexible'.

Clofibrate was developed by a brilliant and eccentric South African scientist, Jeffrey Thorpe. Jeff had started life as an engineer and had somehow changed course to study the effects of drugs on living organisms; he was my closest friend during my time at ICI. One evening in our local, he confided in me that aspirin, like clofibrate, would probably turn out to protect against thrombosis, but "for God's sake don't tell anybody until I'm sure." It is now accepted that aspirin does indeed have a marked protective effect against coronary thrombosis through its action on blood platelets, the tiny particles that initiate clotting when a tissue is damaged. Atromid-S works in a different way by reducing the cholesterol and other fatty substances in the blood that tend to accumulate in the walls of arteries and block them, shutting off the blood to vital organs such as the heart. The human trials that had been set up by Jeff and Kenneth Green were almost complete when I joined the company and my modest role was to analyse the results, write them up and present them at a conference in Buxton. Atromid-S had a somewhat chequered commercial life, although there has been a resurgence of interest in similar drugs called 'statins'.

7

Flying and a Wedding

Three flights at the Midland Gliding Club's hill-soaring site on the Long Mynd in Shropshire inspired me to take up flying. I could see no insurmountable difficulties; the main problem would be keeping my feet on the rudder pedals during the launch by winch because the initial climb was steep and my legs tended to float upwards towards my chest. I contrived a simple arrangement of straps and elastic that would prevent my feet slipping off the pedals and returned to the Long Mynd the following Saturday as a club member. The straps worked well and, since the rudder pedals were linked in such a way that when one was depressed the other moved upwards, I had sufficient movement in my right ankle to operate both in normal flying. My foot was not strong enough in some situations such as landing crosswind or doing aerobatics and I practised flying with the stick in either hand so that I could press the opposite knee down firmly with my free hand. Later, when high performance aircraft demanded a parachute, I added quick-release pins to the foot straps. They were operated by strings threaded up inside the legs of my flying suit to a ring on my belt. There was no point wearing a parachute if my feet were firmly fixed to the rudder when I tried to bail out.

The Club had a resident instructor, Jack Minshall, who did most of his teaching during the week, while volunteers from the experienced club members did the weekend instructing. My most memorable teacher was Hans Wulff, better known as Peter, who became one of my closest friends for thirty years until his sudden death in 1997 while visiting Russia. Peter had worked for the 'other side' during the war and flew *Heinkels* on the Russian front until 1943 when he transferred to fighters. Pilots were being moved to the west to attack the massive formations of American B17s that were destroying German cities. He was shot down near Leipzig on his second flight and was shot down again in a *Fokker Wulff 190* over allied territory on New Year's Day 1945. The New Zealand pilot of the *Tempest* that shot him down at low level saw what he thought was a puff of smoke before Peter's aircraft crashed and burst into flames. It was in fact Peter's parachute. He was too low to bail out normally so he stood up in the cockpit and opened his parachute which pulled him out.[11] He was sent to a prisoner of war camp in South Wales and put to work on a farm near Castle Martin. He told me that when the war ended, "I thought I would try democracy." He married the owner of the farm and lived in England for fifty years!

The best of many Peter Wulff stories describes an event that occurred some time before I joined the club. In sight of the clubhouse he had managed to reduce a glider to a pile of small pieces. Onlookers thought it was the end of Peter, but small movements in the woodpile suggested that life was not quite extinct. A figure emerged, shaking off wreckage, and staggered towards the clubhouse bent almost double – "I'm all right chaps but I think I've done something to my back" – he was still strapped into his seat. Peter passed on several simple rules for staying alive. "Always remember Bill, speed is half of life." Do not stall close to the ground trying to extend the final glide and always look for an emergency landing field before you need one. If you have to land in a field that is too small, so that hitting a fence is inevitable, do not hit the one on the approach side. Rub off as much speed as possible before rolling into the fence at the far end and you may only damage the aircraft. Gliders are safe, the main causes of accidents being stalling and collisions due to pilot error.

During my third weekend visit to the club I had a flight with Bob Neill, the Chairman of the club, who wrote in my logbook: 'Good progress. Rather too much use of rudder.' This amused me because, although sitting in the right-hand seat next to him, Bob had not spotted that I was surreptitiously pushing my knees down with the palms of my hands during strong manoeuvres such as spinning. In spite of my rudder problem I had no difficulty correcting a spin. I successfully handled two winch cable-breaks; the stick is pushed forwards to level off the steep climbing angle and maintain flying speed and the broken end of the cable that is still attached to the glider is dropped. The pilot then has to decide if he has room to land immediately ahead or sufficient height to complete a circuit. The decision has to be right first time. On the 26th September 1959, four weeks after joining the club, I was sent solo.

A first solo in a powered aircraft involves a few circuits with an instructor who then gets out and walks away biting his knuckles and pretending not to be concerned about the safe return of the aircraft. My first solo involved a change of aircraft, a much smaller single-seat glider called a *Prefect.* I completed the take-off drill, checking the controls, instruments, straps, canopy-lock and cable release and shouted, "All clear above and behind?" The wing-tip holder gave thumbs up to confirm that nothing was about to land. "Take up slack." The winch wire straightened. "All out." The wing tip holder ran forwards for a few yards as the glider started to move. It reached flying speed within a few yards and lifted off the ground. I eased back the stick firmly to assume a steep climbing angle and at eleven hundred feet the speed started to fall off. I levelled out and pulled the yellow cable release knob. Only then did it occur to me that I was alone. This was one of my great moments; I think I yelled, "I can't walk but I can bloody well fly." I had plenty of time to get the feel of the aircraft and to plan my circuit. Although it was rather late in the afternoon, I was tempted to explore a thermal that I flew through, but I obeyed instructions to restrict myself to a simple circuit. I had been launched towards the south, and now turned east towards Church Stretton. The *Prefect* was much quicker to respond and lighter on the controls than the *T21*. Turning north for the down-wind leg of the circuit

I checked my height and the landing area. Another glider was on its final glide below me so I did some gentle turns before starting my descent on the crosswind leg, using the spoilers to lose height. Spoilers are small flaps on the upper surface of the wing that 'spoil' the airflow over the upper surface of the wing and reduce its lift. I was still too high. I had been taught in the T21 how to sideslip and did this for a few seconds. With full left rudder and the stick to the right, I pointed the right wing towards the direction of flight. This manoeuvre presents the side of the fuselage across the airflow causing rapid loss of height. I straightened up and flew the *Prefect* down to a gentle landing. I stopped rolling when level with my wheelchair. I had flown solo exactly four weekends after joining the club. In April 1960, on my twelfth solo flight, I completed the first of three tasks for the 'Silver C' (Silver Badge). They required a certified gain of height of one kilometre above the launch height, a flight of five hours and a cross-country flight of fifty kilometres. Carrying a height recording barograph, sealed and signed by an instructor before my flight, I easily reached 1,500m above the airfield. In May 1960, at the annual dinner-dance in Birmingham, the club honoured me with the trophy for the best pupil pilot. The publicity lead to a number of enquiries and requests for advice from other would-be pilots with disabilities. I hope I inspired some of them to take up the sport.

In July 1960 I spent a week on the Mynd in the hope of completing the duration task for the Silver Badge. The conditions were good with westerly winds creating hill-lift so that all launches were by 'bungee'. This is an elastic rope attached to an open hook on the nose of the glider and pulled by six or eight persons. The glider's wheel is positioned in a shallow concrete slot set into the ground. One member of the launching team holds back the tail and a second holds the wing tip and relays the pilot's instructions to the bungee crew. As they run down the hill energy is stored in the elastic rope while the tail man holds back as long as possible. Eventually the wheel lifts out of the slot and the glider catapults forward, reaching flying speed almost instantly. At one moment the pilot is sitting on the ground, the next he is flying. Within a few yards the bungee attachment falls out of the open hook on the glider without any action by the pilot. Bungee launches are the most comfortable of all the four methods of launching that I have used; the other three being winch, aero tow and autotow.

On the 15th of July 1960 a bungee launch went badly wrong for me. For some unexplained reason, as the wheel of the *Prefect* lifted out of the gutter and the tail man let go, the bungee ring detached spontaneously from the nose hook. I was already airborne and could have put the nose down slightly and taken off but unfortunately the man holding the left wing attempted to hold me back. I waved my arm frantically and shouted to him to let go, but he misinterpreted this and redoubled his efforts to hold on as the glider started to slew round to the left. I wrenched the stick to the right in an attempt to lift the left wing and he fell off. I was now at right angles to the intended direction of take-off with the glider banked almost vertically. I was crabbing along the side of the hill with the port wing stalled and the glider trying to roll onto its back. After a few yards the left wing tip touched the heather, the glider cart-wheeled, the nose collapsed and I stopped, upside down with my head through the canopy. The nose had absorbed most of the impact and the main wing spar had snapped. I was hanging upside down and dripping blood from a scalp wound. The crew ran up and extricated me and I made some inane remark about wanting to demonstrate the 'alternative method of landing'. Ten minutes later the bleeding had stopped and I was sent off in another glider on a 'confidence flight'. Teddy Proll, the club's ground engineer, repaired the broken *Prefect*.

Much of the pleasure of weekend flying was the companionship of the club members. Of some two hundred and fifty members about fifty flew regularly and the club owned nine aircraft. We had a comfortable clubhouse with kitchen and bar, male and female dormitories and our own generator. I wrote in a magazine article:

> 'Gliding attracts a remarkable cross-section of society. In our Club we have a heavy sprinkling of ex-RAF types (learning to fly), eight doctors, a gypsy, several women, a man who makes furnaces for crematoria, a number of farmers, accountants, engineers and architects, and a surfeit of 'Trogs' who are in a special category on account of their ability to render any piece of equipment unserviceable in the shortest possible time.'

Back at ICI I had my eye on an attractive lady who used to lunch at a table in the far corner of the staff canteen. A long-term friend and compulsive matchmaker, Ann Smith, who had already made one or two unsuccessful attempts to pair me off, solved the problem by inviting us to dinner. Ann's husband Ken was an ICI technical representative and they had a daughter Nicola (my goddaughter). June Halfpenny was a widow with a five-year-old daughter, Stella, whom she had brought up on her own from the age of three after her husband, Douglas, had been drowned in an accident in Yorkshire. For several years they had lived on the Gold Coast in Tarkwa where Douglas was employed by a gold-mining company and they had returned to England shortly after that country became Ghana. She had moved to Cheshire in 1959 and ran the *Travel and Visitors Office* at ICI. June had been born and brought up in Doncaster, the youngest of four children of Stewart and Elsie Maggs. Stewart had an electrical business in Doncaster and was on the point of retirement when I first met them.

Journeys as a disabled person travelling alone in a wheelchair were often quite eventful. One winter morning I flew to London in a snowstorm. At Heathrow, the passengers were disembarked but I had to wait until I could be carried off. The pilot and a hostess stayed with me and we waited, with snow falling thickly and the aircraft's heating turned off. After several calls from the Captain an ambulance arrived half an hour later driven by a fireman. For some reason linked to insurance and trade union agreements, disabled passengers were handled by the airport fire service not the ambulance service. The Captain and hostess apologised for the delay and went off in a car. "I hope you don't mind the other passenger," said one of the two firemen, pointing to a figure covered with a purple blanket strapped to a stretcher. I didn't mind, his manners were impeccable, although I think if I had been an elderly person of nervous disposition I might have been quite upset. My companion was one of the airport staff who had caused the delay by dying suddenly. The fireman slammed the door and walked round to join the driver. I was seated in a stretcher-chair and not strapped in so I steadied the chair with one hand on the window frame and the other on my companion's shoulder. By the time I had been wheeled into the arrivals hall and the various components of my own wheelchair had been retrieved, I was ninety minutes late for the appointment, and the neurosurgeon I had planned to meet had long gone from the Middlesex Hospital. It was also clear that there could be no flights out of Heathrow that day. British Airways did their best laying on a car to Euston where the Station Master, uniformed and top-hatted in those days, escorted me to a train to Macclesfield. I was met by an office car on arrival and driven to my bungalow where I changed and then drove to June's house to fit electric lights in Stella's dolls' house.

On another occasion I stayed at an old fashioned London hotel where the guests' shoes would be shined if they were left in the corridor. As I leaned forward to put them outside my door I tipped my chair over and fell into the corridor, trapping my unprotected toes between the footrest and the floor. I heard and felt several toes on my right foot snap, followed almost immediately by agonising pain. Fortunately the door did not lock behind me. I towed the chair back into the room and climbed into it. I had broken the heads off the second, third and fourth metatarsal bones of my right foot. The foot swelled rapidly and the following morning I had to make two long cuts down the side of my shoe so that I could get my foot into it. I drove to a meeting to discuss experimental work we were doing to see if female hormones could be used to reduce haemorrhage after removal of the prostate and possibly also in eye surgery. (With hindsight, this was a prediction of things to come a few years later when I became crucially involved with the problem of thrombosis and oral contraceptives). Somehow I got through the meeting and then drove back to Wilmslow, with my left foot on the accelerator. The following morning I went the Casualty Department at Wythenshaw Hospital. I told the doctor that I had broken the heads off the second, third and fourth metatarsals of my right foot. "Doctor," he said, "we never diagnose fracture without X-ray." It was a Saturday morning. The casualty department was busy and two hours later, after an X-ray, he called me in. "Doctor, I very much regret to inform you that you have broken the heads off the second, third and fourth metatarsals of your right foot. You need baloni plaster." A moment's reflection and I realized he meant 'below-knee', even though the fracture was in my foot. Sensing a communication problem, I sighed inwardly and withheld comment as a nurse applied a 'baloni' plaster that started above the fracture site in my foot and ended just below my right knee, leaving my toes and the painful fractures unprotected. "Leave your sock off and come back if the toes swell or go blue," she said. They were already swollen and almost black; I never seemed to have much luck with hospitals. I drove back to Wilmslow, stopping at Boots to buy some plaster bandages, and then on to my bungalow where I hacked off the 'baloni' plaster and made myself a plaster shoe that supported the broken toes comfortably. Later that day I took June out to the cinema.

One day Stella, who clearly approved of me, sat on my knee and said, "Uncle Bill, I wish you'd marry my mummy." June and I announced our engagement in April and were married in July 1962. Forty years later, at a lunch party to celebrate our ruby wedding, June revealed that she had told Stella, "why don't you tell him?" However, I'm moving ahead of my story.

In June 1961 I joined a glider owner's syndicate with Tom Hood, Bruce Bowdler, and Tony Rowson and bought a second-hand *Olympia*. The 'Olly' was a neat little aircraft similar to the German machines in which Luftwaffe pilots had been trained before the war. I also made two painful contributions, each amounting to about a fifth of a year's salary, towards two club appeals. The first was to support a 'fighting fund' to cover the costs of a long argument with a landowner who believed that the spectators and ramblers we attracted to the club were frightening his grouse. The grouse and their chicks meanwhile browsed contentedly within a few yards of the clubhouse and hangar. The second was a substantial contribution towards an Auster *Tugmaster*, a version of the familiar high-wing monoplane used by the army as a spotter plane. It was fitted with a more powerful engine and used for towing gliders. Aero tows have the enormous advantage that the glider can be towed for long distances, for example after a landing away from the home airfield, and can be released well above the height that can be reached with a winch.

During the winter we took the 'Olly' in its trailer to an old RAF aerodrome at Shobden near Leominster. Several barbed-wire fences crossed the runway, but one section seemed long enough to experiment with 'auto tow'. A crowd collected while we rigged the glider and I rather enjoyed overhearing some of their comments about the man in the wheelchair who had been helping to rig it and who then got in to fly it. I found a 'volunteer' who had a Ford drop-head fitted with a tow bar and had recruited several others to keep the sheep away. The first launch was a short hop with a landing straight ahead. I had asked the driver to accelerate as fast as he could after I released the wire so that he could get well clear of the runway before I landed. What may have been the first auto tow from Shobden, now a thriving gliding site, took me to fifty feet. The second launch was to one hundred and fifty feet and I landed a long way short of the end of the runway. I judged that if I got to three hundred feet I was committed to a circuit. On the third launch I pulled back on the stick as much as I dared, released at five hundred feet and made a leisurely circuit of the airfield, much to the appreciation of the audience who applauded my return enthusiastically. The fourth flight took me to six hundred and fifty feet at which point the Ford stopped suddenly and inexplicably. I released at once and was relieved to see the car moving once more. The reason he had stopped was that I had almost lifted the back of his Ford off the ground and the wheels had started to spin. One weekend Bruce flew the Auster to Shobden and towed me to five thousand feet with the objective of completing my five-hour flight for the Silver Badge, but lack of thermals forced me to land back at Shobden. After a dozen auto tows we decided that Shobden was not a practical alternative site for regular flying by our Olympia syndicate.

In March 1962 I joined a second glider syndicate. It included Ric Prestwich, one of my old wildfowling chums at Cambridge, Stephen Wills, Tim Corbett and Henry Maslowski. Stephen is the son of the late Phillip Wills, the doyen of English glider pilots and author of many books on gliding. Tim was a farmer and later Lord Lieutenant of Shropshire, who lived near the gliding club. Henry was the Manchester neurosurgeon who I had introduced to gliding while working with him on a project to treat brain tumours. We bought a Slingsby *Skylark IIIB* that had competed successfully in the National Championships the year before. It was a large machine with an eighteen metre wingspan, instrumented for blind flying and plumbed for oxygen and we planned to fit two-way radio to enable us to report progress to the retrieving crew. Without a radio the recovery crew had to set off in the direction of the intended flight and telephone the club at intervals to enquire if the pilot had landed and left a message and a map reference. I was always somewhat apprehensive about being unable to leave the glider after landing away from the

Mynd. On the few occasions that I did, small boys appeared to grow out of the ground within minutes and I carried a supply of coins and pencil and paper so that the one who looked most reliable could pass my message back to the club.

My eighth flight in the *Skylark* was a Silver Badge distance attempt to fly to a small airfield to the north of Wolverhampton. I bungeed off the Mynd in a westerly wind that was gusting up to twenty-five knots and climbed rapidly to two thousand feet. I found a 'cloud-street', a line of weak thermal lift extending downwind and marked by a long line of dark grey clouds, and flew along its northern edge towards Bridgenorth. I flew over a small airfield at Halfpenny Green, where I had planned to land if I ran short of height; then I turned due north which I judged would allow me to track at about forty-five degrees from Halfpenny Green because of the strong westerly wind. The visibility was deteriorating with frequent showers of rain and patches of low cloud so I switched on the artificial horizon. I could see Wolverhampton to my right and pressed on, looking for a 'V'-shaped junction of the Shropshire Union and the Staffordshire and Worcestershire canals, at the apex of which I should find the airfield. I was approaching the outskirts of Wolverhampton and good-looking 'emergency fields' were becoming few and far between and I started to think about turning back as I was not going to attempt to cross the city. Then I saw the junction of the canals and the airfield. There was nothing moving, but I could see a neat row of parked aircraft and guessed the strong wind and poor visibility had grounded them. This was obviously the day of the glider. I was still about three thousand feet above the airfield. I put on a small aerobatics display to use up my spare height, a couple of loops, a stall-turn and two turns of a spin before completing a left-hand circuit that took me over the canal on my final approach. I rolled the *Skylark* up to the end of the row of parked aircraft near the clubhouse. Two men sauntered over and asked where I had come from and invited me in for a drink. I enjoyed their surprise when

I said, "Yes please, if you wouldn't mind carrying me." They plied me with beer and questions. "Yes, I did plan the flight to Wolverhampton. No, it wasn't a fluke." I looked at my watch. I had taken thirty-five minutes to complete the fifty-kilometre flight and I suggested that if they looked out of the clubhouse window they should see another glider in the circuit and there it was; Tony Rowson, from my other syndicate, had taken off immediately after me in the slower Olympia and had not seen me throughout the flight. I hope the 'power-types' were suitably impressed: a paraplegic co-owner of both gliders, landing away from home at the same site on a day that was too uncomfortable for small powered aircraft. An hour or two and several drinks later, two retrieve crews arrived with trailers and my wheelchair. The gliders were dismantled and we were driven back to the club, each with a leg of the Silver C completed. Sadly, the grass airfield at Wolverhampton has fallen to the creeping pestilence of housing development.

Five days later, I completed the third test for the Silver Badge with a flight of five and a quarter hours from a winch launch in good thermal conditions at heights of up to four thousand feet. I put in some practice in cloud flying and flew to Bishop's Castle, Welshpool and the 'Stiper Stones'. My Silver Certificate issued by the British Gliding Association on behalf of the FAI (Fédération Aéronautique Internationale) and the Royal Aero Club is number 1151. I don't know if any other paraplegic beat me to it, but judging by the difficulties persuading people that I was safe to fly, I was probably one of the first.

Driving home from the club one night I followed a Volkeswagen *'Beetle'* driven by another club member, Dr. John Butler (who died in a flying accident in Canada a few years later) and his fiancée, Margaret. We were travelling down a particularly dark and steep stretch of road between high banks near Shrewsbury when the *Beetle* suddenly stopped dead and, to my astonishment, a cow flew over its roof upside down. It landed on its back in front of my Land Rover. I just managed to avoid it by swerving to the side of the road and up the steep bank, ending with the Land Rover leaning over with the off-side front bumper locked in John's rear wing; a trivial addition to the severe damage to the front of his car. John and Margaret got out, shaken but uninjured – where was the cow? I saw a small man pushing his bike up the hill on the opposite side of the road. I enquired, not too politely, what he thought he was doing driving a cow up the road in the middle of the night? "Very sorry Mister," he said with a strong Eastern European accent, "is not my cow." We set off in various directions to find the animal that had left several inches of brown and white hide on the front of John's car and could have been severely injured, but we failed to find it. The normally slightly convex front of the Volkswagen was now distinctly concave and the front wings were touching the wheels. John managed to lever them out with a jack-handle and we drove to the police station in Shrewsbury to report the accident. Later, when the insurance representative called at my office, I noticed that his file was labelled *The Case of the Flying Cow.*

Later in the year, with another club member, Ken Woolley, I had an aero tow to four thousand feet in the club's T42 *Eagle*, to practise aerobatics. Two weeks later Peter Head, an experienced and popular club member, was killed flying solo in the same aircraft. A wing came off and, although he had borrowed our syndicate's parachute, he made no attempt to get out. I often wondered if he had a temporary loss of consciousness and over-stressed the aircraft. This was the first fatal accident to a member of the Midland Gliding Club. A passenger had been killed in an accident in 1938 and a private owner in 1946.

June and I were married at Macclesfield Registry Office on July 21st 1962. The office was up a flight of stairs and I organized a number of 'pall bearers' to carry me up. We had a small lunch party before departing for our honeymoon during which Henry Maslowski had to own up to having broken a wing off our *Skylark* when he landed in a field that was too small.

June and I drove to London and the following day to Southend where we loaded the car onto a *Carvair*, a four-engine freighter, and flew to Basel. Some of our so-called friends had spiked our luggage, breaking the door-lock of the car in the process and we arrived in Basel with the door held shut with my belt (in a wheelchair it was not essential for keeping my trousers up). Next morning I asked at the desk of the small country hotel if there was any Austin agent in the area and a porter set off on a bicycle. Miraculously he returned quite soon with the door handle and fittings and completed the repair himself. We toured northern Italy, intending to stay for a few days in Sirmione on the southern shore of Lake Garda, but as the temperature was over 90° in the early morning we drove north to Bolzano, which was only slightly cooler, and then over the Brenner Pass into Austria to black skies and thunderstorms. In Kitsbühl, I was enjoying a bath when the phone rang and the receptionist said, "Very sorry, a bus has just driven into the backside of your car." Fortunately the damage was slight. It was added to later in Paris when I ran into the backside of a car driven by an extremely charming Dutchman.

I had always argued that the format of the traditional wedding reception was unsatisfactory. You invite a lot of friends, including some you haven't seen for years, who have a few drinks and a meal with speeches and telegrams from sick relatives. The bride and groom do a quick circuit of the tables in an attempt to say something to everybody and then drive off and the party that should have been has not even started. Supposing there are a hundred guests and the reception lasts four hours. In the unlikely event that only one hour is spent sitting at a table, that gives you less than two minutes per guest. Inevitably, someone will immobilise you for ten minutes while she tells you about her operation. Not for us. June and I had a handful of local friends to lunch at my local pub and invited people we really wanted to a wedding reception a month later after our honeymoon.

I flew only occasionally throughout the remainder of 1962 because the *Skylark* was out of action while the wing was rebuilt. I had two further flights in March the following year and then the *Skylark* was totally destroyed when Stephen Wills flew it into a tree, slightly damaging his back. A few days later we trooped silently into his hospital ward in Shrewsbury and dumped various instruments and assorted artefacts from our beloved glider on his bed; without comment we silently trooped out.

The following year, on June 22nd 1963, the family grew to four with the birth of Rosemary. We had decided that I would formally adopt Stella so she would also be an Inman, keeping 'Halfpenny' as a middle name throughout her life. As only married couples could adopt children, this meant that June had to appear with me in Court, so becoming both her adoptive and natural mother.

Hans ("Peter") Wulff in a Messerschmitt 410

Hugely pleased with myself after my first solo

Inverted 'landing' after bungee accidentally detached during the launch and wing-holder failed to let go

Neill Trophy for most successful pupil pilot, 1959.
Presented by Mrs Hardwick, widow of Espin Hardwick,
the founder of the Midland Gliding Club

Olympia

My last flight at the Long Mynd about 1996

June

Stella

8

Thalidomide and The Pill

In 1956 a small German pharmaceutical company, Chemie Grünenthal, synthesised a compound called thalidomide and in 1957 they started to market it under the name 'Contergan'. At the time barbiturates were the most frequently used sleeping tablet and they were also the commonest reason for the admission of comatose patients who had tried to kill themselves. Several times at Addenbrooke's I had sat with deeply unconscious patients, injecting a highly poisonous antidote called picrotoxin until their reflexes returned. Thalidomide was effective as a sleeping tablet and had proved to be safe when taken in overdoses; some had survived doses of one hundred tablets. It was to bring my career in ICI to an abrupt end and it led me into many fascinating and controversial situations that dominated my life and that of my family for nearly forty years.

In December 1961 the *Lancet* published a letter by Dr. William McBride of Sydney, Australia, reporting that twenty per cent of babies whose mothers had taken thalidomide during pregnancy were born with abnormalities. The most characteristic deformities were missing limbs. McBride's letter had been sent to the *British Medical Journal* but the Editor had decided not to publish it and had missed the medical scoop of the century. At a meeting in Hamburg a month earlier a paediatrician, Dr. Widukind Lenz, reported that he had seen fifty-two babies with similar abnormalities. Three hundred and forty-nine malformed children were born in the United Kingdom and between two and three thousand in Germany. Lenz's data were more impressive than those reported by McBride and he was the first to make his results public, but McBride's letter monopolised the publicity in the United Kingdom. Several years later McBride damaged his professional reputation by claiming without adequate supporting evidence that a drug commonly used to treat depression had similar effects to those of thalidomide.

The Distillers Company marketed thalidomide in the United Kingdom under the brand name 'Distaval'. Possibly more by good luck than good management, ICI avoided involvement in the tragedy and did not market thalidomide although we had a concession to distribute several other products produced by the same company. The tragedy had not been predicted and was probably unpredictable with the technology then available. One thing was clear however; no manufacturer could be relied on to monitor and make sell-or-withdraw decisions on his product.

I could see a possible role for myself and wrote to the Department of Health. My interest and ideas became known to Sir Derrick Dunlop, Chairman of the Committee on Safety of Drugs (CSD) that was being set up in response to the disaster. He was looking for someone to develop a national scheme for gathering and analysing reports of suspected adverse reactions to drugs and invited me to meet him at the Department of Health's headquarters at Alexander Fleming House in London. The interviewing panel included Sir Derrick, Dr Dennis Cahal, who was in overall charge of the Secretariat of the new committee, Wilfred Turner, the Secretary, and a number of officials from the Department of Health. I suggested that although occasional accidents could never be avoided completely, the numbers of victims could be minimised if problems could be detected early. Laboratory animals might not respond to drugs in the same way as humans and human clinical trials were often too small to distinguish uncommon but important drug side-effects from events that were unconnected with the drug or were manifestations of the disease being treated. In many clinical trials certain types of patient were excluded because they might be especially sensitive to the experimental drug. This could apply for example to elderly or frail patients and children, or as thalidomide had shown, pregnant women. It was already hoped that the Dunlop Committee would be able to set up a reporting system and I recommended that a team of medically qualified field officers should be recruited to visit the doctors who had reported suspected adverse reactions.

I was offered the post at Medical Officer grade but said that I felt this was too junior for work of such importance. I was asked to leave the room and then a few minutes later called back to be offered the job as a *Senior* Medical Officer (SMO). I promised to let them have my decision within a few days. I was putting my future and that of our growing family at risk by exchanging a secure and well-paid job for one with the ever-present risk that 'red-tape' could stifle any scheme that I might be able to develop. The salary of about £3,000 as an SMO was slightly higher than I was getting at ICI, but there was no company car and living in the London commuter belt was more expensive. On the positive side I could see a potential for involvement in something of immense public interest. Moreover, although I had the highest regard for ICI and especially for the integrity of its Medical Department and my medical and research colleagues, I was unhappy about the methods that drug companies were using to promote their products. Top of my worry list was the lavish entertaining of doctors at all levels of seniority. I could already see the beginnings of a takeover of medicine by the drug industry. For example, during the promotion of ICI's new anaesthetic (fluothane), almost every consultant anaesthetist in the United Kingdom, and many from overseas, had been entertained during visits to the research laboratories. Although I was aware of no substantial gifts, food and drink flowed freely in expensive restaurants and all expenses were paid by the company. I had enjoyed many parties and made many friendships outside the company. Several outstanding and totally honourable experts had, however, allowed themselves to become gold-plated unpaid 'super-reps.' for the company, without thinking about the consequences. At general practitioner and junior hospital doctor level the drug industry invested millions in subsidies to postgraduate medical centres that had been set up throughout the country. They paid for meals in exchange for a few minutes to screen a promotional film and distributed literature and free samples from a display stand. Company representatives made no secret of the fact that they regarded GPs from overseas as a soft touch. I had joined the Association of Medical Advisers to the Pharmaceutical Industry (AMAPI). Ken Green, the Head of our medical department, had played a major role in setting it up although his boss, Alec Stewart, had serious reservations believing it to be nothing more than an attempt by doctors in the industry to protect themselves from their employers. I could see little wrong with that but doubted that this was its main objective. AMAPI organized frequent symposia at the Royal Society of Medicine (RSM) in Wimpole Street, London. Like most postgraduate medical centres, the RSM was heavily sponsored by the drug industry and served as a club, providing meals and accommodation. Over the years I attended many meetings and delivered many papers there. AMAPI was later replaced by the British Association of Pharmaceutical Physicians (BrAPP). During the next thirty years the drug industry's grip on medicine tightened, and I am now one of few people who saw it happening from the start.

Writing at a time when the National Health Service seems to be disintegrating, it is worth reflecting on the role of the drug industry in its decline. In 1948 the provision of free drugs opened the floodgates to drug promotion at a cost that was effectively uncontrollable. Large numbers of new companies were created. European and US drug houses set up sales centres in the United Kingdom and several built huge complexes of research laboratories. Some of the larger companies started satellite companies with new names. These were designed to look like competitors; in reality they were marketing satellites with a separate sales force but without separate research facilities. Their main function was to sell minor chemical variants of products already marketed by the parent company. I shall refer to these products throughout this book as *'Me Too'* products and I will have more to say about them, the way that the medical profession has been conned into prescribing them and the taxpayer into paying for them. Doctors should prescribe new variants of established drugs with extreme caution until genuinely independent large-scale studies have established their safety. Most 'me too' products offer no significant advantages and may have serious defects that go undetected because familiarity with the class of drugs from which they were derived has bred contempt.

ICI had looked after me well. They kept me in their pension scheme and promised to keep my job open for me if the CSD should be short-lived. June and I did some house hunting in Surrey and Kent and settled for a bungalow in Hever, near Edenbridge in Kent. We drove to Kent in October 1964 passing our furniture vans on the way.

The Committee on Safety of Drugs (CSD) was housed in Queen Anne's Mansions at the corner of Petty France and Queen Street close to Westminster Abbey. The Mansions had been built of brick and were thought to be the tallest un-reinforced building in London. The Admiralty had used it during the war. My room on the tenth floor was No.1007 but somebody had unscrewed the '1'. Perhaps I had already created a 'James Bond' image. The first Chairman of one of three sub-committees dealing with various aspects of new drug appraisal and specifically responsible for reactions occurring after new drugs had been marketed, was Prof. Leslie Witts of Oxford. He reminded me of my old mentor, Leslie Cole. Almost painfully polite and diffident, Leslie was a thoughtful listener who inspired loyalty and backed up those who worked with him. He was one of the leading figures in scientific medicine but somehow escaped the recognition and honours he deserved. Colleagues in my section included a pharmacist, Diana Hine, and a small team of clerks headed by Sidney Cardy. Later I was joined at various stages in their careers by a number of Medical Officers —Doctors Sutcliffe ('Cliffe') Ruttle, Roger Vaughan, Alan Wilson, Gillian

Greenberg, Paul Dendy, Peter Weber, Mary Glenn-Bott, Derek Zutshi and Keith Lovel.

After I had been working in the Department for several months, I was horrified to be told that my job and those of John Broadbent who looked after clinical trial submissions, and our Chief, Dennis Cahal, were not 'Established'. We had been totally misled and should have been warned that our posts were temporary. Presumably, as a result of some administrative cock-up (sadly all too frequent in the service, as I was to discover) the normal protocol for appointments had not been followed because of the pressure on ministers in the aftermath of thalidomide. The Establishment and the Unions now demanded that this anomaly be corrected; the jobs were advertised and we had to appear before a formal Civil Service selection board and compete with other applicants. I posted an application form and received three identical printed cards acknowledging the form and telling me that my application was being considered! I attended for interview and remember the astonishment on the faces of several applicants known to me who were waiting to be called for interview. Later I learned that they had no inkling that the three people already in position would be candidates and told me later that they would have ignored the advertisement had they known. If we had not retained our jobs we would have sued the Department. I have little doubt that the interviews were rigged and all three of us did return to our offices in Queen Anne's Mansions.

Although working with a tiny staff and lacking legal teeth, the CSD had considerable power. If a company failed to co-operate the Minister could advise doctors not to prescribe their drug. In practice the companies and the Committee treated each other with 'arm's-length' but mutual respect. A staff of about two dozen managed the committee's affairs and processed the submissions of data on new drugs efficiently for nearly eight years until the Medicines Act of 1968 became effective in September 1971. After that, although the throughput of new drugs remained very much the same, layer upon layer of officials, at least a tenfold increase in number of staff, were required to administer the new law. They absorbed most of the resources, leaving little to finance my small group who were attempting to monitor hundreds of currently marketed drugs. I had to wait nearly five years before I could get the data processed on a computer at the Department's installation in Reading. A single request for data could take three weeks to process because the Committee's work was done during 'off peak' periods. I was not joking when I complained that by the time I got the answer I had often forgotten why I had asked the question. Fortunately my staff invariably finished vital tabulations by hand long before they arrived from the computer in Reading; so we were able to meet committee deadlines.

The mainspring of the monitoring system was then, as it still is forty years later, the 'yellow card' system. Yellow business reply cards are issued to all doctors and some other health care workers who report their suspicions about drugs that may have caused some unexpected side-effects. Several hundred cards arrived each week and almost immediately in 1964 I noticed a potentially serious problem among women using oral contraceptives. Some women had unexpectedly developed thrombosis. During the next six years I was able to make two important contributions to our understanding of the risks of the pill.

I have told this story in some detail in my earlier book *Don't Tell the Patient* and in numerous technical journals [12]. As this was probably the most important work to come out of the CSD, this autobiography would be incomplete without at least a summary of the discoveries that I was fortunately able to make. In 1965 I set up what turned out to be the first study to produce statistically valid evidence that the pill was an occasional cause of fatal thrombosis. What was to have more far-reaching effects, however, was my discovery that the risk of thrombosis was mainly related to the *dose* of one of the two classes of hormone used in the contraceptive pills. This eventually led to worldwide adoption of much safer low-dose preparations and to my being called by some – 'Father of the Mini-Pill', or by less charitable people in the pharmaceutical industry who were hard-hit by my discovery – 'Bill the Pill'.

Thrombosis in the veins or arteries may occur spontaneously or because a coincidental risk factor may predispose to it. Recently, for example, there has been much publicity surrounding sudden deaths after long flights in aircraft, but this risk is well known and was mentioned as an example of a risk factor in several of my papers published thirty years ago. Thrombosis in the leg veins is especially likely to occur within a few days of a surgical operation or after childbirth. Coronary thrombosis is much more common in smokers, diabetics or the obese and it becomes progressively more frequent with increasing age. It is virtually impossible to say whether or not any particular risk factor (of which the use of oral contraceptives is only one) was the most important for the patient who suffered a thrombosis.

In September 1965 it was estimated that about four hundred thousand women were using the pill. In a population of women of this size about a dozen deaths from pulmonary embolism (blood clots lodging in the lungs) would have been expected each year even before the pill had been introduced. The Committee had in fact received reports of sixteen deaths during the first twelve-month period, a figure that was similar to the expected number. This negative finding led to the first of many misunderstandings. Against my advice the officials seized upon the close similarity in numbers to reassure the Minister and the public that there was no risk in taking the pill. This was nonsense because it assumed that every death had been reported to the Committee. That was a most unlikely and dangerous assumption when our experience with all other drugs was that only a small fraction of adverse reactions was being reported.

I recruited a team of more than fifty part-time doctors who

could follow up reports by visiting the general practitioners in their surgeries. I called them *Derrick's Dolls* after our Chairman. Many of them were mothers with growing children who had enough spare time to make occasional visits. Some were older women whose families had grown up and half a dozen were men. Next I obtained copies of the information supplied on death certificates for every woman between the ages of fifteen and forty-four in England and Wales who had died from blood clots in the lung, brain or coronary arteries in 1966. The 'dolls' were asked to interview each doctor whose patient had died and find out if she had been using the pill and if she had any other condition that might have caused thrombosis. At the same interview the notes of six living women of similar age attending the same doctor's practice were examined to see if they were using the pill at that time. This allowed me to roughly estimate the overall usage of the pill in the medical practices in which the deaths had occurred. The preparations for the study were rapidly completed and follow-up of deaths started in the second quarter of 1966. By August it was obvious that relatively more dead women were pill users than would have been expected if the pill had played no part. It was the first study to provide strong evidence that the pill was probably a cause of thrombosis. Before this, however, I had already made an even more startling discovery.

The struggle to keep the Committee serviced with hopelessly inadequate equipment meant that I was forced to do much of my work at home at night or during the weekends. Repeatedly I broke the rule that no confidential information about patients must leave the office. Night after night I worked on more than a thousand yellow cards reporting that a woman using the pill had suffered a thrombosis. I repeatedly sorted them in various ways into piles on the sitting-room floor to see if I could find some clue that might confirm the thrombosis hypothesis. After many passes through the whole suitcase full of yellow cards, I found it.

All versions of the pill marketed at the time contained a mixture of two kinds of sex hormone known as progestogens and oestrogens. There were several variants of progestogen but only two types of oestrogen (mestranol and ethinyloestradiol) that I shall simply call 'M' and 'E'. Almost exactly half of the UK market for the pill was for products that contained M and the other half for products that contained E. The most important clue to the role of the pill was staring me in the face. Three quarters of all the reports of thrombosis were associated with M and only one quarter with E. For all reactions other than thrombosis linked to use of the pill such as headache or nausea, half of the reports referred to a product containing E and half to those containing M — exactly what would be expected from knowledge of the market distribution of the two oestrogens. There was no reason why doctors should report M-related cases of thrombosis selectively and this uneven distribution of reports must either have been the result of chemical differences between M and E or simply because the dose of oestrogen in the pills containing M was larger than it was in those containing E. My problem was that I had noticed this possible explanation for a thrombosis risk before we were certain that there was any risk. The Committee needed corroborative studies before releasing any information to the public.

In the second half of 1966 Leslie and I had several meetings with the College of General Practitioners and the Medical Research Council (MRC). At that time the GPs had no arrangements for large-scale epidemiological studies. Their current research activities were conducted in a very small number of practices. The MRC were unimpressed with their data and I agreed absolutely that with the health of millions of women at stake it was essential to challenge the results of my study before making them public. With some difficulty we persuaded both bodies to set up studies to confirm or refute our conclusions. The College set up a small survey, mainly of women with minor superficial forms of thrombosis, and the MRC another small but high-quality study of patients admitted to hospital. We had agreed that the early results of all three studies would be published simultaneously in the form of a report to the MRC. However, early in 1967 as soon as all three studies were found to show similar trends, the College of GPs jumped the gun and published their study unilaterally in their own house journal. By itself the College study could hardly be considered to provide evidence that the pill was a cause of thrombosis although it produced a CBE for one of its authors. Their self-seeking action was most distasteful to the MRC and Committee. The task of writing the preliminary report fell entirely on Martin Vessey and Richard Doll of the MRC and myself. The College of GPs had assembled one hundred and forty-seven patients, mostly with minor cases of thrombosis. The MRC study compared twenty-nine women with more serious thrombosis with a similar number of women admitted to hospital with other conditions. My earlier study for the Committee already included one hundred and forty deaths and about six times as many living controls. The MRC study suggested that the pill was likely to increase the risk of thrombosis about five times and my study that the annual death rate was comparable to the risk of death while bearing and giving birth to one child [13].

Discoveries are rarely attributed to those who make them. During the months that followed, the fact that I had been responsible for the first statistically validated evidence that the pill was a cause of thrombotic disease and that Leslie Witts and I had encountered so much scepticism and difficulty persuading other bodies to set up studies to confirm or refute my findings, was overlooked. The College of GPs and MRC vied with each other to grab the credit but both their studies started after mine had already reached the stage where the Committee had to take action.

If I had predicted the trouble that the comparison with risks of pregnancy would cause I would have left it out of the discussion. The notion that a year on the pill carried the same risk as one pregnancy became firmly embedded in the minds of the administrators and infected the advice they passed on to ministers and the public. No arguments from me could persuade them that *a woman has to get pregnant before she can run any risk of death from being pregnant* and that women are not pregnant for the whole of their reproductive lives. Thrombosis is not the only risk associated with pregnancy and we had no idea at that time what other serious risks might be associated with the pill. The officials were unwilling to accept the obvious need only to compare like with like and persisted with the intellectually dishonest comparison between one risk in women using the pill with all potential risks in non-users. Arguments raged for several months culminating on April 30th 1968 with totally contradicting advice given in both Houses of Parliament on the same day! Baroness Summerskill, who was a doctor and had read our carefully worded statements in the *British Medical Journal*, got the story right. Kenneth Robinson in the Lower House churned out the propaganda fed to him by the administrators and stated that the risk of thrombosis with the pill appeared to be *smaller* than was the risk of pregnancy.

I flew to Uppsala and was met in a snowstorm by my opposite number in Sweden, Barbro Westerholm (who later became the Swedish Minister of Health). She heaved my wheelchair on top of a pile of skiing equipment in the rear of her Volvo and we set off for my hotel. After a few miles I said that I thought I could hear a baby crying! "That's Bjorn," Barbro replied, "he probably doesn't like your chair on top of his carry-cot." I found that the Swedish data on thrombosis was very similar to ours; I then flew to Copenhagen and found the same thing. Throughout 1968 and 1969 I continued to work on the yellow cards, adding new data from the Swedish and Danish drug safety centres. I concluded that the risk of thrombosis definitely depended simply on the total dose of oestrogen in the various versions of the pill, and was most unlikely to be due to any chemical differences. In November 1969 a new Minister, Richard Crossman, decided that he must reveal these findings in Parliament. I had been careful to advise the Department that the other components of the pill, the progestogens, might also play a part in thrombosis and that my study was incomplete because I had not had time to investigate their possible influence. My advice was brushed aside. The Committee held a meeting with the manufacturers and recommended to the Department that there should be an embargo on release of the story until we had time to inform GPs who in turn could reassure patients that the risk was small even with the larger doses. They too were overruled. The story was leaked to the *Daily Express* and Chapman Pincher wrote it up next day. Crossman no doubt got a few votes for appearing to be on the ball but many women spent a miserable Christmas worrying unnecessarily about an extremely small risk. The media had a bonanza and the medical profession called upon the CSM to resign. The manufacturers, for whom my findings were no surprise, miraculously produced half strength pills at the same price and with all the supporting literature within a few days. The 'mini pill', later known as the 'Second Generation' pill, had arrived. Ten months later Sir George Godber, the Chief Medical Officer, noted a small rise in the birth rate and wondered if the new low dose pills were less effective as contraceptives. He suggested to me that I might have been the father of rather more than I had bargained for.

There was the inevitable witch-hunt for the person responsible for the leak to the press and I was the prime suspect. For some weeks I was exposed to an atmosphere of suspicion and mistrust fermented by the lay officials. I suggested that if they did not believe me why not ask the *Daily Express* if I had leaked the story? Many years after I had left the Department I discovered who had in fact been responsible. Philip Brown, owner and Editor of the industry's newsletter *Scrip*, revealed to me that he had been told about the impending announcement from the Committee while travelling home in a train with the late Ed Harris, a future Deputy Chief Medical Officer at the

Department of Health. Ed obviously had more faith in the ability of the Press to keep a secret than I had.

More than twenty years later it was suggested that certain progestogens in what were now called 'Third Generation' pills might carry a slightly increased risk compared with those that I had been studying. There was a further explosion of media speculation and administrative panic. Any possible risk was still much smaller when compared with that of the first generation pills of the 60's and 70's. Once again the profession's anger vented on the Committee and there were more demands for its resignation. The latest batch of arrogant civil servants and armchair 'experts' had obviously not bothered to read the files of a quarter of a century earlier that would have told them of mistakes in public relations that had been made that were now perfectly avoidable in the light of our earlier experience. As Winston Churchill once said "Those who ignore history are doomed to repeat it".

During the 1960s I was visited several times by thinly disguised emissaries from the Vatican, most often Irish and beguilingly and delightfully vague female doctors. They were avid for evidence of the alleged dangers of the pill. It was widely known that, although I had highlighted a problem with oral contraceptives, I had shown that the risk was very small and that for the majority of women the pill was almost completely safe. This had obviously not been the answer they wanted. They had been seeking any scraps of evidence that might be used to support the current Catholic teaching on birth control. But had I inadvertently added to society's burdens? The pill had certainly contributed to the emancipation of women by giving them control of their reproductive lives. It offered the possibility of limiting their family to a size they could afford. On the other hand it fostered promiscuity, teenage pregnancies, abortion for convenience rather than medical necessity, a divorce rate approaching fifty percent and the 'single-parent family.' Would this have occurred if the Committee had found the dangers of the pill unacceptable or had yielded to pressures from the media? I have views on many facets of these trends. Should the taxpayer, for example, foot the bill for the single parent family? DNA testing could identify the father of children for whom benefit is claimed. Refusal to name the father or his refusal to be tested should lead to withholding benefit or forfeiture of the father's earnings.

Our new home in Kent was a bungalow built on a triangular site of about three acres, hence its name — *Wedgewood*. I had ambitions to develop a fruit and vegetable garden and bought a small second-hand crawler-tractor and a plough. I soon mastered the technique of steering with two levers. Ploughing was fun and the so-called kitchen garden grew. I built a substantial shelter for a Welsh Cob called 'Lucky' that we bought for Stella. To build such a large structure without help and in a wheelchair required careful planning. I set up six brick pillars on the floor of the garage to bring the work up to wheelchair level and I prefabricated the frames in six-by-four inch timber, cutting mortices carefully and securing the joints with wooden pegs. I then knocked out the pegs and two friends carried the timbers out to the field, reassembled the frame and covered it with sheets of galvanised iron. Lucky's shed was still standing sixteen years later when we left Hever, though Lucky himself had been sold when the lure of riding had given way to other teenage attractions.

The winter of '69/'70 was a miserable time for both of us, especially for June. Her father was beginning to show the signs of the brain tumour from which he died in March 1970. I began to think about a change of job. Could I survive the frustrations of commuting to London each day in increasingly difficult traffic conditions? What chance had I of continuing to produce good work while dominated by politicians and administrators who believed that expediency overrides scientific integrity?

The Cummins 'Stairlift', Caloundra, Queensland.
Chris and Cynthia providing the power,
Bob Cummins and June guiding

June and Rosemary, 1963

A WHO Taskforce on Drug Monitoring

9

Lowest Ebb

Our third daughter, Valerie, who had been born shortly after we had moved to Kent, died in an accident when she was only eight months old. On Tuesday October 26th 1965 I returned home earlier than usual. June met me at the front of the house. She asked me not to disturb Valerie, who was asleep in her pram on the patio at the rear of the house. I wheeled across the lawn to the greenhouse and pottered for half an hour and then returned to the house along the path leading to the patio. I looked into Valerie's pram. She was lying on her stomach, still and blue. The cord of the pram beads suspended horizontally between the wing nuts that secured the pram hood was wound round her neck. I released the cord and picked her up and hammered on the window with my fist to attract attention. Cradling her in my arms with my mouth over her mouth and nose and her jaw supported by my left hand, I started to ventilate her gently at the same time compressing her chest between my knee and right hand. After several minutes I almost convinced myself that I could feel a weak pulse and our GP, Andrew Russell, arrived with miraculous speed. He inserted a small breathing tube and I then took over the ventilation of her lungs while he concentrated on trying to get her heart started. After about half an hour we agreed to stop. That this was *my daughter* did not overwhelm me until the police had left with Valerie and her pram and June and I were alone. I still have nightmares.

The police were sympathetic but raised the possibility that somebody might have interfered with Valerie. I was asked if someone might have climbed over the fence that ran along the bridle path. She was a large, healthy and vigorous eight-month-old who we knew as 'Happy Val' because she was always smiling and giggling. She was almost able to sit up in her pram unaided and at the inquest the forensic pathologist described how she had fallen or rolled over the cord and pulled a loop over her head. The Coroner said that it "seems hardly possible to have left the child in safer circumstances" and added "the manufacturers will no doubt hear of this and endeavour to ensure better safety in the future". His verdict was Accidental Death. Eight days after the accident a sad little procession lead by Mr. Smith the undertaker with Happy Val's small white coffin in the crook of one arm, laid her down in Hever churchyard.

June and I had always examined toys carefully but had failed to think of this particular risk. The cause of the accident was the excessive length to which the elastic cord could be stretched. There should have been a component that limited its extension. The elastic cord had a loose braided cover and it would have been easy either to include a secondary, non-stretching, cord of appropriate length within the cover or to ensure that the cover itself was made of a material that limited the amount of stretch. This accident should not have been possible.

I have frequently been involved with patient action-groups through my work in drug safety and well understand their frustration with official bodies and manufacturers. Compensation was never in our minds, such loss cannot be compensated, but I became a one-man action group to force the manufacturer to take the beads off the market until what now seemed to be an obvious fault had been corrected. I decided that the first approach should be to *Kiddicraft* whose Managing Director was notified while on a trip to Australia. He replied:

> 'We have very carefully re-examined the design of the toy from the safety point of view and quite frankly we cannot see that any danger arises when the toy is used in the complete form as manufactured by us.'

He went on to point out that one million strings of beads had been sold and no other trouble had arisen. *'Its complete form as manufactured by us'* referred to the fact that two of the plastic beads were missing from the string on Valerie's pram.

They had been broken and we had removed them to prevent her cutting herself on the sharp plastic. The implication was that we were to blame for Valerie's death for failing to use the beads 'in their complete form'. With an extension-limiting modification that would allow the total length to increase only an inch or two more than the width of a pram, the loss of two or more balls should not have affected the safety of the toy. As *Kiddicraft* would not act instantly I got in touch with my old friend Ronnie Bedford of *The Sun* newspaper. They printed a nine-inch photograph on their front page showing Valerie in her pram with the beads. The headline read – 'Four Months after Beads Strangled Baby, Coroner warned, "Why this delay?" The beads were out of the shops the following week.

Preliminary enquiries at the Office of the Registrar General (now the Office of National Statistics) suggested that similar accidents had occurred rarely but they could find no evidence that specifically implicated *Kiddicraft* beads. I wrote to all UK Coroners, a large number of retailers and several official bodies. I did not restrict my enquiries to accidents with pram-beads; I asked for information about any cases of strangulation by toys. I wrote to: The British Toy Manufacturers' Association; The British Toymaker's Guild, The National Association of Toy Retailers, The Retail Distributors Association, The British Standards Institute, Boots the Chemist, The National Association for Maternity and Child Welfare, The National Society for Children's Nurseries, The National Federation of Women's Institutes, The Department of Health and Social Security, The Royal Society for the Prevention of Accidents, my Member of Parliament and all the national newspapers and appropriate radio and TV programmes.

With a very small number of exceptions the responses ranged from poor to pathetic. The coroners were the most helpful; one of them described an inquest on a child who had been strangled when the wooden button on the end of an electric light cord had jammed in his cot so that he got his head in a noose. Another recorded a similar tragedy when the parents had dangled a rubber toy on a long string hanging down into the baby's carrycot. A search of death certificates for the whole country for several previous years revealed a few deaths of infants from strangulation, mostly when toddler's clothing had become trapped in cots or play-pens, but no death closely resembled Valerie's. Cliff Michelmore, the TV presenter, wrote sympathising with the trouble we were having and saying that he was having similar problems with a campaign to fit devices to stop children pulling hot pans off cookers.

The article in *The Sun* had been the most decisive, and a number of other actions had been triggered. For example, Lord Stonham for the Home Office wrote to my MP, Sir John Rodgers, on April 13th 1966:

> 'The manufacturers, Kiddicraft Limited, who are gravely concerned at the accident, had already decided to adopt one of Dr. Inman's suggestions and the box in which the pram beads are sold now bears a warning that the toy should not be used on a pram without its full quota of beads. The manufacturers have also agreed to adopt a suggestion we put to them that, in future, the elastic cord should be braided in such a way as to limit its extendibility to 40 %.'

It was ironic to read how the official who drafted the letter for Lord Stonham had twisted the two ideas around. I had not wasted energy discussing what might be written on a box that would probably be thrown away within a few minutes of opening it. The idea of reducing the extendibility of the cord was entirely mine. I had frequently encountered this kind of deceit by civil servants trying to impress their superiors. When processing official replies, they draft them in such a way that they appear to be the people with the bright ideas.

As a sequel to this chapter I quote from a press clipping sent to me by my eldest daughter some twenty years later:

'A baby strangled herself with a toy, an inquest heard yesterday. R...F... became entangled in a rope holding plastic rattles across her cot. She died an hour later, three days before her first birthday. Toy makers, J. L. Randall, said that 23,000 had been produced. There had been no complaints.'

Nothing changes.

FOUR MONTHS AFTER BEADS STRANGLED BABY

Coroner warned.. Why this delay?

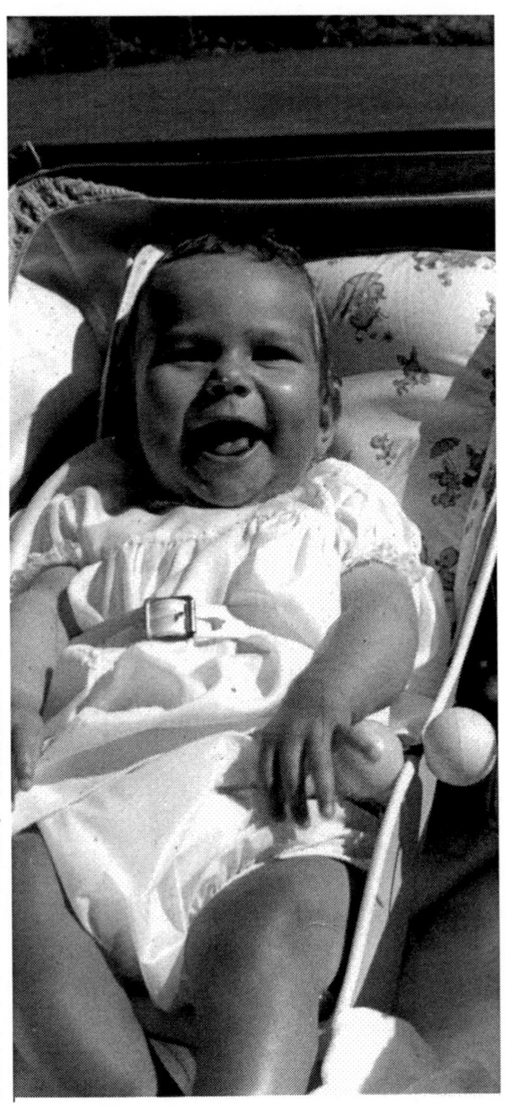

PRAM beads, identical to those which strangled an eight-month-old baby girl, were still on sale in shops yesterday—without the safety warning urged by a coroner at an inquest nearly four months ago.

The baby, Valerie Inman, died as she played with the plastic beads—the size of ping-pong balls—which were suspended across her pram by an elastic cord.

Two of the eight beads were missing.

At the inquest in Tonbridge, Kent, on November 1 last year the coroner, Mr. David Morgan, said: "No doubt the manufacturers of this toy will hear of this and will endeavour to arrange better safety precautions in future."

Valerie's father, a doctor at the Ministry of Health, wrote to the toy's manufacturers, Kiddicraft Ltd., of Godstone Road, Kenley, Surrey, asking them to modify the toy to prevent a similar accident.

REGRET

On December 9 he received a reply from Mr. David Day, the firm's managing director.

It said: "We have very carefully re-examined the design of the toy from the safety point of view, and quite frankly we cannot see

SUN newspaper reporting the death of Valerie

10

A Tragedy Nobody Noticed

Forty years ago there was an 'epidemic' of deaths from asthma in the United Kingdom. Suspicion fell on the pressurised aerosol inhalers containing adrenalin-like substances that had proved to be a rapidly effective means of alleviating an attack. In *Don't Tell the Patient,* I described it as the 'Silent Epidemic', because it was slow to be recognized, attracted little publicity at its height or after its passing and left about three thousand patients dead.

The Riker pharmaceutical company had introduced pressurised aerosol inhalers under the brand name of *Medihaler*. These inhalers could be carried in the pocket or handbag and nearly always worked. In 1964 Martin Greenberg, one of my former chiefs at Addenbrooke's in Cambridge, wrote to me about several sudden and unexpected deaths of asthmatics who had used the inhalers. The Committee did not feel that his letter called for official action at that time and any adverse comment from them could damage an important and usually beneficial product. I advised Martin to write to *The Lancet* and in June 1967 I managed to persuade the Committee to publish a 'low-key' warning, emphasising the great value of the inhalers but advising patients to stop using them and seek help urgently if they failed to produce the relief that they had usually experienced. Meanwhile, I arranged with the Registrar General for the mortality data to be released to the Committee a year before the normal date of publication. In August 1969 with Abe Adelstein, the Chief Medical Statistician of the Registrar General's office, I published a paper in *The Lancet* entitled *The Rise and Fall of Asthma Mortality* [14].

The death certificates revealed an horrific picture. Only children under five years of age, who were too young to use the aerosols, were unaffected. Amalgamating the figures for patients aged five to thirty-five, deaths in England and Wales (Scotland had a separate arrangement for processing death certificates and we did not include them) averaged about one hundred and fifty each year. By 1966 it had risen to four hundred and fifty. In 1967 there was a modest drop to three hundred and seventy-three, all the reduction being in the second half of the year after the Committee's warning, and then in 1968 it fell to two hundred and sixty-one. Similarly in people aged over thirty-five we estimated the excess deaths over the whole period of the epidemic to have been about two thousand three hundred. The rise and fall in the death rate closely followed the sales of pressurised aerosols. There had been about one death for every two to three thousand aerosol canisters sold.

I was a member of the Medical Research Council's committee of enquiry into asthma deaths that had been set up under the chairmanship of Sir Cyril Clarke. Numerous hypotheses were considered and it seemed likely that several factors were involved. I believed that the majority were caused by *over-reliance* on a treatment that was normally effective (I nearly used the words *over-dependence* but realized that this might wrongly suggest addiction). Although the drug itself was not intrinsically dangerous, a point of no return could be reached when the beneficial effect ceased and continued use had no further beneficial effect on the asthma. Unless resuscitated immediately a patient could die from asphyxia and heart failure. Doctors and patients had probably been lulled into a false sense of security by the availability of this normally excellent form of treatment. The worst affected group were children aged between ten and fourteen who were old enough to master self-treatment, but not sufficiently mature to recognize its limitations and seek help when it was most needed. Any new treatment must be introduced gradually under close supervision. Drug companies cannot be relied on and doctors and patients should be especially cautious when new treatments are massively advertised. Among more than half a dozen ideas that I suggested, one was that during the epidemic a particularly vulnerable sub-group of young people might have been decimated. Ten to twenty years might elapse before a new sub-group of asthmatics, who were similarly at risk, had reached the same age. I was concerned about the tactics used by Glaxo to promote its product *Serevent* in the 1990s at a time when it was generally recognized that asthma appeared to be becoming an increasing problem. They were employing so-called 'research assistants', who were nothing more than sales representatives, to recruit GPs for post-marketing studies, ostensibly to confirm the safety of the product but in reality to promote it.

I searched the literature to see if there was any evidence that the propellants used in the aerosols might have unpredicted dangers. They were the chlorofluorocarbons, generally referred to as "CFCs", carbon-based chemicals containing fluorine and chlorine and they were used in many commercial aerosol canisters such as hair or paint sprays and as refrigerants. CFCs are nowadays thought to be 'environmentally unfriendly' because of the damage to the ozone layer in the upper atmosphere. I found that in some experiments, animals had developed cardiac problems, especially when oxygen levels were deliberately reduced to simulate an attack of asthma. While explaining this to the MRC Asthma Death Committee I could see that Colin Dollery, from the Postgraduate Medical School at the Hammersmith Hospital, was fidgeting and stuffing his papers into his briefcase and he was half out of his seat by the time Cyril Clarke had called for 'any other business'. He rushed from the room and in the record time of about two weeks published a paper in *The Lancet* on the effects of CFCs in volunteers. Colin had returned to Hammersmith and recruited some 'volunteers', one of whom was Charles George whom I would meet in Southampton as Dean of Medicine some ten years later and who remembered the incident well. It was eventually decided that CFCs were not likely to present a danger in the small amounts that would be inhaled by asthmatics.

11

The Old Rectory at Hever

In 1970, at a festival to celebrate the 850th Anniversary of Edenbridge, we attended a reading from Dickens by the actor Emlyn Williams. During the performance I heard a loud noise in my right ear followed by a continuous ringing sound. These were the first effects of Ménière's disease, a condition of the inner ear that causes deafness, disturbance of balance and, worst of all, tinnitus – a loud high-pitched continuous noise in the head. I have now lived with tinnitus for more than thirty years. Few noises are loud enough to mask it. A low fly-past at the Farnborough air show almost obliterated the noise, but day or night it is there and I have adapted to it. Several weeks after my 'big bang' I also developed severe vertigo, falling back into bed when half into my wheelchair. The children bouncing on the bed made me feel sick and I remain intolerant to high-pitched noises that increase my tinnitus and can start an attack of vertigo lasting for an hour or more. I was thoroughly investigated but no treatment worked. My hearing deteriorated over several years and I am now totally dependent on an aid. In common with many deaf people I usually miss the first few words of a conversation. Here was another disability to add to my collection; it has run a close second in nuisance value to the polio that put me in a wheelchair.

In May 1971 June and I flew to the WHO in Geneva to spend a week helping Bruce Royal plan a conference on drug monitoring. On the desk in my temporary office in the headquarters building the morning after I arrived, I found a telegram from my mother to say that father had died during the night. I had felt that he might be unwell when I spoke with him on the phone before leaving for Geneva. My great sadness was the feeling that there was so much that had yet to be said and now no chance to say how much I had appreciated his support over many difficult years. My brother Chris handled the funeral arrangements while I spent two days trying to cobble a conference programme together and then we flew back in time for the funeral. My mother seemed to get over her bereavement reasonably well when we visited once or twice each month, her only complaint being persistent 'rheumatism' in her hip.

Later in 1971 June had a call from a solicitor in Cambridge asking if she was the wife of a Dr. William Inman? Had he worked at Addenbrooke's in the fifties? Had he ever looked after a certain 'Miss X'? June had visions of a lawsuit, but he went on to say that he had some good news for me and would I phone him as soon as possible. Thirteen years previously I had indeed looked after his client. She was an elderly diabetic whom I had admitted and readmitted repeatedly in diabetic coma. Both her legs had been amputated above the knees because of gangrene, a common complication of diabetes, and she was nearly blind. Senior colleagues, including the consultant, had taken me aside and suggested that I was under no ethical obligation to keep resuscitating her as her 'quality of life' was minimal. I never cease to worry when judgements are made about quality of life. Miss X never seemed to have visitors and it was difficult to communicate with her because she was deaf, confused, argumentative and sometimes violent. In her lucid periods I discharged her as soon as I could, knowing that a week or so later I would be seeing her again or perhaps receiving a note from her GP to say that she had died. She was one of my 'regulars' who would try the patience of a saint and I was fond of her in spite of many interrupted nights. She was the sort of person I had gone into medicine to help – for better or worse. Thirteen years later this remarkable story emerged.

Miss X's last discharge had coincided with my leaving Addenbrooke's. Her diabetes had remained under control and she had taken on a new lease of life. She had bought a new wheelchair and started spending her money at the Newmarket races. Somehow she had followed my career without getting in touch with me directly and I have no idea how she did it. Eventually she went blind and ended her days in a nursing home. She left a quarter of her estate each to me, her solicitor, a relative of his, and the British Diabetic Association and nothing to her family. She left all her jewels to "Dr. Inman's wife, if there be one". Her jewel box had been broken open and rifled, presumably after she went blind, and no record of its contents was ever found. It had not, as stipulated in her will, been deposited at her bank. A second larger box of costume jewellery, including one or two quite valuable items, survived. The costume jewellery provided an endless supply of 'lucky dips' for my girls in the years to come.

Though not large in present-day terms, the legacy enabled us to look for a larger house and the value of the shares increased many times over the years. The old lady's legacy changed the course of our lives, as without doubt my persistence with her treatment had changed hers. The greatest reward was the thought that I might somehow have inspired her through my own performance in a wheelchair and added thirteen years of 'quality' to the already long life of an old lady who had been written off by her family and the medical profession. Nowadays she would have been labelled 'not to be resuscitated'.

As the sophistication and cost of health care escalates and the proportion of elderly people increases, the spectre of rationing and so-called 'euthanasia' starts to haunt us. I had learned never to allow my judgement to be over-ridden by the negative attitudes of some relatives. Too often, a well dressed relative (who might have recently taken on a larger mortgage), visiting a tatty and neglected elderly parent perhaps for the first time in many years, talked too glibly about a hoped for 'happy release'. Pressure on hospital beds has led some nurses to persuade young and inexperienced doctors to agree to 'do not resuscitate' notices or to withdraw positive treatment of elderly patients. The Department of Health rightly advises that such situations always require the participation of the consultant and the relatives. After fifty years in a wheelchair and aged over seventy I feel particularly vulnerable. At first sight, in an emergency situation and perhaps unable to speak for myself, a stranger might easily assess my 'quality of life' to be so impaired that it would be a kindness to let me slip away. I do not disagree in principle with so-called 'living wills', but I tend to wonder if the patient had been the first to suggest it. I expect all possible measures to be taken to resuscitate me, or any of my relatives, until experts have confirmed either that 'brain death' has occurred or that I and no one else had clearly indicated that it is time for me to go. I have devised a letter to be shown on admission to hospital. My solicitor will look for any evidence of a 'Do Not Resuscitate' order, verbal or written, and their presence will be regarded as grounds for litigation. To deliberately withdraw fluids from a patient who may be 'locked in', able to hear and understand but unable to communicate, is probably one of the worst forms of torture that any human being could inflict on another human being. I fear sudden death and strongly disagree with people who express the wish to die suddenly from a heart attack or accident. I would far prefer to die slowly (pain is controllable) and have time to prepare, to complete some of the tasks that were important to me, to make provision for the family and to delegate responsibilities.

Towards the end of 1971, we heard that the Church Commissioners were planning to sell the Old Rectory a short distance from where we were living in Hever. It was a beautiful building standing in about four acres of land with a coach house and stables. A new and smaller rectory was being built nearby. According to Lord Astor, Hever Castle, St Peter's Church and the Old Rectory had been built about eight hundred and fifty years previously. The first recorded occupants of the Castle were a Norman family who took the name of de Hevere from the old English word for a deer forest. A later owner was Sir Thomas Bullen, Anne Boleyn's father. Henry VIII courted Anne in Hever and Sir Thomas is buried at St. Peter's near our tiny daughter, Valerie. A small hamlet was built around the church, opposite the *Henry VIII* pub. This pub was formerly the *Bull and Butcher* a derivative of *Bullen Butcher,* so named because Sir Thomas's son, his daughter Anne, and his daughter-in-law had all been executed.

At the auction of the Old Rectory I was carried up a flight of stairs and sat towards the back of the room. I remained silent as the bidding proceeded in multiples of £100. When I felt the time had come for a decisive bid I called £500, waited for two more small bids and then raised it by another £500, precariously close to the limit agreed by the building society. I became the proud owner for £31,500. Twenty-five years later an advertisement in the national press showed the Old Rectory was on the market at £850,000.

We moved from the bungalow at the end of April 1972 and lived with an aerosol mist of red brick dust that crept through keyholes and around polythene screens, while a new roof, a lift, an extra bathroom and thirty-three radiators were installed. The northern and oldest part of the house was constructed of oak beams and 'wattle and daub'. There was a large ground floor study with the principle bedroom above and an attic room above that. In the study there was a small modern grate with a hideous blue-tiled surround, behind which was a hollow void about eight feet deep containing two chimneys. A short passage led alongside this dead space to a long drawing room that had originally been two rooms. Through a doorway at the end of this long room was a Victorian dining room. A hall, kitchens, laundry and pantries had also been added in the nineteenth century and the passage to the 'servants' quarters' (if we had any) was approached through a green baize door. The eastern elevation of the building had been revised in the early nineteenth century and included a row of seven tall windows, two of them opening to the main lawn. I installed a wheelchair lift that allowed access to four levels including the extensive cellars, one of which I used as a workshop.

The house was full of surprises. One day I climbed up to the attic room on my bottom and could see, through a hole in the plaster, that the bedroom ceilings over the Georgian middle section of the house had been lowered several feet, presumably to save heat. In the basement I demolished part of a wall and uncovered another large cellar extending the full length of the oldest part of the house. The floor had once been at a much lower level than the other cellars and had been filled with rubble. The top half of an outside door and the tops of window frames were still visible. The drive outside had also been raised some six feet and on the other side there was evidence of other buildings that had at one time stood at a lower level in a peculiar sunken gully that we used as a bonfire area and rubbish dump.

One evening with dinner guests, and fortified by several bottles of claret, we attacked the blue tiled grate with a brick-bat and a four-pound hammer and immediately found a Victorian grate one brick's depth behind it. I was disappointed because I had hoped to find a much earlier fireplace with an inglenook and bread oven. We persisted and found, at another brick's depth, Elizabethan corbels blackened with the soot of centuries and soft mortar mixed with horsehair. At this point our architect and next-door neighbour, Bob King, vetoed further excavation until a new mantle had been let into the brickwork to support the stack that was thirty feet high. June and the children later removed thirty barrow-loads of jackdaw nests, some ancient eggs and numerous skeletons. A new throat was constructed and a specialist restored the old brickwork. For the next eight years the fireplace smoked whenever we lit it and we understood why it had been bricked up. Had we not left in 1980, my plan had been to install a fan in the chimney.

The rectory once had its own gas-making plant in a lean-to shed backing onto the kitchen wall. There was no public gas supply, although pipes were found all over the house and had been used as conduits for some wall lights that had been converted to electricity. Jack Collins, the Rector, told me that the gas had been made from petrol by some process that I have not been able to trace.

On returning to Kent after one of our overseas trips, the news about my mother was not good. She had complained of pain in her back and hip for several months and had been admitted to hospital for transfusion after a bowel haemorrhage. The surgeon told me that, although her bowel X-rays showed no abnormality, he must do an exploratory operation. My mother had not consented to an operation unless I agreed and I certainly did not agree. I suspected that her pain-killing tablets had caused the bleeding. He then threatened me, saying that if I refused to let him operate and she bled again, no more blood would be available for her. After he had gone I asked to see the X-rays of her spine and hip that had not yet been reported on by the radiologist. To my horror and disgust the diagnosis was obvious at a glance. She had numerous secondary deposits of cancer in her spine and pelvis. I had no idea that nobody had taken an adequate history or examined her breasts. This was a diagnosis that would not have been missed by a medical student. I wondered how much he made in fees for unnecessary operations on private patients.

I took Mother to see a radiotherapist at St.Thomas' Hospital. There was no point in removing the painless tumour in her breast that measured more than an inch in diameter and had probably been present for several years. He advised local radiotherapy to any parts of her body that were painful. This was done as an outpatient while she stayed with us and she then returned to Cooden. She became confused and started to write her diary in her accounts book with such entries as: 'Treatment came began' and 'Bill in came'. She wanted to die in Bexhill where her friends could visit her and she settled fairly well in a nursing home with a view of the sea that she loved and some of her own furniture. As she seemed to be reasonably comfortable and the children had not had a holiday, we decided to risk a brief trip to Yorkshire. We borrowed a caravan and drove to Castle

Howard but were recalled after only a few days. Mother's room was on the first floor of the nursing home and there was no lift so I was carried up two flights of narrow stairs with the help of an elderly porter and several nurses. Mother's head had shrunk into her shoulders because the bones of her neck had collapsed. I am not sure if she recognized me; she made peculiar grunting sounds in an attempt to talk but I could distinguish no words. I did not say goodbye in case she realized that I would not see her again. I left frustrated by the difficulty of visiting. It was at times such as this that inability to cope adequately with a crisis because of one's disability is most painful. She died on August 19th 1973.

Fishing had taken over from gliding and shooting. I still enjoyed an occasional evening shooting pigeon in the woods near the Castle with the Astor's agent, Victor Hoare-Nairne, or one of the local GPs. A small reservoir at Bough Beech was easily accessible in a wheelchair and I needed assistance only to hold the boat steady while I climbed in. I had no difficulty rowing and usually caught my 'limit' of trout. On another local lake, Bewl Water, the boats were much larger and had outboard motors. I constructed a portable seat that spanned the middle and stern thwarts so that I could sit comfortably facing sideways and handle the outboard motor and fish without shifting my position in the boat. If the engine failed to start I could slide onto the middle thwart and row. I was not able to reach the anchor rope but solved this problem by tying a short length of thin line to it, about a boat's length from its attachment at the bow. By pulling on the line I could then drag the anchor rope within reach. This is a useful tip for a disabled angler. The Y-shaped arrangement of the two ropes also helped to set the boat across the wind and greatly helped casting the fly-line with a weak arm. Sometimes I fished with a friend, David Chamberlin, but many trips were single-handed.

I have fished on lakes in Sussex, Cumbria and Cornwall that were equipped with 'Wheely-boats', specially designed for disabled anglers and placed there by the Handicapped Anglers Trust (HAT). They comprise an aluminium pontoon resembling a miniature tank-landing craft and a ramp at the bow can be lowered for the angler to embark in a wheelchair. To reduce pollution in these reservoirs, they were driven by an electric outboard motor but it was seriously underpowered and made poor progress in windy conditions. Fishing in a chair from the bank of a lake or river can be dangerous. Even a small slope may be disconcerting because wheelchair brakes that depend on the friction exerted on the tyre by a simple metal lever can easily slip, especially when both hands are occupied playing or netting a fish. Electric chairs must be switched off while fishing, because a loop of line may easily foul the joystick and set the chair in motion. I have heard of a sea angler fishing from a jetty who had drowned, strapped to his electric wheelchair.

When on holiday with the family on the Isle of Arran the owner of the boats, Mr Laird, solved the problem of wheeling me over the sand by sitting me on a pallet on his forklift tractor and driving me through the water to his boat. One day I heard a commotion on the beach and saw Rosemary running up and down screaming "Daddy, Shark, Shark, I love you." A basking shark twice as long as the dinghy quietly basked about six feet away from the boat, fortunately without trying to rub the barnacles off his back against the boat.

As a child, Rosemary earned a few shillings during the pheasant-shooting season by beating on the Hever estate. The Queen was a fairly frequent guest of the Astors and on one occasion, when I asked Rosemary how the shoot had gone, she casually mentioned that she had chatted to the Queen during the lunch break. At her age I would have run home bursting to tell everybody, but I had difficulty extracting the story. "Was she wearing her crown?"

"No, just a scarf."

"What were you doing when she came over to talk to you?"

"Sitting on the step of the hut."

"Did you stand up?"

"No I was eating my sandwiches"!

My winter local was the Henry VIIIth near the Castle. One day when I was alone in the bar, a middle-aged rather stout visitor with thinning reddish hair joined me in a drink. We enjoyed each other's company and had reached the point in our conversation when we started talking about our jobs; he told me he was an actor. I explained that I had an annoying habit of guessing what strangers' occupations were and had decided he was probably a bank manager. Privately I could not imagine anybody looking less like an actor or more like a bank manager. A long time later I discovered that I had bought a pint for Arthur Lowe – Captain Mainwaring of the TV series *Dad's Army*. I had cast him perfectly as a bank manager several years before he played the role.

Our friends in Hever included our neighbours at the New Rectory, Keith and Dora Russell. Keith had been a Bishop in Uganda before coming to Kent and was now the Assistant Bishop of Rochester and Rector at Hever. We played snooker each Saturday in the 'Riviera', a wooden summerhouse in his garden in which he had installed a half-size table. Perhaps it is a characteristic of bishops that they always play to win. If, for example, I accidentally caught a ball with my sleeve he demanded his four points. If he did it, it was "Didn't see that did you Bill?" Our standard of positional play was such that we usually potted the colours one at time and we were evenly matched. Many of our games depended on who potted the last black. If Keith missed an easy shot he had a number of episcopal expletives. Most often he raised his eyes to heaven, struck the floor firmly with the butt of his cue and shouted — "Confustication", a word that I have since learned he must have borrowed from Tolkien. Very sensibly our conversations never once touched on religion, mostly snooker, current affairs, family or lawnmowers.

One Saturday evening Keith's house guest was Archbishop Luwum, whom Keith had ordained as a priest in Uganda years earlier. We decided to teach him how to play snooker. Not even a distinguished visitor was allowed to interfere with our snooker so we decided to teach him how to play. Luwum found the cue action difficult. I suggested that he should hold it like a throwing spear only the other way up! We were soon prancing round the table pretending the cues really were spears. Shortly afterwards the Archbishop returned to Uganda and was murdered by General Idi Amin.

The Old Rectory, Hever, Kent

12

A Ghost Goes West

As a consultant to the World Health Organization I often flew to Geneva and other countries to help them set up drug reaction reporting systems. Friendships formed with the leaders of the national systems were invaluable. The relaxed atmosphere of international conferences, the parties and the sightseeing were the best part of the job and were some compensation for overtime and bureaucratic frustration at the office. All the drug monitoring centres were under-funded and under-staffed and most of them were held together only by the enthusiasm and self-sacrifice of the individuals who had set them up. Noteworthy was the dedication and persistence of Karl Kimbel in West Germany, Ronnie Meyboom in Holland, Ed Napke in Canada and Judy Jones in the USA, to mention only four who perhaps had a rougher ride through their national bureaucracies than others. The politicians and civil servants hoped that another disaster on the scale of thalidomide was unlikely and, quite wrongly, that drug-company trials on laboratory animals and small numbers of humans were a sufficient safeguard. It was easy to draw up a set of rules about the number of animals that must be used in each test or the duration of toxicity studies and so on, and the Medicines Act of 1968 made only passing reference to the desirability of monitoring adverse reactions *after* marketing. The influence of the drug industry on the drafting of the Medicines Act was very obvious, especially the deliberate omission of rules about the relative efficacy of new products. There was no obligation to show that a new product had a measurable margin of superiority over similar products already marketed. This omission set the scene for the explosive increase in the number of expensive copycat products – the 'me too' drugs. They flooded the market during the next thirty years, soaked up a large proportion of company research budgets and diverted billions of taxpayers' money into drug company profits rather than into building and equipping hospitals and paying adequate salaries to doctors and nurses.

Flying while dependent on a wheelchair was packed with incident, frequently amusing and sometimes traumatic. On September 14th 1968, June and I, with Rosemary and our fourth daughter Charlotte in her carrycot, set off to Heathrow so that I could take a flight to Washington for a WHO conference. There had been heavy rain and we had reached a point just north of Edenbridge where a flood blocked the road to the north. Some opportunists in thigh boots were charging £5 to push cars across the deepest part. We turned back and called at the police station. They had lost touch with most of their men and they had no idea of the extent of the floods. It seemed likely that our road back to Hever would already be blocked so I drove to a service station that was on higher ground, parked the car on the forecourt and the owner volunteered to drive us home in his Land Rover. For several days, except for the occasional sound of helicopters, there was almost complete silence. The phones were down and we depended on bulletins on the TV and radio. Edenbridge was extensively flooded and many shops and houses suffered severe structural damage. Colour TV sets were seen floating down the river. Hever Castle was flooded and oil and sewage contaminated tapestries and panelling. Residents in the 'Elizabethan Village', built by Lord Astor to house his retainers, had to be rescued by boat. There was no way I could contact Washington to report that I would not be able to speak at the WHO conference. When I failed to show up at breakfast the following day, Bruce Royal, who headed the WHO team, phoned the hotel and was told that I had checked in late the previous evening but was not answering the phone. When I had still not turned up at the coffee break immediately before I was due to speak, Bruce took a cab to the hotel. He demanded to be taken up to 'my' room fearing I was lying in a pool of blood after falling out of my wheelchair. He found I had checked in only in spirit.

The following month I did get to Washington. I had not yet reached the seniority that would normally justify first class travel, but the Chief Medical Officer, Sir George Godber, took account of my two hundred pounds, six foot five inches and paraplegia and very thoughtfully ruled that I needed more space. I flew first class to Washington with Bob Wilson, a systems analyst who had the task of designing a computer system for the Committee. We inspected the WHO pilot scheme that had been set up by the Food and Drug Administration (FDA). The programme was managed by Lloyd Christopher and ideas for signalling potentially important adverse reactions were being developed by him and a bright young statistician from Ceylon, Kim Patwari. We located the WHO computer in the basement of a row of shops near the airport. A flight of stairs led down to the basement and I had to wheel through a ladies' boutique and along a narrow passage, flanked by naked dummies, to a goods lift. The installation was liberally carpeted with computer paper, creating an obvious fire hazard. I was quite pleased to get out after a cursory look at the 'system'. The data was hardly more than an amalgamation of the printout from the national centres, including our own. Over the next thirty years the centre developed progressively and was relocated in Uppsala in Sweden where it currently collects and analyses data from more than sixty national centres under the direction of Ralph Edwards.

About this time June had started to suffer from chronic abdominal pain. Rex Laurie, a surgeon from Guy's Hospital who visited Edenbridge regularly, investigated it and I was shown her X-rays. She had a fixed constriction of the large bowel that had to be regarded as a cancer until proved otherwise. No cancer was found, but she had an extremely painful post-operative wound infection from which she had barely recovered when we embarked on a six-week round-the-world lecture tour. Our first stop was New York. While June, with a barely healed abdominal wound, was pushing me across one of the main avenues, a castor of my wheelchair collapsed. I leaned sideways and she continued to push me on three wheels. We made no attempt to retrieve the wreckage of the castor. Fortunately a cab driver knew of a shop that sold wheelchairs and, as it was an American chair, we replaced the whole assembly. Breakdowns are a problem for disabled overseas travellers; many wheelchair parts are not readily interchangeable. Nuts and bolts may have metric, British or American threads. Local mechanics will do their best to help, and my luggage always included two adjustable spanners, a small selection of nuts and bolts, a spare spindle, a ball-race, some plastic gloves to keep grease off my hands and a pump, because connectors also have different threads. Mobility for a wheelchair in New York put England to shame. All public buildings had disabled toilets, taxi drivers did not look the other way and many buses had electric lifts.

I gave a paper on the pill at the 5th International Congress of Pharmacology in San Francisco and we then flew on to Honolulu. The British Consul sent his secretary to meet us and arranged for us to rest and refresh in the VIP suite for an hour or so before changing aircraft for an evening flight to Fiji. I mentioned to the stewardess that, as we crossed the International Dateline during the flight, my birthday on August 1st would last only four hours. The 707 had to make a short unscheduled stop at Pago Pago in Samoa to attend to a problem in one engine. While the rest of the passengers 'deplaned', June and I remained on board and when the flight resumed I was presented with a birthday card signed by the Captain and all the crew and a bottle of champagne. We arrived at Nandi at 4.00 a.m. and were met by a tobacco planter, Murray Charters, and his son. Murray was a mutual acquaintance of some friends at the Queen Victoria Hospital in East Grinstead. We could easily have made our way to the hotel under our own steam, but he and his son had got out of bed at 4.00 a.m. to ensure that we were well looked after.

The following evening Murray invited us to dinner at his plantation and seated me next to a beautiful young lady called Shirley. Proving that the world really is a small place, within a few seconds I discovered that Shirley was the daughter of my 'favourite patient' at Addenbrooke's Hospital. Her mother, Lucy, had been one of the bravest patients I had ever had the privilege of looking after and she had died under my care. I had admitted her to Hatton ward on many occasions in advanced cardiac failure, a victim of rheumatic fever whom the surgeons had been unable to help. Nowadays she might have had a heart transplant at Papworth. On each admission her legs were swollen to such an extent that I used to drain off more than two gallons of fluid in a single night after inserting 'Southey's tubes' under her skin, a procedure for which she was always pathetically grateful. Lucy endured these painful indignities with a seemingly inexhaustible store of good humour. Like her daughter, Lucy was beautiful and I can still see the smile with which she greeted me as I stopped every morning and evening at the second bed on the left, even on the day she died. Patients make medicine worthwhile, and Lucy was one of the special ones.

Next day we set off in a large steam yacht to an island at the southern end of the Yasawa group, a few miles from Nandi. It was a flat mound of coral sand and palm trees with a thatched shelter and brick barbecues. There was no landing stage and I was rowed ashore in the dinghy and carried up the beach. We had caught a small tuna weighing about thirty pounds on the way and this was chopped into cubes and served raw with a pinch of lemon on palm leaves. Occasionally a disconcertingly loud thump as a coconut fell onto the sand reminded us of the wisdom of eating in a pavilion protected by a thick thatched roof.

On returning to the dock in Nandi the tide had dropped some eight feet. The other members of the party disembarked from the upper deck, leaving me stranded below the dock level. There was no ladder or steps but there was a motor tyre, used as a fender, hanging a few feet above the boat's rail, suspended by a thin piece of cord (thick string might have been a better description). The Fijian boatman told me to put my arms round his neck. He stood up and climbed onto the rail but could not reach the edge of the dock. He grasped the cord with both hands and reached up with one leg until his toes were gripping the rim of the tyre. There was a heavy swell and when a wave lifted the boat, he transferred his other leg to the tyre and then straightened up while I hung from his neck by my arms. He inched his fingers up the cord until he had both hands on the edge of the dock and then, with no more effort than a swimmer getting out of a pool, swung the pair of us onto the dock and rolled me off his back. Throughout this painful exercise I trusted that my arms were strong enough to prevent, at best, a ducking and at worst being crushed between the boat and the dock. We spent a few days touring the island and enjoyed a *meke* with dancing, singing and feasting on flying fish and turtle meat. I would have liked a longer holiday in Fiji; the climate was wonderful although not long after we left for New Zealand a hurricane blew the roof off the hospital in Lautoka.

We flew to Auckland and then in three hops in small commuter planes to Wellington, Christchurch and finally Dunedin, where we were met by Professor Garth McQueen, my opposite number in drug monitoring and a friend for many years as a consultant to WHO. Garth ran a drug monitoring scheme similar to ours, using a blue card inspired by our yellow one. We arrived in the late afternoon and Garth thrust a yellow poster into my hand advertising my lecture and told us that he had arranged a reception for us. Having travelled most of the day and changed aircraft four times, we had about an hour to rest and get ready for the reception. The top doctors in Dunedin seemed to be almost exclusively Scottish and we had a strong feeling of passing backwards through a time warp to the early fifties, of shiny dark suits and 'winkle-picker' shoes.

After a weekend with Garth in Queenstown, in the space of one day I gave a presentation to a group of doctors, a radio interview and a press conference in the morning in Dunedin, flew to Christchurch for a meeting of the New Zealand Adverse Reactions Committee in the afternoon and on to Canberra, changing planes in Sydney. Next day we were met by my opposite number in Australia, Annette Walshe, and attended a meeting of the Australian Adverse Reactions Committee (ADRAC). Their philosophy was identical to ours. Relations with the pharmaceutical industry were cordial and there were no barriers to free exchange of information. Annette drove us to the nature reserve at Tidbinbilla where we saw three species of Kangaroo, emus and flocks of white parrots, although the koalas failed to show.

After a conference and another speaking engagement in Sydney we then flew to Brisbane to start the second part of our holiday. We were met by old friends from Cambridge, Chris and Cynthia Cummins, their son Robert and his wife, Marion. I had last seen Robert having his airgun confiscated for shooting at telephone insulators in Papworth. We were to spend a week in Caloundra at their holiday chalet that was raised on stilts over a garage and boat park and approached by an external wooden staircase. Chris had devised the *Cummins Stair-Lift*, a novel way of lifting 200lb of man and chair twelve feet up a steep external staircase. It comprised two long planks clamped to the wooden staircase, a double block and tackle and a hook attached to a wooden chair fitted with castors. Two chair legs on one side had been cut short to keep the seat roughly horizontal during the ascent. Chris and Cynthia sat on the ground facing the staircase, their feet braced on the bottom step and hauled, taking great care not to let go of the rope. There was no braking device to prevent the chair slipping backwards if their grip on the rope relaxed.

Each morning I was woken by the unfriendly neighbourhood Kookaburra perched on the rail of the veranda about ten feet from my head, the most effective alarm clock in the world. Chris kept a cabin cruiser called *Omphalos* (umbilicus) parked on its trailer under the house. I am not sure why he chose the name; perhaps the boat was the lifeline that linked his dreams to reality. Next day we launched *Omphalos* from the beach and Chris settled me comfortably in the stern. We set off in typical Cummins style — flat out — but he had misjudged the state of the tide, or forgotten that there was a smooth standing wave over the sandbar that we had to cross to reach the open sea. We hit this wave hard and I found myself floating in the air several feet above my seat. Fortunately, as the boat and I were travelling in the same direction at about fifteen knots, I subsided fairly gently back in my seat after a brief 'out-of-boat' experience. Bob was less lucky; he floated up into the air and struck his head on the cabin roof. Chris apologised and we put out spinners and started trolling, hooking a beautiful Spanish mackerel of about twenty-five pounds. Ten miles north of Caloundra the engine died. By law in Australia, boats have to carry a reserve engine and we had a small outboard that we fixed to the side. We returned slowly to Caloundra, arriving far later than we intended and were met by the somewhat anxious ladies. As Cynthia cranked the winch handle, three turns at a time, and pulled the boat onto its trailer, I heard her muttering a litany in time with the crank-handle, 'one two three, – I hate boats, one two three, – I hate boats...'

On our last day in Australia we returned the Cummins' hospitality at a splendid fish restaurant where I demonstrated my penchant for oysters, consuming two-dozen. Next day seeing us off at Brisbane, Chris had secretly arranged for a large jar of fresh oysters in brine to be delivered to the plane. I was carried backwards up into the 707 that would take us to Singapore, clutching my jar of oysters with one hand and waving to the Cummins with the other. I handed it to the stewardess and asked what was on the menu for lunch; it included oysters. We arrived in Singapore late at night. The carpenter at the *Ladyhill Hotel* had built an enormous gently sloping ramp at least twenty feet in length across the courtyard, directly to the French window of our room. I was pushed up the ramp still clutching my jar of oysters. In the early hours of the morning I was sleepless, rather sad at leaving Australia and hungry; so I sat cross-legged like a Buddha on my bed in my red pyjamas – and ate my oysters. After a day in Singapore, we flew to Penang and on to Bangkok where we were met by a WHO representative with two large estate cars. One, he assured me, was for the 'honoured doctor and his wife' and the other for the luggage and the wheelchair and we were driven to the *Erewan Hotel* (the double-headed elephant).

I had been invited to Bangkok by the Director of a WHO project in Thailand, Doctor Ranjit Roy Chaudhuri. WHO was proposing to spend many thousands of dollars on a family planning project in Chiang Mai because they were worried about thrombosis and oral contraceptives. In Thailand, because of differences in diet and in spite of the oriental habit of sitting cross-legged on the floor, a posture that might precipitate clotting problems in western women, venous thrombosis in the legs was a rarity and pulmonary embolism was virtually unheard of. I advised that, although the high-oestrogen did increase the risk in western women, a tiny risk was likely to be even smaller in oriental women. On the other hand, because Thai women had a significantly lower average body weight compared with western women the dosage of the pill might be important for a variety of reasons other than thrombosis. Following my discovery of the oestrogen dose effect, the drug industry was still selling off stocks of the high-oestrogen pills that they could no longer sell in the West. The industry has a different set of standards for the 'Third World'. I gave a seminar on drug monitoring at the Chulalongkorn Hospital to a large and appreciative audience of young doctors, students and health workers who, I suspect, hardly understood a word I was saying. They sat on the edges of their seats and clapped at all the right places in response to body signals from their professor.

Our return to London was quite the worst journey I experienced in fifty years as a disabled traveller. There was a long delay before leaving Bangkok in a thunderstorm. There were problems with the first class lavatories on the 747; no English-language tape could be found for the public address system and much of the economy section was filled with Muslim pilgrims on their way to Mecca. During the flight they tried to light a camping-gas stove to cook their own food.

We landed in Teheran in daylight and were immediately surrounded by men with machine guns under orders to keep us on the plane, even though we were to stay more than an hour. Thankfully the pilgrims did leave the flight at this stage and their debris was cleared up. We sweltered in the heat with the doors open until the flight crew returned, only to apologise that they had been reminded that they had not had their 'statutory rest period', so we waited another hour while they put their feet up. Ever since, June and I have described our after-lunch snooze as our 'SRP'. Finally the doors of the 747 were closed for take off, but again nothing happened. A huge Arab wearing a djellaba and a red fez sauntered across the tarmac swinging a sledgehammer. He disappeared under the nose and after a few solid clouts somewhere under my seat, the engines started; I suspect that the pin in the towing attachment had jammed. We took off for Tel Aviv but could not fly directly because British planes were not allowed to fly over Iraq or Syria, so flew over Turkey and then turned south, enjoying a spectacular view of Cyprus and east again for some two hundred miles to Tel Aviv. When we landed, more men with machine guns surrounded us and again we were not allowed off the plane. Finally, after a further stop in Frankfurt, we reached Heathrow.

I flew to the United States three or four times each year and more frequently to the Continent. During forty years of flying I used most types of commercial aircraft from DC3 to Concorde. The facilities for disabled passengers have improved progressively over the years, but it still pays to know your 'equipment' (as the airline personnel describe their aircraft). I have experienced almost all the snags, from lost wheelchair parts to a loo that did not have a wide enough access in the Concorde lounge at John F. Kennedy. Probably the most convenient equipment was the DC 10 where I could embark in my own wheelchair and slip directly into the aircraft seat. The first class section of a 747 used to be excellent until an extra pair of seats was added behind the table in the centre of the cabin. It then became difficult to reach a seat even in the narrow on-board wheelchair provided by British Airways. In some 747s two of the ten toilets were joined to allow room for the on-board chair. With careful attention to diet for several days before flying I have always been able to avoid using the loo. I have relied on a blanket and a plastic screw-top bottle that may either be emptied by a companion or taken off the aircraft without embarrassment to the cabin crew or passengers. I stuck to 'shorts' in spite of the well-known risks of dehydration and thrombosis, reducing the latter risk as far as possible by frequent contraction of any muscles in my legs that could still be moved. I was also recommended to take a small dose of aspirin before the flight.

I always resist requests from ground staff at the check-in that I should transfer to an airport chair and I hang on to my own folding chair as far as the door of the aircraft. Most airport wheelchairs are not self-propelled. Before a flight it is vital to visit the loo, an embarrassment if you can't propel yourself and especially if the pusher is of the opposite sex. Frequently, the steward would store my wheelchair in the cabin, or if this was not possible it could be loaded into the luggage hold last and unloaded first enabling me to get into it immediately at the door of the aircraft rather than in the baggage hall. Officials generally listen once they realize that the particular disabled passenger they are 'processing' knows the cabin layout of each kind of equipment.

I used Concorde frequently but nearly missed one flight to London. My wheelchair had already been loaded into the hold with the baggage and I was sitting in the departure lounge in an airport chair. The Sky Caps who were supposed to carry me on board had failed to turn up and the staff were becoming increasingly agitated because they had been instructed, sensibly enough, not to attempt to lift or carry passengers. All except two passengers had boarded and a hostess said that she was sorry but the Concorde flight could not be delayed any longer. Fortunately the other missing passenger turned out to be a VIP; after a further ten minutes Richard Attenborough ran into the departure hall red-faced and breathless, and apologised to everyone, including me. He was followed by two Sky Caps with a 'Captain's Chair', a device that combines the functions of stretcher and wheelchair specially designed to fit the aisle in an aircraft's cabin.

Arriving one day at San Francisco Airport from Hawaii, I was reunited with my chair in the baggage hall and noticed that there was a cut in one of the tyres through which a rapidly expanding balloon of red inner tube was protruding. It burst with a loud bang and a dozen passengers nearest to me 'hit the deck'. I spent the whole of the following morning driving round San Francisco trying to find a replacement tyre. I had an American wheelchair that had been assembled in England and fitted with wheels made in Germany. No tyres could be found and I had to pay $80 for a pair of wheels that had narrow solid tyres, not intended for outdoor use. The original wheels haunted me on each subsequent flight for engagements in Portland, Indianapolis, Kalamazoo, Philadelphia and New York, getting lost twice and delivered separately to my hotel after travelling on different planes. If the chair had not belonged to the Ministry of Health I would have dumped the wheels.

13

Some were caught but one slipped through the net

While I was with ICI, James Raventos, a Spanish pharmacologist, developed an anaesthetic called halothane. Its potential usefulness as an anaesthetic had already been recognized by Dr. Charles Suckling at ICI's research laboratories in Widnes, Lancashire. Suckling had been researching the properties of fluorocarbons during the war. They were normally used as refrigerants and degreasing agents, but ICI's secret objective at that time was to find non-corrosive gasses that could be used in the separation of the isotopes of uranium (chapter 2). Dr. James Fergusson, the Research Director, was now interested in the toxic effects of some of the fluorocarbon that could be used in a peacetime role to destroy pests in grain such as weevils, and I suspect it was Fergusson who first suggested that, if they could put weevils to sleep (permanently), fluorocarbons might have a use as anaesthetics to replace ether and chloroform. Suckling set to work with James Raventos at the Dyestuffs Laboratories in Manchester under the direction of Alfred Spinks. This research continued when Raventos and Spinks moved to the pharmaceutical laboratories when Imperial Chemical Pharmaceuticals Ltd. (ICP) was formed, shortly before I joined the company.

An anaesthetist in Manchester, Dr Michael Johnstone, supervised the early human trials of halothane, but very soon after first marketing almost every anaesthetist in the country, and many from overseas, attended local promotional meetings or visited the company headquarters in Cheshire. Although I had not been involved in the work on halothane, I was expected to do my share of entertaining these groups of visitors. The meals were enjoyable but I regarded this as an unwelcome chore. I invariably made it clear that I had never been an anaesthetist;

my role was merely to greet them and prepare them for what should be a fascinating tour of the laboratories and discussion with real experts during the following day.

The possibility that halothane, like other fluorocarbons, might cause liver damage was a contentious subject. It was feared by some clinicians and contested by many anaesthetists and all the company reps. It was ironic that almost as soon as I left the company to join the CSD, I was responsible for confirming that the fears about the risk of liver damage due to halothane were justified. My research into cases reported to the CSD undoubtedly damaged the product's reputation and it is to the credit of my former colleagues that few harsh words were ever said. Only one of them felt that I should not have been allowed to work on any product manufactured by a former employer.

Reports of cases of jaundice after halothane, some of them fatal, arrived on my desk in small numbers in almost every post. Many of the patients had been exposed to it on more than one occasion, but because its use was so widespread this was hardly surprising. Halothane's advocates were reluctant to admit that it could cause a potentially lethal complication such as liver failure and I was well aware that many similar cases were not reported to the CSD. I found the vital clue in 1968 but almost five years passed before I had collected enough detailed information about the individual patients to confirm that halothane was definitely hazardous, albeit rarely. I had already broken the rules and taken home large numbers of the CSD's confidential reports on oral contraceptives to work on at night. Now I had to do the same with the halothane reports. One evening I noticed that when patients had had more than one halothane anaesthetic, the interval between the most recent exposure and the onset of jaundice was often considerably shorter than after a first-ever exposure. When jaundice occurred after multiple exposures, it often did so within two to three days of the most recent anaesthetic. After a single exposure, on the other hand, jaundice had been reported at almost any time interval from a few days to more than a month. I showed my results to Bill Mushin, the Professor of Anaesthetics in Cardiff, who was a member of the Adverse-Reactions Committee. Bill had some rough estimates for the number of patients exposed to halothane and I calculated that the risk of death reported after multiple use was between sixty and seventy per million or about ten times the risk of death from naturally occurring virus hepatitis. I drafted a paper for the *British Medical Journal* and invited Bill Mushin to be a co-author. Our conclusions could not have been more circumspect and we finished:

> 'Only the anaesthetist is in a position to balance this risk against other possibly more common risks that may attend the use of an alternative to halothane. In planning a series of anaesthetics it may be prudent to reserve halothane for the one operation where its advantages may be greatest, but only if the alternative agents are as safe and effective as halothane has proved to be.'[15]

To avoid the obvious dangers of public alarm, the chairman of the Committee, Sir Eric Scowen, agreed with Sir George Godber, the Chief Medical Officer, that it was undesirable for the CSM to issue a public statement at that time. This sensible low-key approach was, however, overturned by senior officials who clearly felt that this would draw attention to Inman and Mushin (who had done the work) and give insufficient credit to the Department of Health. The Committee were persuaded to issue a public warning and it had disastrous but entirely predictable consequences. The Committee stressed that they were 'aware of the valuable role of halothane' but suggested that halothane should not be regarded as the agent of first choice for minor surgery and that it should never be employed more than once within a month. However, there was a huge difference between an opinion from Bill Mushin and myself in a scientific article and a statement that carried the full authority of the Committee.

The Committee's statement provoked a storm of criticism, sometimes amounting to abuse. During the following weeks senior anaesthetists published thirteen letters of complaint in various medical journals. The one I enjoyed most suggested that it was time for 'Dr. Inman and Dr. Mushin to seek a less demanding occupation.' Professor Jimmy Payne, an old friend from my days with ICI, wrote in his capacity as Chairman of the Association of Professors of Anaesthetics, complaining that the letter from the CSM was 'needlessly alarming, putting anaesthetists in difficulties because of its medico-legal implications'. He felt that the CSM should have given more thought to the consequences of their letter (they had not wanted to send it). The letter removed the element of judgement that the anaesthetist could apply in individual circumstances and it turned the use of halothane into a 'wilful act without regard for the patient's safety.' His letter, and a similar one from Professor R.A. Millar from Glasgow on behalf of the Anaesthetic Research Society, urged the Committee to withdraw their statement. The response from the profession was exactly what Bill Mushin, Eric Scowen, the Chief Medical Officer, the members of the CSM and I had all been so eager to avoid. It illustrated, as had the fracas about the oral contraceptives, how politicians and civil servants sometimes ignore the cautious and generally sensible views of the scientists advising them.

None of our critics remarked that the reports to the Committee probably represented only a small fraction of the jaundice cases, since anaesthetists who did not believe that halothane could cause jaundice or who did not want to admit it, would not have reported any cases even if they had encountered some. This was borne out when we learned that one hundred and seventy-five cases had accumulated at the London Hospital, none of which had been reported to the Committee. This number, collected in one centre, exceeded the one hundred and thirty the Committee had collected from the whole of the UK up to the time the statement was issued and it confirmed that there had indeed been a large element of under-reporting.

Fortunately, unlike the public furore that followed the publication of Committee Statements about the pill, the halothane story displeased anaesthetists but caused comparatively little reaction in the press. Halothane jaundice carried a relatively high mortality but when halothane was used in the way the CSM recommended it had several advantages. It was easy to administer, and several of the anaesthetists who had criticised the CSD pointed out that it was especially safe in the hands of inexperienced anaesthetists. It is still in use thirty years later. The same lack of publicity had followed the 'epidemic' of asthma deaths described in chapter 10 when, in spite of our observation that more than three thousand patients had died, there had been no public alarm. On that occasion the media response had been limited to two column-inches on the second page of one of the tabloids. In May 1976 the London Hospital group, headed by Professor Roger Simpson who had always been critical of our work, published their results in the BMJ. Submerged in a massive paper was a somewhat reluctant vindication of our work. Analysis of their material led them to conclude that it 'now supports the findings of Inman and Mushin'[16].

In 1967 the Department of Health decided that the yellow card scheme should be used to report adverse reactions to vaccines as well as drugs. I was asked to collaborate with the *Joint Committee on Vaccination and Immunisation* (JCVI). Although the CSM had promised that the yellow cards would never be shown to anybody outside the Committee's Secretariat unless their names and those of their patients had been obscured, photocopies of the cards were now to be passed to the JCVI. An *Association of Parents of Vaccine Damaged Children* (APVDC) had been started by Mrs Rosemary Fox, whose daughter had been severely brain-damaged, and Jack Ashley put pressure on the Department to reconsider the safety of the vaccine. The JCVI set up a *Subcommittee on the Complications of Vaccination*. They showed little interest in the CSM's opinions about the dangers of whooping cough vaccine even though we had been assessing the yellow cards for more than seven years. We had accumulated twenty reports of encephalitis (brain inflammation), sixty-eight of convulsions and fifteen children had died. This was a small number when considering the numbers of children vaccinated over a seven-year period but we were well aware that only a small fraction of vaccine reactions were being reported. Interpretation was difficult because the whooping cough vaccine was often combined with vaccines for diphtheria and tetanus and polio. Frequently it had not been possible to decide which if any of them might have been responsible. This became painfully true when I had the opportunity to examine a much larger number of cases from Mrs Fox, almost none of which had been reported independently to our Committee. Mrs Fox now sent us details of more than five hundred and fifty children known to have developed severe problems. Two hundred and forty of these cases were well documented and by themselves amounted to three times the number already reported to the Committee from all other sources.

In April 1977 I planned a strategy for investigating them and included a preliminary opinion that I had formulated after examining the first sixty case records supplied in detail by Mrs Fox; her reports were much more complete than the brief summaries we had collected from GPs. The APVDC children had been hospitalised and assessed by brain specialists. The majority had residual disability ranging from weakness or convulsions to idiocy or a 'persistent vegetative state'. Most of the parents had been told at the hospitals that the vaccine was the probable cause of the damage. In the parents' letters the general tone was one of dignified acceptance of their child's misfortune, concern about their care in later life, and anxiety about the safety of other children. Surprisingly few hinted at litigation. In many cases communication between nurses giving the injections, parents and general practitioners had failed; some children who had a temperature or had screamed repeatedly or had muscular spasms or convulsions after the first injection, had been given further doses of vaccine, with catastrophic results.

I spent a weekend drafting letters for our field officers but did not distribute them because the officials insisted all the numerous committees and sub-committees involved with the vaccine problem should first approve the wording. This delayed the start of the investigation. I was then called into the Under Secretary's office and carpeted for the delay in starting the investigation that had left the officials vulnerable to criticism by the Minister! By the end of 1977 no fewer than eight separate groups were involved, each insisting that copies of all the documentation should be sent to them.

The reports to the CSM amounted to only one serious reaction per three hundred thousand children vaccinated. Although this was probably less than one tenth of the real incidence, this low figure was seized on as a defence of the Department's forthcoming publicity campaign to promote the use of the vaccine. In other situations when eager to ban a drug or put pressure on a drug company, the officials would have argued differently. They would have emphasised that it was probable that only one in ten reactions had been reported and was therefore necessary to multiply the number of reports by ten to estimate the risk. Only one of the first eighty of Mrs Fox's cases had been reported independently to the Committee by the patient's doctor! If this was typical of all the reports, it suggested only one or two percent of the cases might have been reported. It was also quite possible that Mrs Fox's group had assembled only a fraction of the reactions that had actually occurred. By the end of September 1977 I concluded that one hundred and sixty-seven serious reactions had been caused by or aggravated by the vaccine. I circulated a note suggesting that the incidence of serious reactions was probably about one in thirty thousand and certainly not one in three hundred thousand as proposed by the Department.

On October 19th 1977 the new Chief Medical Officer, Sir Henry Yellowlees, wrote to all doctors to advise them about a campaign soon to be launched to promote vaccination; I was told it would cost £3million. I made one more attempt to avert a potential disaster and Dr. Diana Walford, a colleague in the Department who had also looked at the APVDC cases together with even more material provided by Professor Gordon Stewart from Glasgow, wrote in strong support of my memorandum. Diana was destined to become a Deputy Chief Medical Officer at the Department. Professor Gordon Stewart, who was one of the best opinions on vaccine safety in the UK, had been invited by the APVDC to conduct an independent assessment of their case-material and it was proposed he should join Professor Dudgeon's Advisory Panel. This had been vetoed by Dudgeon. His antipathy to Gordon Stewart had led to the formation of yet another group to consider the whooping cough vaccine problem. The conflict boiled over during one of the meetings. I had never before seen a professional colleague so shoddily treated as Stewart was and the incident left a bad taste in my mouth for many months. Our concern about the incidence of vaccine reactions at last had some effect and Sir Henry sent a second letter to all doctors on November 24th advising them that the campaign had been cancelled. The vaccine would still be available but he stressed the great importance of avoiding its use in conditions that might make children unduly sensitive. My popularity in the Department was diminishing.

In the JCVI's final report, based on three and a half million children believed to have received a total of ten and a half million injections, their estimate for serious central nervous system side-effects was one in twenty-nine thousand! The estimate for the risk of permanent brain damage was one in fifty-four thousand. These were regarded as minimum risks because of the likelihood of under-reporting. I was too fed up with bureaucracy to feel smug that their estimates had coincided so precisely with mine (one in thirty thousand) rather than the figure of one in three hundred thousand grasped so enthusiastically by the officials. An official at the 'top of the office' told me that I had seriously damaged my career by criticising the Department's position on the safety of the vaccine and possibly causing embarrassment to the Minister. "You know Bill, you blew your K' (the anticipated reward for the "mini-pill" and developing the yellow card scheme) by daring to question the party line." To which I replied, "Well, bugger me."

At one of the Committee meetings the owner of a small drug company, Dr Gottfried, had been asked to give evidence in support of his treatment for stomach ulcers that had unusual effects. The drug was a derivative of liquorice that he had marketed successfully as 'Biogastrone'. He had developed a variant that he called 'Duogastrone'. The drug was put into capsules made of a material that resisted the acids in the stomach but dissolved when it encountered the alkaline secretions in the duodenum after passing through the stomach. In this way it had proved to be effective for the treatment of duodenal ulcers. However, a problem had been detected during hospital trials. The capsules swelled and exploded within the patient's abdomen with an audible pop! Staff and visitors could hear these pops and, although not dangerous, they were disconcerting for the patients and their relatives. I had already visited Dr. Gottfried, a charming and enormously overweight Romanian, at his small and well-run factory. He shuffled breathlessly into the committee room in Queen Anne's Mansions and was asked by Sir Derrick Dunlop, from the other end of the long table, to take a seat. At my suggestion a thoughtful clerical officer had provided the largest tubular steel chair that could be found to accommodate his enormous bulk. He took his seat and slowly and silently subsided to the floor as the legs of the chair bowed and then bent to a right angle. Only his head was visible.

Sir Derrick, always cool in an emergency, stood up: "I say, my dear Doctor Gottfried, are you all right?" Nobody laughed and the poor doctor was helped to his feet with considerable difficulty by several civil servants. With remarkable composure he gave his presentation standing. Duogastrone disappeared shortly afterwards.

One scientist joining ICI at the same time as I did in 1959 was responsible for two of the most successful classes of drug discovered in the second half of the twentieth century. He was Jimmy (later Sir James) Black and he earned a Nobel Prize. An entirely new range of drugs called ß-blockers proved to be very useful in the treatment of heart disease. The first four were developed by ICI and more imitative products were introduced later by several other companies in the hope of capturing a portion of a lucrative market. After a few years with ICI Jimmy may have seen himself being drawn into a prolonged, soul-destroying competition to develop and sell other minor chemical variants of the same group of drugs. He left the company to join Smith Klein and French where he developed a novel range of drugs called H_2-antagonists that revolutionised the treatment of stomach ulcers. The first of these was *Tagamet* (cimetidine). Its rival, *Zantac* (ranitine), sold by Glaxo, was probably the most successful money-earner on the world markets at that time. They made surgery for stomach ulcers virtually obsolete.

I seemed to be fated to encounter problems with the products that my previous employer had marketed. The first of the ß-blockers, called *Alderlin* (pronethalol), did not survive because of doubts about its safety in long-term animal tests. The second was *Inderal* (propranolol) that has proved its safety and efficacy in heart disease over forty years. The third, *Eraldin* (practolol), first marketed in 1970, was recommended mainly for angina and high blood pressure and was responsible for the worst drug disaster since thalidomide. Few problems were noticed until May 1974 when two skin specialists, Doctor Robin Felix and Dr Francis Ive, reported that they were seeing unusually large numbers of practolol-treated patients who had developed a rash resembling psoriasis, a very common skin complaint, and that some of these patients were also suffering from severe dryness of the eyes. Peter Wright, an ophthalmic surgeon at Moorfields Hospital, called at my office and told me that he was preparing a paper in which he would describe a number of patients with severe dryness of the eyes that in some individuals had progressed to ulceration of the cornea. We had seen only one yellow card reporting an eye problem, a case of mild conjunctivitis, hardly sufficient to raise an alarm when it was estimated that one hundred thousand patients had been prescribed practolol.

ICI issued a general warning and within a few days we received ninety reports of eye damage and fifty of psoriasis. I also saw four reports of patients with acute bowel obstruction due to a condition known as sclerosing peritonitis in which the membrane that normally encloses the bowel becomes massively thickened and then contracts. This was normally so rare that few surgeons would see a single case in a whole professional lifetime. Towards the end of 1974, ICI circulated a second warning letter to doctors and they now believed the coverage had been adequate. Distrusting this, I arranged a random postal survey and found that thirty-nine per cent of general practitioners claimed that they had seen neither of the company's two letters. Like much of the huge amount of material dropped through doctors' letterboxes, I suspected that many letters had been 'binned' unopened. ICI tried to persuade the CSM not to issue a public statement that might irreparably damage practolol's reputation. The evidence against it, however, was now so strong that in January 1975 the Committee posted a strongly worded leaflet to all doctors and reproduced it in all the leading medical journals. In the meantime I had alerted all of our overseas contacts. Later I learned that a complaint had been sent to the Chairman suggesting that I was trying to 'clobber' ICI's export market!

I invited doctors from companies manufacturing ß-blockers to a meeting in my office. Six companies were represented and all agreed that the practolol experience could reflect a 'class' effect — similar problems might occur with other drugs of the same type. We reviewed other ß-blocking drugs regularly for several years and although there were a small number of cases of psoriasis and mild dry-eye symptoms, nothing resembling the severe problems that had led to blindness after practolol was ever found.

ICI introduced a compensation scheme. All the regulations for licensing a new drug had been adhered to and there was no question of culpable negligence. With the possible exception of some pathological changes in long-term animal studies that came to light retrospectively, none had been mentioned in the data submitted to the CSM that would have led the company to predict what would happen in humans. Except for sclerosing peritonitis, which was extremely rare and developed only after prolonged treatment, the other side-effects such as dry-eye, psoriasis, and deafness (another complication of treatment that was discovered relatively late) were commonplace and doctors would not have been expected to link them to any specific drug treatment. After ICI announced its compensation scheme there was another wave of reports to the CSM, many describing cases that had developed several years earlier. Even if no allowance was made for under-reporting, the rate of serious reactions was very high. The practolol incident clearly demonstrated that it was dangerous to rely completely on voluntary reporting by the yellow card scheme and I started to plan an entirely new strategy for drug-safety monitoring that would complement it. Critics of the non-governmental scheme that I eventually set up several years later accused me of attempting to sabotage the Committee's scheme (that I had spent sixteen years of my life developing) in order to secure a monopoly position. In the sense that I was responsible for developing both of the only two independent monitoring schemes currently operating in the United Kingdom on a national scale, it was true.

The yellow card system had failed because doctors had not recognized the skin and eye symptoms for what they were — adverse reactions to practolol. The disaster stimulated a complete reappraisal of the arrangements for monitoring the side effects of new drugs *after* they had been marketed. The need for closer surveillance after marketing was later exploited by the industry as a means of promoting new products and this was encouraged by the Licensing Authority and the Medicines Control Agency (MCA) that later replaced it. I shall show how drug companies were able to set up post-marketing studies that were nothing more than promotional exercises. Doctors were paid by drug companies to change patients' treatments without, in many cases, obtaining the patients' consent.

The arrangements for scrutinising drugs *before* marketing had also failed even more dramatically. Similar events, including one or two cases of sclerosing peritonitis, *had been observed* during the clinical trials of practolol and were mentioned in the licence applications. But they had not been recognized as adverse reactions to practolol. In fairness, one could not expect the medical assessors on the licensing staff to be expert in all aspects of clinical pharmacology, pathology, dermatology, ophthalmology, biochemistry, toxicology and dozens of other medical or surgical specialities, even though some of the more arrogant of them tried to create the impression that they were. None of the professional secretariat was, for example, a psychiatrist, an anaesthetist, a paediatrician or an obstetrician. This is why large committees, that include members from many disciplines, are essential and why the appropriate specialists must read all the original material submitted by the manufacturer relating to their particular area of expertise. They should not rely on the summaries prepared by officials.

Fast tracking a new drug through its clinical trials and the speedy assessment of licence applications, so much sought after by the industry, is dangerous. Few new drugs have such a large margin of advantage over older remedies that fast tracking is important for patients. Even fewer new drugs are effective in conditions that were previously untreatable. The industry argues that delay in licensing erodes the residual patent life that a new product will enjoy when it is marketed. My answer is to change the law and extend the period of patent protection for entirely novel new discoveries so that their competition-free marketing life (before the identical generic copies could be sold by other companies) is lengthened. This would discourage companies from frittering away research budgets and taxpayers' money on the minor imitative variants. There could be a substantial reduction (perhaps a halving) of the nation's general practice drug bill and greater safety, without loss of benefit.

Another way of reducing or perhaps containing the nation's drug bill would be to reduce the remuneration of the 'fat cats' that run the industry. Can there be any justification for Glaxo's Chief Executive being offered a pay packet of £22million that, I was pleased to read, the shareholders turned down at an annual general meeting. I began to feel sorry for Sir David Barnes' paltry £1.6million in 1996 that remained unchanged in 1999 after his spell at the helm of Astra Zeneca. Well I remember David in the Sales department in my earliest days with its founding company ICI Pharmaceuticals. The Glaxo offer would have covered the cost of the Drug Safety Research Unit that I was about to found in Southampton which became the leading national monitoring scheme in Europe, for many years. Whatever may be said in defence of these salaries (for example that they deter top people from moving to even better paid posts overseas), they are unacceptable in an industry paid for largely from taxes.

Sometimes it may be unethical to delay the release of an important new drug. The release of a treatment of a 'new' disease such as AIDS or of a cancer for which no effective treatment is currently available, may justify short cuts in the procedure for assessment. In these circumstances all the recipients of the new drug must be clearly identified and followed up periodically to see if there is an abnormal incidence of any particular disease. Although it was a major objective of the Drug Safety Research Unit that I founded in 1980, routine *long-term* follow-up over a period of several years has not so far been achieved.

In the wake of practolol, my battles with the administrators over the answers to Parliamentary Questions (PQs) intensified.

Although irritating and often time-consuming, many PQs were sent to us from someone I would come to regard as a friend – Jack Ashley. The famous safety-conscious rock-climber, Joe Brown, used to say 'Never use one belay when four will do' and Jack used a similar strategy, often tabling a whole string of short PQs each phrased in a slightly different way. Sometimes a dozen or so PQs from Jack would land on my desk in one post. To draft truthful answers could take several hours. By the time many layers of civil servants had done their worst, my answers would be unrecognizable. When, for example, Jack asked if the Department or the Committee were 'satisfied with the arrangements for early detection of drug safety problems' there was no chance that I could get away with an honest, 'No, the Committee is not satisfied', followed by a statement about the reasons why the current arrangements left a lot to be desired. The sanitized reply would dodge the question by saying something like 'The CSM is constantly reviewing methods for speeding detection of safety problems with new drugs'. We could not admit that the resources allocated to my small Adverse Drug Reactions (ADR) monitoring section were hopelessly inadequate or that we had no computer or that I had to process data on a hand-cranked 'Facit' adding machine. Nor was the Minister told that several members of the ADR sub-committee, such as Ekke Kuensberg and David Finney, had threatened to resign if nothing was done about it. Almost invariably the answers to PQs were distorted by the 'Doctors on tap but not on top' attitude of officials. The PQs did not come to me immediately. Officials would spend days circulating them up and down their chain of command and then seek my opinion at the last minute, for example on a Friday afternoon when the answer was due on the Minister's desk on Monday morning. Sometimes, if they anticipated an argument with me, they used the 'Dr Inman was at a meeting all day' ploy and showed the draft answer to some other member of the technical staff who was totally uninvolved in ADR monitoring and had no idea what the truthful answer should be. He or she would be told that they couldn't contact me but that this was the kind of answer that I always endorsed.

My requests that MPs should spend time with us so that we could explain the problems of interpreting the incomplete material that we had to work with, fell on deaf ears. On one occasion Laurie Pavitt MP, who knew ways to beat the system, approached me personally and arranged a meeting with me and a few of his colleagues in one of the Commons committee rooms in an attempt to get to grips with the problems posed by practolol. On the comparatively rare occasions when I was asked to attend a meeting with the Minister of the Day I would find myself separated by a phalanx of departmental officials, political advisers and sycophants and parked at the end of the table, without introduction. The chance of making any useful contribution to the discussion was virtually zero. Ten minutes person-to-person discussion with the Minister could have saved weeks of defensive paperwork, avoid embarrassment to him and cost to the taxpayer. The cost of processing one PQ could easily run into four figures. Why was it never suggested that a meeting between the writer of the PQ and the technical people behind the scenes might clear up many misunderstandings?

I could not accept the argument that the answers to PQs must always be consistent with previous answers; there must be no ministerial 'U-turns'. Nothing must be said that might embarrass him or her. The departmental procedure for answering PQs was defensive and allowed little room for correcting wrong impressions. Administrators found it difficult to understand that expert opinion must change as new information accumulates. 'There is *no* evidence that A causes B' can change overnight to 'There is now *good evidence* that A may cause B'. Officials repeatedly fell into the trap of quoting figures for the number of adverse reactions reported to the Committee as if they were the same as the number of patients who really had suffered adverse reactions. They ignored repeated warnings that probably as few as one in ten serious reactions was reported to the Committee.

Jack Ashley asked what steps were being taken to determine the number of patients who had been disabled by practolol. I thought we should try to explain that the yellow card system could not be relied on to answer this kind of question with precision. The scheme was designed to give an early warning in a simple way but that there were two important reasons why it could never provide reliable estimates for the total number of patients who had been damaged. Firstly, we had no means of knowing how many doctors had seen an adverse reaction but had failed to report it. Secondly, although the total volume of drug use could be estimated from prescription statistics, the actual number of patients who had used a drug could not. It was not possible, for example, to distinguish twelve prescriptions issued at monthly intervals for one patient over a period of a year from twelve prescriptions issued to twelve patients, each of whom had used it for only one month. This was because of the sacred cow of confidentiality; the patients' names were not entered on the computers of the Prescription Pricing Authority (PPA) where they are processed.

Jack Ashley asked if the Government intended to establish a 'watchdog' to check on the inadequacies of drug monitoring. The Committee had itself been set up as a watchdog, but the facilities required to do the job adequately, and especially a computer, had never been provided. The 'Watchdog' could take several weeks to raise a snarl. There was no 'Fax' or e-mail in those days, only the telephone and the post to keep the members up-to-date. Calling an emergency meeting would require busy members to travel from as far as Aberdeen. There was no way that the yellow cards alone could provide answers to several of Jack Ashley's questions. I had already put forward proposals for a new system that might go some way towards answering them, and the Sub-Committee were very much in favour. However, as we shall see, there was to be no support from the Licensing Authority.

Jack also asked what steps we proposed to ensure that patients were more closely involved in checking adverse reactions. This question touched on whether patients should report reactions independently of their GPs and was difficult to answer. The best chance of early detection of a previously unsuspected hazard depended on close observation by doctors and complete reporting of suspected reactions. Patients would usually be unable to judge which events were drug reactions and they would have difficulty describing the events that they had experienced. It would not be helpful for them to report directly to the Committee in lay terms what their doctor should be doing *as part of his professional responsibility*. The doctor was in the best position to provide relevant medical history backed by the results of investigations. While not totally opposed to the idea, I believe reports that bypassed the doctor could cause confusion and could upset relations between patients and their doctors. There are, of course, a number of situations in which patients become extremely knowledgeable about their condition and manage their own treatment. A good example is the control of diabetes with insulin.

Jack asked about the possibility of an independent enquiry into the practolol accident. I had no fears about the outcome of such an enquiry but it would have diverted us from work designed to plug the gap in our defences that practolol had uncovered. In the end, by the time the officials had processed Jack Ashley's PQs, little of what I had to say found its way into the answers. When I met him twenty years later to discuss a problem about which we were in full accord, he was under the impression that we had been on opposite sides of the fence!

My thoughts increasingly focused on the difficulties of attempting to conduct research while working within the Civil Service. In the first five years I had developed yellow card reporting almost as far as it has ever been developed, being hampered mainly by the Department's failure to provide computer facilities and staff. Recently some gloss has been added to monitoring with yellow cards by the development of ADROIT (Adverse Drug Reactions On-line Information Tracking). This has speeded the retrieval of information but the fundamental weaknesses remain. Long after I left the Department, the number of reports sent in by doctors each year was still about the same as my tiny staff had been handling thirty years before. At best the yellow card scheme is a valuable early-warning system capable of drawing attention to potential problems but it has never been able to measure the size of these problems. This is because the extent of under-reporting is never known and it is usually only possible to speculate about the number of patients using a drug. I had made important contributions to safer oral contraception and had solved a problem in anaesthesia by finding subtle variations in the pattern of voluntary reports. It was unlikely that many other situations would arise in which it would be possible to apply such a degree of sophistication.

Practolol did, however, have one good effect. It stimulated the Department to go to a contractor for help with a computer. I had already done some work with a systems analyst, Bob Wilson, on the Department's machine at Reading. The CSM had very low priority but we were occasionally able to get some time on it during slack periods at night. Data had to be transported by road and printout was often returned two or three weeks later. I used to claim that by the time I got a reply to a question, I had often forgotten why I had asked it or had already worked out the answer by hand. I was not joking.

I was now joined by Eric Middleton and we worked with a small but rapidly expanding software company called *Logica* to design a computer programme for adverse reactions monitoring. Typical of my difficulties was an infuriating exchange of memoranda with our Under Secretary. Eric and I had produced a specification for the new system and I was told that as soon as the Department had completed its 'internal consultations' she would be pleased to sign the contract with *Logica* to implement the system; but she did not think it would be appropriate for me to show the document to members of the Committee before the Department had approved it. Surely, I suggested, I should at least discuss the report we had prepared with Richard Doll, the Chairman of the Adverse Reactions Sub-Committee, and with David Finney, the Subcommittee's statistical adviser. I received, in writing, the dusty reply — 'when I said internal consultations, I meant internal consultations.'

Between 1976 and 1979 my efforts to introduce a complementary system that might offer a reasonable chance of preventing another major accident, although greeted enthusiastically by the Committee, failed to make any progress within the Department. Using the practolol experience as a model, David Skegg, a New Zealander working in Oxford, conducted some pilot studies among a small group of general practitioners that suggested that *event-monitoring* (David Finney's idea that I will describe later) could be conducted effectively in general practice. We needed a national scheme that would embrace a substantial proportion of all the patients who received a new drug during its first few months on the market.

From 1964, when the CSD was established as a voluntary system for scrutinising new drug applications and adverse reactions, officials had been busy drafting legislation to give legal teeth to the 'Watchdog'. It was to be known as the Medicines Act of 1968 and it did not become effective until September 1971. By the mid-Seventies it was glaringly obvious that the bureaucrats were going to make it difficult to provide the kind of service that a committee of experts might reasonably expect. The time to move was rapidly approaching. Before doing so, however, I felt I owed it to the Committee to make one more attempt to design a better system that would fill the hole in the net through which practolol had fallen. An entirely new system of drug-safety monitoring was needed. Much as I had respected and admired Derrick Dunlop and the members of his committees, I realized that I was increasingly being placed in a false position by administrators whose interpretation of the data differed from that of the researchers responsible for collecting and assessing them. The administrators' attempts to adjust the results of my studies of the pill to suit what they thought the Minister should know, had been ample proof of what was going on.

14

Southampton via Honolulu

In October 1970, the CSD was invited to a meeting at the National Academy of Sciences in Washington and Derrick Dunlop and I spoke on behalf of the United Kingdom [17]. The US speakers in particular highlighted the difficulties experienced by their Food and Drug Administration in recruitment of quality staff and the need to shield them from political bias; and the conference recommended that in any monitoring centre:

> 'Neither the Director nor the staff of the centre should participate in regulatory decisions ... they must be free to seek the truth wherever that may lie.'

This wise advice fell on deaf ears at the United Kingdom's Department of Health when the first opportunity to improve the UK system occurred in September 1971. A Medicines Commission was established to oversee the Medicines Act of 1968 and had become effective that month. The Committee on Safety of Drugs (CSD) that had worked so well with a small staff for nearly seven years, was disbanded and replaced by a Committee on Safety of Medicines (CSM) with at least a ten-fold increase in the number of officials, lawyers, inspectors and their infrastructures. Most of the members of the old Committee and its professional staff were retained. The word '*medicines*' replaced the word '*drugs*' in its title because the word '*drugs*' was by now firmly entrenched in the public mind in the context of abuse, a problem that was outside our remit. The new arrangement should have provided a golden opportunity to increase the effectiveness of the Adverse Reactions Sub-Committee by giving us independence. We needed freedom to warn the public about newly discovered hazards without wasting time in prior discussion with the CSM that from past experience would merely rubber stamp them. It would have given us more clout in the struggle for resources and would certainly have enabled us to *'seek the truth wherever that may lie'* as the Washington conference had recommended. Leslie Witts had retired and the new Chairman of the ADR group, Owen Wade, was carefully briefed about this essential need for a change of status. He seemed to be in full agreement, but when the question of sub-committee versus independent committee was raised at a meeting of the newly formed CSM, he was overruled. I was abroad when this capitulation was relayed to me on the phone. A Sub-Committee we were to remain.

Shortly afterwards, Owen Wade was appointed to the Medicines Commission and a new Chairman had to be found for the Adverse Reactions Sub-Committee. Sir Richard Doll of the Medical Research Council was an obvious choice, but almost at the last moment, immediately after I had returned to the UK, I discovered that Richard's name had not been included among the people who were to be considered for the post. This omission had been engineered by officials and I suspect endorsed by the incoming Chairman, Sir Eric Scowen, Chairman of the parent Committee (the CSM). Richard out-shone all the other members and the civil servants realized that when it came to advising Ministers or making statements in public, he would be less 'tractable' in the handling of scientific affairs. I phoned Derrick Dunlop late that evening. He was horrified and immediately saw to it that Richard was appointed. I am not sure if Richard ever realized that I had been responsible. His appointment had unfortunate consequences for me because it tied me to the civil service for the next five years or so. Having involved him I could not leave until his term of office had expired.

After developing the yellow card scheme, I realized that there was a most pressing need for a surveillance system capable of measuring the frequency of adverse reactions (the yellow cards cannot do this). I am still the only person who has so far been able to set up a monitoring scheme that worked *on a national scale* and yet remain outside the control of the drug industry or the government. I was not the first person, however, to point to the important distinction between *events* that might have occurred anyway and *adverse drug reactions (ADRs)* caused by treatment.

One of the committee members, and my friend of forty years, Professor David Finney, had proposed as early as June 1964 that every *adverse event* and not merely *every suspected adverse drug reaction* should be recorded. This distinction between an adverse reaction and an adverse event is difficult for members of the public or juries to grasp; the media find it impossible and lawyers grow fat on the confusion. They find it difficult to understand that while all adverse effects of drugs are adverse events, comparatively few adverse events are adverse reactions to drugs. The majority of events are either coincidental and have no relation to drug treatment or perhaps more often are manifestations of the disease being treated rather than the effects of the drug that has been prescribed. The Department had already ignored David's far-reaching proposals for ten years and another six were to pass before I was able to put them into effect in an independent national scheme based on the Unit that I established in Southampton in 1980.

In January 1976 I outlined my ideas for improved post-marketing surveillance at a conference at the East-West Centre in Hawaii. The Japanese and American governments had jointly set up this cross-cultural centre to provide low-cost conference facilities within comparatively easy reach of both countries. The meeting was organized by Michael Gent of McMaster University, Canada, in collaboration with Ciba-Geigy to discuss a recent 'epidemic' of drug-induced disease in Japan [18]. Large numbers of Japanese had suffered severe damage to the nervous system after using Ciba-Geigy's drug, clioquinol, that was sold 'over-the-counter' (OTC) without prescription as a treatment for traveller's diarrhoea. Sporadic cases had been noted in other countries but the clinical problem was almost exclusively Japanese. The disease was called *subacute myelo-optic neuropathy*. I have seen it spelt in various ways and will use its acronym, SMON. The Japanese delegates presented the clinical picture and defined the possible extent of the problem and around this framework about twenty delegates from other countries exchanged ideas for improved monitoring schemes.

I chaired the first session on various drug-monitoring systems and contributed two papers. We had not seen SMON in the UK but the Japanese experience had illustrated how totally unexpected hazards could arise with widely used drugs. I described the 'epidemic' of asthma deaths associated with aerosols and I proposed a new scheme that I called *Recorded Release*. The idea was that as soon as a new drug had been licensed and until the Committee was satisfied that it had an acceptable level of safety, doctors would be permitted to prescribe it only if they submitted follow-up documentation to a central monitoring agency.

Exactly a year later in January 1977 I was invited to return to the East-West Centre to join the late Franz Gross, Professor of Pharmacology in Heidelberg, in running a second conference to expand the theme of post-marketing surveillance of new drugs. Franz was one of the best conference chairmen I have ever met. He could speak five languages fluently and had a remarkable ability to smooth ruffled feathers and he contributed significantly to the progress of drug safety monitoring for many years. Sadly, one evening after supper at his home, his wife found him dead at his desk. My paper on Recorded Release was published in the book that we jointly edited.[19] Ciba, the manufacturer of clioquinol, sponsored both conferences. In addition to their medico-legal interest in the epidemic of SMON, they were genuinely concerned that non-commercial and non-bureaucratic systems should be developed to monitor safety after marketing. Their experienced and much under-rated medical officer, Oliver Pinto, played the leading role in the organization of the conference and stimulated the development of the scheme that I was to start up three years later. The gathering of more than forty of the leaders in drug safety monitoring from sixteen countries was a considerable achievement. I have not encountered a more lively, experienced and innovative group of experts during the quarter of a century that followed this conference.

During the late seventies I was invited several times to lunch at the House of Commons with David Ginsberg. David was a labour MP who defected to the Social Democrats; he was also the Director of the market research firm, Intercontinental Medical Statistics (IMS) that had been helpful to me in my work on the pill. Without the IMS estimates for drug sales I could not have completed the research that had led to the safer mini pill. David saw me as the leader in the field of adverse reactions monitoring. IMS planned to set up a medical department and he wanted me to head it. I much enjoyed our lunches together and meeting his colleagues from both sides of the House, but I turned down the offer because I was convinced that independent, non-promotional, monitoring could not be done by a commercial institution.

In July 1977 I wrote to Dr. Alan Wilson who had been one of my assistants in the Adverse Reactions section at the CSM. Alan was now the Medical Director of the Association of the British Pharmaceutical Industry (ABPI). I said that I would welcome a visit to discuss the Committee's plans. I was, however, ordered by the then head of the Medicines Division, Dr John Griffin, not to hold any discussions with ABPI until a so-called 'top of the office' meeting had taken place later in the year. In spite of my protests to the Chairman of the CSM that the concept of *Recorded Release* and most of the documentation that had been prepared for just such a meeting had been prepared by me, I was excluded from the meeting that, perhaps significantly, took place in a London hotel rather than within the walls of the Department of Health. A flimsy excuse was that I was on holiday at the time and would not wish to be recalled, even though half a day's notice would have been sufficient to ensure my participation. The proposals for post-marketing surveillance were presented by John Griffin and Dr. Peter Fletcher (who had not been involved in ADR monitoring during his relatively short period of employment with the Department). Griffin left the Department almost immediately afterwards to succeed Alan Wilson as Medical Director of ABPI. Fletcher also left to become medical head of Intercontinental Medical Statistics (IMS), the post that had been offered to me by David Ginsberg. Both of them declared openly that post-marketing surveillance of new drugs should be a commercial undertaking conducted by the drug industry.

Although the Committee had strongly approved of my Recorded Release scheme, it was clearly going to be impossible to obtain support from the Licensing Authority that was now firmly under the spell of the drug industry. It was ironic that, when I eventually succeeded in setting up the 'Post-marketing *Drug* Surveillance Research Unit' at Southampton University, IMS immediately advertised a rival organization that they called the 'Post-Marketing Surveillance Unit'. Their prospectus offered a participating company a surveillance programme that would cost £900,000 for a study embracing 10,000 patients (with a supplementary cost of 50% in addition if data were to be provided on another similar drug). Doctors would be paid £5 for every patient registered and every follow-up report. As a charity depending on voluntary donations, my Unit charged nothing and participating general practitioners were not paid.

One of the most impressive speakers at the second Honolulu conference was Kenneth Hammond, Professor of Social Psychology at the University of Boulder, Colorado. He was a noted pioneer of decision theory and his description of the difficulties encountered by scientists in governmental institutions described exactly those I had experienced when trying to develop the yellow card system. Ken explained that the role of scientists was supposed to be quite different from that of policy makers. Scientists assembled the evidence and presented it to the policy makers who then decided the social policy that best served the public. In his own words – *'not only are these functions confused, but legislators and scientists exchange roles'*. Legislators demand that their scientific advisers should participate in policy-making and the scientists may even offer policy suggestions before being asked for them. This was one of the reasons why government departments frequently mishandled controversial problems affecting public safety. He said:

> '... scientists who intend to serve merely as expert witnesses become policy advocates and are frequently pitted against one another as adversaries. In the process, scientists become incompetent amateur legislators at best, and self-serving advocates at worst.'

The policy makers, on the other hand, become interested in scientific affairs and rapidly come to believe that they understand their social and political significance better than the scientists do and they start to argue with the scientists:

> 'Rather than concerning themselves with the social values that should control the application of science and technology into social problems, they seek out details that enable them to do battle with the scientists. Thus scientists become incompetent social legislators and social legislators become incompetent scientists. No one benefits from this confusion.'

This confusion, he emphasised, led to the greatest perversion of science – deliberate bias.

The relations between the Medicines Control Agency (MCA) and the Industry have always been, putting it mildly, unhealthy. There has been an attempt to combine two widely divergent and mutually conflicting functions – public safety assurance on the one hand and promotion of the interests of the pharmaceutical industry on the other. The Department of Trade and Industry and not the agency responsible for safety should handle the latter function. To this day, the drug industry continues to have far too much influence on government policy and I shall comment later on the lamentable failure of the Department and its advisers to stop drug companies exploiting the gullibility and greed of a minority of doctors who take part in pseudo-scientific post-marketing surveillance (PMS) studies that amount to nothing more than sales promotion.

By the end of 1977 it was obvious that I would have to leave the Department. I had to find a University prepared to accommodate a self-financing institution and I had to raise funds. The medico-legal, ethical and confidentiality issues had to be discussed with the British Medical Association, the General Medical Council, the Medical Research Council, the Department of Health, the Prescription Pricing Authority and several other bodies. My experience with committees over sixteen years had shown that if you have to band together to beat the bureaucrats, the probability of winning is minimal. Wars are won by maverick generals who meet problems head on and brush aside the risks of failure.

I decided to produce a textbook to record a body of scientific and administrative experience on which the work of an independent unit could be built. Many of those I had persuaded to attend the second Hawaii conference contributed chapters. This was a task that would have been quite impossible without June's help. I drew a diagram based on a wheel. The hub represented the patient and closest to the hub were his three main sources of information about drugs and diseases: his general practitioner, his newspaper and his TV. Arranged around the rim of the wheel and connected by the spokes, were the other bodies involved in health care. They included the Department of Health, hospital consultants, statisticians, epidemiologists, the drug industry, lawyers, pharmacists, consumer organizations and many others. I asked one or more representative of each of these groups to describe their personal role and to examine their relations with every other institution on the diagram. I hoped that this would help the authors to organize their thoughts, and this was how it turned out. The book was arranged in five sections, each linked by an introductory chapter written by myself. The plan worked well and the first edition of *Monitoring for Drug Safety* was published in 1980 in time for the opening of the new institution in Southampton.[20] Sir John (later Lord) Butterfield wrote the preface. Fifty-nine men and three women from twelve countries contributed to the work. One reviewer described it as, 'not the only book on this subject, but certainly the best'. The first edition included a chapter by the well known TV presenter, Dr. Charles Fletcher, who was the pioneer who gained acceptance and the respect of highly critical and initially suspicious medical colleagues for the BBC's landmark series *Your Life in Their Hands*. The textbook ran to two editions and still sells a few copies more than twenty years later. For the heavily revised second edition I was fortunate to recruit the help of an experienced medical writer, Elaine Gill, to work on the book as Assistant Editor and it was published in 1986.

Recorded Release evolved slowly to become *Prescription-Event Monitoring*. Users of a new drug were identified through photocopies of the prescriptions written by general practitioners and sent to the Unit in huge numbers by the Prescription Pricing Authority (PPA). This is an independent government body that was set up when the NHS was formed so that pharmacists could be paid. More than four hundred and fifty million prescriptions are processed each year in England. I aimed to collect all the prescriptions for up to ten new drugs at any one time, until the first ten to twenty thousand patients who used each of them could be identified and followed up. I was particularly indebted to Eric Stabler, a senior executive at the PPA, who processed my application to use photocopies of tens of thousands of prescriptions. This was the first component of PEM. The second, an account of the events that followed their use, had to be supplied by the GP who had written the prescription.

My first choice for a home for the Unit was Cambridge and the Regius, John Butterfield, made some encouraging enquiries at the University. I soon realized, however, that it might take two or more years to get anything started. Donald Acheson, who had founded the medical school in Southampton, thought there was no reason why the Unit should not be accommodated there if I could raise the funds. I had been promised some support from the Chief Scientist's Office at the Department of Health and my salary as a Principal Medical Officer at the Department would continue for a while on secondment to Southampton. I would have to look for the bulk of the funds as 'no strings' donations from the pharmaceutical industry.

I convinced several companies that they had everything to gain by supporting the Unit. If the scheme worked they could obtain a large amount of information about their products, much of which would be reassuring; most drugs turn out to be reasonably safe. Occasionally severe problems would be identified early, reducing harm to large numbers of patients and the extent of their company's liability. We would not be a contracting organization where the sponsoring company held any intellectual rights to the results of the studies and there was no possibility that a subscriber could influence what was published, especially any results that were unfavourable to a product. We, and not the company, would choose the drugs or the problems that would be studied. We would publish the results of the studies, good or bad and would share the results with the international regulatory agencies as well as the manufacturer. There was no question that a company offering financial support could modify good news or suppress bad news.

In 1979 I enlisted the help of Ken Carter, an English doctor who was on the point of retirement from the Syntex Corporation in Palo Alto, California. His long experience in the industry was invaluable especially as he was qualified both in medicine and pharmacy. Together we secured several six-figure pledges and a large number of smaller ones and on December 12th, 1979, the Southampton University Senate approved the establishment of the Unit. During the subsequent fifteen years I raised nearly £10 million in 'no strings' support, without signing a single contract or making any special arrangement with the companies.

In April 1979 I was invited to be co-chairman of the Kyoto International Conference Against Drug-Induced Sufferings (KICADIS). The main topics were SMON and the more general aspects of drug safety monitoring. En route for Japan, June and I visited Delhi. There I met Dr. Ramalingaswami, head of the Indian Medical Research Council, who was interested in the possibility of setting up drug monitoring schemes in India. I recommended that limited resources would best be concentrated on diseases such as malaria or leprosy that were not a problem in countries with sophisticated monitoring arrangements already in place. There was no point spending time or funds setting up adverse reaction reporting schemes for expensive new western medicines that might be used only by a few wealthy people in the cities.

In Kyoto I gave two papers, chaired the final plenary session and summarised the conference. June and I had a suite of rooms overlooking the city and surrounding hills. Four medical students had been recruited to travel by train from Osaka each morning to look after me, their main task being to carry me up and down the numerous staircases in the buildings. Though recently built, there were no facilities for the disabled at the conference centre. I was told later that I had created quite a stir in a country in which it was unheard of for a severely disabled person in a wheelchair to play a prominent role in full public view. One morning, while still suffering from a mild attack of 'Delhi Belly', my 'Four Musketeers' as I called them carried me into a lavatory cubicle, too narrow for the chair. I had almost got my pants down when they all rushed back in a high state of excitement, apologising profusely for disturbing me and shouting 'no rid, no rid, no rid'. They picked me up and carried me with pants half off into the adjoining cubicle. They had seated the honoured professor on a toilet without a lid!

KICADIS was atypical in several ways. Victims of SMON sat in the front row of the auditorium, with relatives carrying photographs of those who had died decorated with black ribbon. There were street demonstrations against the drug industry and we were uneasy at times that the violence might spread into the conference centre. There was considerable disagreement about how many of the 30,000 alleged Japanese cases had been caused by SMON or by other diseases of the central nervous system such as multiple sclerosis or polio, or by environmental pollution such as mercury poisoning of fish. There was overwhelming evidence that most SMON cases had been caused by clioquinol. There was uncertainty, however, about the reasons why the companies that manufactured clioquinol and other similar drugs had not cut their losses and removed them from the market. To do so, however, could invite massive litigation and possibly bankrupt some of the companies. It was also unclear why, although the drugs were heavily promoted worldwide, apart from isolated cases in a few other countries the epidemic mainly affected the Japanese. I suggested that the manufacturers might have been advised by their lawyers not to make any change in marketing policy until the litigation had been decided. Removal from the market could be interpreted as an admission of guilt. I also suggested a possible explanation for the lack of cases outside Japan. The Japanese are exceptionally 'bowel conscious' and were known to take remedies for bowel upsets in large amounts over long periods. Clioquinol could be taken safely for 'traveller's diarrhoea' by holidaymakers from the UK, simply because few could afford to take a holiday overseas for more than two to four weeks. In my summing up I said:

> 'Rather than argue endlessly about the causes of SMON it seems to me to be more important to ask ourselves what we are going to do about other people with disabilities, whether drug-induced or not. Some of the Japanese SMON cases did not take clioquinol, so it seems that the drug is not the cause of all the problems. These people need just as much help ...

> Before I finish, I would like to turn to the SMON sufferers themselves. Some of them have joined us at KICADIS ... I have spent about sixty per cent of my life in a wheelchair. I try not to identify with disability except when it suits me. I do know that most disabled people come to accept their misfortune with dignity and almost always with humour ... I am pleased to see that our disabled colleagues who are present today have retained both their dignity and their humour.'

For the first time in five days I could see the SMON victims and their relatives, exchanging looks and some even smiling. I made two final diplomatic gestures:

> 'We must introduce, I hope through insurance rather than litigation, some means of dealing with the tragedies that will inevitably occur in the future. Above all, I think we must continue to communicate with each other as colleagues and human beings and we must avoid confrontations of the kind we witnessed on Saturday (a near riot in the streets outside). SMON and other tragedies occurred because we do not yet have effective methods for post-marketing surveillance. We will never eliminate risk, but we must do everything we can to minimise it.
>
> I would like to record very special thanks to our interpreters who have delighted our senses in at least two ways – first, our sense of hearing and secondly, for those like myself who have spent some time looking at their little windows, they have delighted our eyes. May the cherry trees continue to bloom ... '

The effect behind the glass windows on the interpreters' balcony was electric. Tiny hands flew to mouths; blushes and giggles all round and one or two discreet waves at the speaker.[21]

Contraception Clinic in Delhi

Anthony, Richard, Lara, Arran, Riley, Rufus, Nina, Mathilda, Zeljka, Mia

15

Setting up the DSRU and our First Experiment

After numerous house-hunting journeys to Hampshire, June found a Georgian house near Botley that was being divided in half. The southern half was still an empty shell and we were able to alter the plans to accommodate a lift. The house was wheelchair-friendly with doors and corridors six inches wider than in all but the most opulent of modern buildings. We moved in June 1980 and the Drug Safety Research Unit (DSRU) opened its doors the same month.

I recruited two secretaries, Frances Gibson and Susan Richards, and a statistician, Nigel Rawson. A research officer, Dr Lynda Wilton, joined me in January 1981 together with Keith Castle who had been one of my yellow card team in London. Lynda was about to start a family and worked only part-time for most of the next twelve years while the children grew up. I also set up a small advisory committee under the chairmanship of Sir Ronald Gibson, formerly President of the BMA, the main purpose of which was to convince critics that the Unit was not a drug industry stunt. Keith's job was to train a small team of clerks to process the prescriptions and follow-up forms. I believed, wrongly as it turned out, that this would be an excellent first clerical job for school leavers. I had no experience as an interviewer at this level. In large organizations recruitment is through personnel departments or agencies and it opened my eyes to the defects of secondary education. Most of the applicants were girls who, although ill-prepared for employment, were well turned out and motivated. The performance of the small number of boys who applied was uniformly abysmal. Typically, a lad would slouch into my office in trainers and an open neck shirt, a day's growth of beard and heavily nicotine-stained fingers. He avoided eye contact, slumped into a chair and fixed his gaze on the garden. He seemed reluctant to discuss why he had applied for the job or to enquire what it entailed. A polite enquiry if he supported a local football team might raise a flicker of interest. When I asked if he would like a job in the Unit, he continued to inspect the garden and eventually, without turning his head, shrugged "wouldn't mind". None of the males was offered a job. The girls seemed to grasp my description of our objectives and understand that to maintain an acceptable processing speed, they would need concentration, accuracy and discipline.

I soon learned that my idea of recruiting school leavers was not going to work. For example, when Keith had to discipline one of them for running noisily up the staircase while I had a meeting in my office, the whole group would stomp up and down the staircase in unison. They behaved like schoolchildren and used group disobedience as a weapon. The frustration proved too much for Keith who retreated to his family fruit farm in Kent. I had been warned about falling into the maternity trap. It was common practice for a young woman to assure a potential employer that she did not intend to start a family in the foreseeable future; she would then have a child soon after starting, claim maternity leave for which we would have to pay, return to work for the minimum period required to qualify for benefit and then resign. No small business or charity such as ours could afford such luxuries. I announced that I was looking for 'impregnable women', something I would not have got away with in today's atmosphere of political correctness.

I replaced all the schoolgirls with mature women and they proved to be dedicated and reliable. They recognized the importance of their work and enjoyed the companionship and family atmosphere that we had created. An information scientist, Gillian Pearce, was appointed to develop the Unit's computer, and Marilyn Skipp replaced Keith Castle in charge of the clerical staff. Later at various times the central office and professional staff were joined by Dr. Joan Clark, Bill Cox, Nadine Dingley, Lesley Flowers, Barbara Hunt, Dr. Kiyoshi Kubota, Tom Lucas,

Nigel Rawson, John Rogers, Linda Roxburgh, Georgina Spragg, and Dr. Patrick Waller, supported at any one time by thirty or more clerical and data processing staff. Of the original team, Lynda and Marilyn were still working in the Unit twenty-five years later and more than ten years after I retired. Our first office was a small comfortable building that had been used as student accommodation in the grounds of the science campus.

Founding the DSRU was the biggest gamble of my life. We had moved to Southampton before I had even obtained approval to use NHS prescriptions as the starting point for our safety work and without knowing whether or not general practitioners would co-operate with the Unit. Failure to secure either of these components of Prescription-Event Monitoring (PEM) would destroy any hope of establishing the second national monitoring system that would supplement the yellow card scheme. I was entirely dependent on Eric Stabler of the Prescription Pricing Authority (PPA). Prescriptions are confidential documents and the PPA had to be satisfied that no harm would come to patients or doctors if they were made available to the DSRU. Eric deserves a large share of the credit for making PEM possible.

Dr. John Ball, a general practitioner from Worcester, also played a vital role. John was Chairman of the General Medical Services Committee (GMSC) of the British Medical Association whose backing was essential if I was to secure the co-operation of general practitioners. At the crucial meeting with the GMSC, I explained that I planned to post up to one hundred thousand questionnaires each year. At first sight a very large number, but it would amount to an average of only four or five per GP. I explained that there could be no payment for doctors as this could lead to accusations that we were trying to stimulate prescribing of a particular drug. We would be approaching each doctor up to a year after he had prescribed the drug, and PEM could have no bearing on his choice of treatment. When a doctor is 'recruited' by a commercial organization to take part in a study where the new drug is prescribed for a patient who is not a *fully informed volunteer*, he could (and in my view should) be sued if a severe adverse reaction occurs. This could not happen in a DSRU study because our retrospective enquiries could not have influenced him. I shall refer later to the way patients' trust in their GPs is exploited in drug company studies and how the official bodies and the Department failed to stop it.

When I turned to the question of confidentiality, John Ball from the Chair interrupted after a few moments, saying that I was being far too modest. On no occasion during the sixteen-year life of the yellow card scheme had any doctor been in medico-legal trouble or any patient been harmed as a result of my handling tens of thousands of confidential reports to the CSM. He regarded this as the strongest argument in favour of support for PEM in Southampton. To my surprise, about fifty members stood up and clapped. The meeting was over. I was told at lunch that the Committee had agreed to the proposal only because they trusted me to resist political interference. Specifically they said that they would not have agreed if PEM were to have been run by the CSM or the Department of Health.

Meanwhile, Eric Stabler had convinced the PPA that it was feasible to photocopy all the prescriptions for up to ten new drugs at any one time. This would enable us to identify the first ten to twenty thousand patients who received each of them. The two components of Prescription-Event Monitoring (PEM) had now been brought together.

I was invited to lunch at the BMA with Michael Mungavin, a former colleague at ICI, who was for a short time the Medical Director of the Association of the British Pharmaceutical Industry (ABPI). Clearly my judgement had been at fault when, in confidence, I had given him a copy of the plans for PEM that were being considered by Southampton University in order to keep ABPI in the picture and in the hope that they would encourage the British companies to support us. From 1978 to 1980 I had shared my ideas with several people whom I trusted.

Michael should have told me that ABPI planned to start up a company known as *Medical Monitoring and Research Ltd.* in collaboration with the Royal College of General Practitioners as a rival to the DSRU. I did not accept a subsequent invitation to attend their launching ceremony and press conference on October 15th 1980, but I obtained a copy of their prospectus. They promised to provide *'a full service to the pharmaceutical industry'*. With a few exceptions, the wording and logistics in their proposal seemed to be identical to the specification that I had submitted to Southampton University. However, I estimated that the cost of monitoring a drug using their scheme would be at least five times that of PEM because they intended to pay a fee to the doctor for each patient who started treatment with the new drug and to make a profit for themselves. Their homework had not been as thorough as mine; the PPA would never have allowed them access to prescriptions. *Medicines Monitoring Ltd.* foundered soon after it was launched. This was the first, but by no means the last attempt by ABPI to delay the development of PEM.

By April 1981 we were ready to start our first PEM study and I published a two-part paper in the *British Medical Journal* describing PEM and its objectives.[22] In order to avoid bias, I did not mention the names of the two drugs that would be tested and to ensure that GPs were not caught unawares, I arranged for reprints of both papers to be posted to all general practitioners in England exactly one week before the questionnaires. PEM was exclusively an English system: Scotland, Northern Ireland and Wales were not included because they had different arrangements for processing prescriptions. The two drugs that had recently been introduced for the treatment of arthritis were *Opren* (benoxaprofen) and *Lederfen* (fenbufen). Exactly a year after the first prescriptions for each of them had been written, we dispatched fifteen thousand questionnaires, identifying individual doctors and patients. They were sent by road to distribution points throughout the country and were then posted to individual doctors to reach them exactly one week after they had received the reprints. The reprints from the BMJ, however, were to be distributed by a different route, starting from a single central distribution point in London. This was the plan. It came to a grinding halt when a railway strike by the Association of Locomotive Engineers and Fireman (ASLEF) brought sections of the rail system to a standstill, including the Post Office's main rail link. Thousands of reprints were held up. Many doctors complained about our apparent discourtesy in failing to brief them about what the scheme was all about and many others no doubt threw their questionnaires into the waste bin. The strike undoubtedly delayed our research into what soon emerged as a serious public health problem and probably cost some elderly patients their lives.

Fortunately, perhaps because I was well known to GPs after writing to thousands of them during my days in charge of yellow cards, some six thousand of the first fifteen thousand questionnaires were returned. Among these were eight reports of jaundice. This was not enough to justify a public statement; at least not until my enquiries about these eight had been completed. We reported them to the CSM and I was in the United States talking to the manufacturers about the problem when the news about jaundice reached the press in the UK. If I had risked a public statement about the jaundice problem before following up the eight patients, I could probably have avoided cynical accusations that PEM had missed an important hazard; but it would have been irresponsible to publish anything that might alarm patients before following up the reports. We hadn't failed to detect the problem as some of our critics had suggested. In April 1982 I already decided to expand our study and it eventually included twenty-four thousand patients, among whom we found fifty-four cases of liver or kidney damage. Most of these turned out to have nothing to do with Opren. There were patients with gallstones and cancer that were obviously unrelated but some of these had been reported to the CSM and accepted by them as 'Opren jaundice'. At the end of our extended study, we concluded that Opren might have been responsible for twelve of the cases; most of the others were obviously unrelated to treatment. This suggested an incidence of about one in two thousand treatments.

Opren taught me more about the tricks used by interviewers from the media. During a TV recording one interviewer asked, *'Tell me, Dr. Inman, did your system spot the problem with Opren?'* I explained that we had eight cases of jaundice in the first batch of reports returned by GPs and were following them up when the public alarm went off, overshadowing our efforts to confirm that they had been caused by Opren. When screened a few days later the question had become an accusation. *'Tell me, Dr. Inman, why didn't your system spot the problem with Opren?'* As it turned out the same answer would have been appropriate for both questions, but several sentences had been clipped, changing the emphasis. Put the first way my answer explained how we had acted responsibly, not risking a panic by rushing to the media as soon as we had the initial reports. Put the second way, my answer sounded like an excuse for failure. This may not have been deliberate, but it taught me to beware the dangers of the 'single camera' technique. Rather than use two cameras simultaneously, one aimed at the interviewer and the other at the interviewee, the questions are repeated after the interview is finished. With only one camera available, it has to be turned round, after the interviewee has left the room, so that the interviewer can be seen asking the questions again.

The CSM had to carry the burden of its apparent failure to predict liver damage. That it was allowed a licence for sale at the manufacturer's recommended dosage, however, must have resulted from the incompetence of the civil servants who had processed the marketing application. They had presumably failed to ask appropriate questions about the way the drug was metabolised and the speed of its elimination from the body. In order to avoid any bias that prior knowledge of our intention to study Opren might introduce, I had deliberately made no contact with the Lilly Company, the manufacturer of Opren. I was therefore not aware that vital results of studies of Opren's metabolism had been presented at the *XV International Rheumatology Congress* in Paris, in June 1981, long before we started our PEM study and fourteen months before the media forced the CSM to withdraw Opren from the market. Lilly employees had contributed fifteen papers and clinicians collaborating with their clinical trials a further ten papers. Several papers had dealt specifically with the metabolism of Opren. Some studies had been deliberately set up in elderly patients and had shown that Opren tended to be eliminated more slowly than in younger people. The drug could accumulate and reach toxic levels. In October 1981, the company had asked the Licensing Authority to be allowed to modify the Data Sheet that accompanied their sales literature so that prescribing doctors could be warned about this risk and other data from the Paris conference added to it. The Data Sheet is the officially approved document circulated to all doctors. Important details are also included in package inserts seen by patients. They include recommendations about the dose that should be used and the risks of not following them. Incredibly, Lilly told me that they had *not been allowed* to change the Data Sheet in the light of these new results. Presumably, each change of Data Sheet had to be endorsed by the Committee and this meant more paper work for the officials. It did not carry what should have been the most important warning of all — *that the dose should be reduced in the elderly*. Had this been done, cases of liver failure and some deaths might have been avoided. I am sure that the blame lay with the civil servants and that the Committee members knew nothing about it.

Shortly after Opren was removed from the market in 1982, the yellow card system was seriously and permanently damaged by an action by officials for which no reasons have ever been given. To preserve confidentiality, the normal practice was that the names of patients were not stored on the CSM's computer. The ability to link reports that might be submitted by more than one doctor about the same patient depended on two confidential card indexes that my clerical staff had kept updated for sixteen years. These were a *Patient Index* and a *Doctor Index*. Without these card indexes, reports of a serious adverse reaction could be inadvertently duplicated. I was proud of the ability of the clerical staff to locate any report within about thirty seconds, provided the name of either the doctor or the patient was known. In 1983, inexplicably, these two indexes were put through the shredder. When I complained to members of the CSM they were unaware that they had been destroyed.

Over many years I had established a good working relationship with 'The Boys' or the 'Gentlemen of the Press' as they were sometimes referred to. It was based on mutual trust that little of public importance would be withheld and that a reasonably balanced account of what I had told them would appear. None of the national newspapers could afford to be without a medical correspondent. Oliver Gillie of the *Sunday Times* used to joke that if they got the story right 51% of the time they were doing quite well, but I believe they did a lot better than this when painstakingly briefed. Ronnie Bedford (*Mirror*), Bill Breckon (*Mail)*, Dr. Alfred Byrne (*Sunday Times*), Christine Doyle (*Observer*), Peter Fairley and Michael Jeffreys (*Evening Standard*), John Stevenson (*Sketch*), John Wilkinson (*Express*) and David Wilson (BBC), all contacted me frequently and usually got the story right. I believe I got across to most of them some understanding of the damage that could be done by premature disclosure of results of studies that were incomplete and therefore liable to misinterpretation.

The most detailed and accurate summaries of the studies by the DSRU were often those in *Scrip*, a broadsheet published by the Philip Brown organization mainly for the pharmaceutical industry, or in *The Lancet*, *British Medical Journal* and *Pharmaceutical Journal*. The three newspapers distributed free to doctors, *Pulse*, *Doctor* and *General Practitioner* also kept up a constant stream of short and reasonably accurate items about the DSRU and PEM.

When I entered the drug safety arena I had little experience of the journalistic style required for regular communications with general practitioners. I believe that material intended for the medical profession must be written in plain language that is readily understandable to intelligent lay readers. Medical journals abound with such horrors as "the changes were consistent with..." or neologisms suggesting that the authors had discovered some new phenomena or some new method for statistical analysis that exonerated them from the obligation to give appropriate recognition to the true originators of ideas. I have a special dislike for words like 'pharmacovigilance', perhaps because it apes my original 'post-marketing surveillance' or, even worse, carries the implication that the French might have been at the forefront of drug safety work in Europe. Although individual groups of enthusiasts in France, Spain and Italy had done good work, only West Germany, Holland, three Scandinavian countries and the UK ever succeeded in developing significant national monitoring schemes in my time.

In the *Guardian* of August 2nd 1982, I was libelled by two journalists, Colin Johnson and Arabella Melville, in a short article entitled 'Drugs Under the Influence'[23].

'The number of acceptable people available for all the bodies and institutions requiring experts on drugs is limited. Dr. Bill Inman's career illustrates the consequences of this. He worked for ICI when a cholesterol-lowering drug, clofibrate, was being developed there; later, as Principal Medical Officer at the CSM he supported the drug against the evidence of a massive WHO trial. He left the CSM to found the new Drug Surveillance Research Unit ...'

A court action might have produced massive damages but I decided that this was not worth powder and shot. Honour was satisfied in an American Court some time later. The case concerned allegations that certain hormones used as a test for pregnancy might harm the foetus if a woman happened to be pregnant at the time of the test and it was reported at length in *Don't Tell the Patient.*[12] I spent a hot and boring week in the *Chattanooga Choo-Choo Hilton Hotel* waiting to be called as an expert witness. I had been warned not to leave the hotel on my own because of the danger of being 'pan-handled' (mugged). The hotel had been built around the old railway station and many of the guest suites were converted railway carriages. It seemed to be populated by coach loads of octogenarian nymphomaniacs with blue rinses; any glimpse of a lone male of any age in the restaurant or bar produced whoops of unrestrained joy and desire and a wheelchair or crutches was no protection.

The chief attorney for the plaintiff quoted the Johnson/Melville passage in court as part of the customary attempt to undermine my credibility. "Had I worked for ICI?" "Yes." "Had I then moved to the Department of Health?" "Yes." "Had I questioned the validity of the WHO clofibrate data?" (now as they say, I 'had him over a barrel'). "Excuse me a moment" – I reached into my briefcase and held up a copy of my textbook, *Monitoring for Drug Safety* and offered it to the Judge. He would find in the book a chapter that indeed did comment on the WHO data and the kinds of biases that might have affected the interpretation of the results. "I would like you to note, Your Honour, that the author of the chapter was J. I. Mann, not Bill Inman!' A sickly grin spread over the attorney's face and he went bright red. "Well, I guess I stepped into that one," he said. "I'm so sorry," I replied.

I had begun to understand the capricious nature of perceptions of risk and to realize how difficult it is to convey information about drug safety to patients and their doctors. We worry about chemicals used in agriculture but not the cancer-inducing natural insecticides that plants have evolved over millions of years to protect them from bugs. We tend to be obsessed about the small danger of atomic power stations and ignore the much greater damage caused by the pollutants from fossil fuels and tobacco smoke. We fear flying, even though the chances of arriving home alive are considerably greater than during a journey by car to the local supermarket.

In 1984 an opportunity arose for me to develop some ideas about the risks of drugs at a series of lectures organized by Michael Cooper of the Department of Engineering Sciences and presented at Wolfson College, Oxford [24]. Sir Herman Bondi introduced the series of eight public lectures over several months. I spoke on the risks of medical intervention and later speakers dealt with various industrial hazards, energy generation, biological research and the environment. I had plenty of time to gather my thoughts and found that they had been running parallel to those of John Urquhart and Klaus Heilmann in Germany[25]. We had developed similar schemes for presenting information using logarithmic scales that allowed for the huge variations in perceived risks. Unfortunately, we had discovered each other too late. When John called at my office to share his thoughts and describe what he called his 'Safety Degree Scale', I found that his scale differed from mine by an order of magnitude. Characteristically, John and Klaus fully acknowledged my work as the founder of PEM and used examples from our data to illustrate their scheme.

I started my Wolfson lecture by pointing out that the population of the world has trebled in my lifetime. Since 1840 when records were first collected, infant mortality had fallen from one in seven to one in five hundred per year. Deaths of children have been reduced twenty-fold, and of young and middle-aged adults, ten-fold. Even in the elderly there has been a modest reduction of fifty per cent per year. This is largely the effect of greater affluence, better food and housing and the conquest of diseases such as tuberculosis, syphilis and smallpox. Drugs used for conditions that are still commonplace, such as heart disease, have also played a significant life-extending role. The human race is threatened with extinction by its success in extending life span. If the present rate of expansion is maintained its resources will run out, possibly before the end of the century. Withdrawal or rationing of life-extending treatment for the elderly is already happening. AIDS, malaria, tuberculosis, famine, floods and religious conflict are still major factors that retard population growth, but it seems unlikely that the human race will turn to a more acceptable method of population control — contraception. Unfortunately those who need it most cannot afford it.

Risks of death are best measured as loss of *life expectancy*. It is not a question of lives lost but of *time* lost. The loss of a patient who could reasonably expect to live for thirty years may be perceived to be a greater loss than that of one who could only expect to live for five. I have wondered, however, if it might make more sense to measure risk by the percentage of *residual useful life* lost or put at risk by a particular medical procedure. Otherwise there is a danger that the residual life expectancy of an elderly person may be undervalued. In the aftermath of the Opren incident, I said to the audience in Oxford:

> 'Recent problems with anti-arthritic drugs have sharpened my concern about our perception of risk in the treatment of very elderly patients who have the shortest life expectancy and who are more likely to suffer adverse drug reactions than younger people. As I get older, I think I might opt to trade some years for greater comfort and mobility. On the other hand the less there is to go the more I want to hang on to what is left because there is such a lot still to do and it is such fun doing it.'

Perception of risk depends on the extent to which we identify with risk takers. We insist on protection from accidents at work, however minor, so that we will be fit to go hang-gliding at the weekend. When all the passengers in a plane are killed it is perceived to be a disaster. When the same number die in separate car accidents hardly any notice is taken. If eight jumbo jets crashed in England each week we might give up flying, although this is equivalent to the weekly toll from cigarette smoking. Nobody will have failed to dwell on the appalling slaughter in the World Trade Center in September 2001 in which the number of victims compares with the weekly death toll from smoking in the USA.

Arthritis may not be thought of as a killing disease, but if the complications of immobility, the risks of surgery, drug-reactions or depression from prolonged pain are taken into consideration, there is an appreciable mortality. A diagnosis of rheumatoid arthritis may reduce life expectancy by one third. The incidence of fatal reactions that had led to the removal of several arthritis treatments in the 1980s was far lower than the mortality from the disease. The death rate from Opren was probably more than a hundred times smaller than the death rate from the complications of rheumatoid arthritis. A drug called Zomax was subjected to a 'trial by television' following a single death in the United States. Two million Americans had been treated with Zomax, a death rate perhaps ten thousand times smaller than the risk of complications of the diseases for which it was used.

My Wolfson lecture was received with enthusiasm but publications read by a few hundred already well-informed readers have short-lived impact. In 1984 I obtained permission to reprint my lecture in *PEM News* that had a circulation exceeding twenty-five thousand and this received an encouraging response from many general practitioners. It was also made into a short film with animated diagrams. The GPs felt that it had helped them to understand how public perception of drug risks had been distorted by horror stories in the press and the hasty decisions of civil servants and politicians and how drug withdrawals were often based on inadequate evidence.

In December 1984, while teaching in Bad Neuheim in Germany, I learned that I had been honoured with a personal Chair at Southampton University; apparently the first Chair in any country to be described by the word 'Pharmacoepidemiology'. The title was rather a mouthful, but accurately reflected my life-long attempts to merge the two disciplines of pharmacology and epidemiology. I am not a pharmacologist who spends most of his time trying to find out how drugs work, but I have spent more than a third of a century studying epidemics of drug side-effects and I have developed both the nationwide monitoring systems in the United Kingdom.

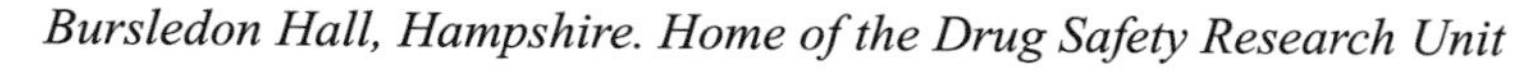

Bursledon Hall, Hampshire. Home of the Drug Safety Research Unit

Our house in Hampshire

DSRU Garden Party at our house. a) Punch and Judy, (b) The Director steamed up, (c) Inflating the balloon for his departure, (d) too rough to fly the Microlite.

A landing in the New Forest

16

Dirty Work at the Crossroads

The DSRU soon outgrew the small house on the University campus, so as a temporary expedient we bought the other half of the property that my family were living in and transferred my office and some of the staff, leaving the Prescription-processing section in Southampton. We now had space to install a more sophisticated computer system – in the kitchen! PEM was the only tried and tested method for measuring drug risks on a national scale in the UK and was gaining impetus. On the downside, I was already fifty-six and, although active and still able to travel widely in spite of increasing weakness, there was a pressing need to appoint a deputy who could take over from me. Unfortunately there were serious obstacles to such an appointment within the University. Most of the people with appropriate experience worked for drug companies and earned two or three times my salary. Although the DSRU was self-financing, the University argued that other university staff would resent any departure from the basic salary structure. Even if this hurdle could be overcome in some way, there was an even more serious problem. The University would not guarantee that anybody we appointed could be assured that they would take over my job when I retired. When the time came, the job would go to open competition and the best performer in front of a large panel of interviewers appointed by the University would get it. I could see no prospect of anybody with sufficient seniority and experience in drug-safety work and with a family being willing to join the Unit as my deputy without a guarantee of succession.

Another problem started to interfere with the day-to-day running of the Unit. I had recruited, trained, paid all the salaries and cared for all the staff since founding the Unit.

As an illustration of the kind of problem that I found I now had to face, a senior administrator started to stir up trouble by insisting that some complaints that had been made by our only chronic troublemaker were 'confidential' to the University Staff Department and could not be shared with me! I knew perfectly well what the trouble was, but the Unit obviously needed to be free from interference that smacked of civil service style bureaucracy that had nearly wrecked the yellow card system. The solution was simple. I set up an independent Charitable Trust, loosening but not entirely separating the Unit from the University. The *Drug Safety Research Trust (DSRT)* was launched on my birthday, August 1st 1986. The retiring Vice Chancellor of the University, Sir Gordon Higginson, was invited to become a Trustee and accepted. Sir Douglas Black, Past President of the Royal College of Physicians of London and former Chief Scientist at the Department of Health, also became a Trustee. We used the change of status to make a small modification to the title of the DSRU. The word 'surveillance' smacked of 'Big Brother' so we substituted 'Safety', retaining the DSRU logo. I doubt if anyone noticed.

I have been asked how I managed to maintain scientific independence and credibility and yet be funded by the industry; it was not easy to convince people that we were not, and never had been, in the pocket of the drug industry. I made it clear that all the results of our studies, (excluding confidential information that would identify individual patients or doctors) is available to the medical profession, the regulatory agencies and the relevant drug manufacturer; the information can never be regarded as the exclusive property of any manufacturer. The intellectual rights remain with the DSRU. Although many companies have contributed to PEM studies, many drugs have been examined without the support of a particular manufacturer. I am proud that I founded the Unit, developed PEM and raised the funds to create more than fifty jobs, without signing a single contract with a drug company, and I believe that it would be better for the Unit to shut down than to conduct studies with strings. Only once in my fourteen years as Director did a company threaten to withdraw funds unless I agreed to halt a study of one of their drugs. This was because they wanted to do a massive promotional study under the guise of post-marketing surveillance. We did our study anyway.

Most companies realized that they had everything to gain by supporting the DSRU. The majority of drugs turn out to be safe, and evidence that large numbers of monitored patients had suffered no serious ill effects was invaluable to them. When, however, serious effects were identified, their early recognition benefited patients and reduced legal liability. Our house rules were formulated to minimise abuse. Under threat of dismissal and litigation, staff were not permitted to buy shares in drug companies or pass information to relatives or others who might profit on the stock market. Senior staff were allowed to undertake ad hoc or advisory work on specific safety problems at the discretion of the Director and trustees, as long as transparency prevailed. Although I realized there were many ways in which they might be circumvented, I made the rules and there were no arguments.

Whether members of the CSM and other government advisory bodies should be regular consultants to drug companies or to have any other financial interests has been hotly debated. As soon as an expert has been identified by the drug industry as someone who has influence with government, they are offered retainers. It is argued that if leading experts cannot supplement their NHS or academic salaries in this way, the government would soon find it difficult to recruit the best people to advise them. Two thirds of the members of the CSM and the Medicines Commission are consultants to one or more companies. Retainers also work in another way; if a problem arises with a particular company's product, any committee member who is a company consultant has to declare an interest and cannot take part in the subsequent debate. He may well be one of few, or even the only member of the committee with the specialized knowledge relevant to that problem and his elimination from the debate about a company's product could be a considerable advantage to that company.

Another major concern has always been the proliferation of minor modifications of successful products that I call 'me too' drugs. They account for a large part of public expenditure on drugs. By the time that a drug of a completely new kind is developed, much of its useful patent life has been used up in laboratory and clinical trials. Even a 'break through' drug may have burnt up half of its useful patent-life by the time it is first licensed. Once its patent has expired, any competitor may sell a so-called *generic equivalent* under its own brand name at a fraction of the original price. The rival company can do this without investment in research or expertise with the product. Since a generic drug does not usually differ in its side effects or efficacy from the parent product (there have been dangerous exceptions), no appreciable safety issue arises and generics are usually considerably less expensive. With one proviso, I do not mind if a generic drug is substituted by the pharmacist even though a branded product may have been prescribed by the GP, but I do want to be sure that the manufacturer of the treatment that my patient is given can be identified with certainty so that appropriate action can be taken in the event of an accident. I believe this is, or should be, a legal responsibility resting on the shoulders of the pharmacist (provided, of course, that the doctor wrote the correct instructions on the prescription).

For most of the second half of the twentieth century an insidious practice has been permitted and even encouraged by the authorities. To capture a small share of a lucrative market, many companies obtain licences for 'me-too' products that are already patent-expired or have used up much of their patent life before they were licensed; or they may apply to market very minor modifications of existing products. The industry argues that such products are essential to fund research on more novel projects. This is a circular argument, however, because each variant costs many millions of pounds to develop and survive the licensing process and each has the potential to be another thalidomide. There have been several situations where fairly minor chemical variations have led to major problems. An obvious solution would be to grant *more prolonged patent protection* for completely novel treatments. This would make the copycat products unprofitable and would prevent a huge waste of effort on products that rarely have any advantages over the originals. The NHS drug bill could be reduced by several billion pounds each year.

However, reducing the flow of 'me too' products is not the only way in which the public might benefit from changes in the licensing laws. When the Medicines Act of 1968 was drafted, the industrial lobby successfully blocked the inclusion of one essential step in the logical assessment of safety and efficacy. The Act specified that a new drug must show some efficacy, but it specifically avoided any requirement that it should show a *margin of greater efficacy* over available alternatives. Frequently a submission for a new 'me too' drug includes the results of comparisons between the new product and a placebo (an inert substance) or an old remedy known to have little efficacy. This is simply not good enough. A new product must be compared with the best alternative therapy available and must have a margin of superiority in efficacy as well as being of equal or greater safety. I argued relentlessly in this way with my colleagues in ICI before leaving the company in the early Sixties. Legally enforceable requirements to stop using placebos and to produce evidence of superior efficacy over existing products would eliminate many of the 'me-too' products, greatly reduce NHS expenditure and channel resources into exciting new areas of research. Only the 'fat cats', drawing seven or eight figure annual salaries at taxpayers' expense need worry. Some countries do insist that manufacturers produce evidence that their new product has undergone comparative studies with other similar drugs and that it does show a margin of greater efficacy, otherwise the company may receive a letter saying "We see no need for this product in our country".

Driving to Bournemouth one evening to speak at a postgraduate meeting, I was involved in a rear end 'shunt' at a road junction. I had stopped at a point where I had to give way, when my Peugeot was rammed from the rear. Suffering from the whiplash, I drove over to the other side of the crossing (I had already been pushed half way) and got my chair out to see if anyone was injured. Neither the woman driver who had run into me or her children were hurt, but their car seemed likely to be a write-off. My heavy estate car had suffered comparatively minor rear-end damage. I continued the journey and subsequently received a nice letter thanking me for an interesting presentation, though I have no memory of delivering it. Some time later it turned out that I had been rather more seriously injured than I had thought. The effects of the whiplash injury had got progressively worse for a few weeks and then began to improve considerably over several months until I began to wonder if the hassle of the insurance claim was worth the trouble. Not long after a modest out-of-court settlement, however, the pain became worse and I lost much of the muscle power in my right hand. The orthopaedic experts explained that this was because nerves had been trapped by scar tissue formed in the blood clot caused by the original accident. Another side-effect of this accident changed my appearance; because of the discomfort of stubble while wearing an orthopaedic collar, I grew a beard.

Summer garden parties played an important part in maintaining morale at the DSRU and I remember how my father had encouraged similar functions when he was Chairman of ICI's Alkali Division, fifty years earlier. His were called the 'Pensioners Garden Party' and it brought the families together and gave faces to the management. Father's ability to address by name hundreds of members of his staff at all levels was legendary. At various DSRU events we had Morris dancers, a ride-on miniature steam railway and a Punch and Judy man. 'Throwing the Wellington Boot' separated the athletic from the overweight husbands. I had thought of hiring an elephant one summer, but nearby Marwell Zoo did not have one, so in 1988 I hired a hot-air balloon. My idea was to fly it to a height of about fifty feet on a tether and give rides for the children. The wind was too strong and gusty however and for most of the afternoon the balloon remained in its basket. Having paid quite a lot to hire it, however, I decided to persuade the pilot, Tony Bolger, to let me finish the party in style. I was lifted out of my wheelchair and seated on an office stool in the basket. Our field is narrow and flanked with massive oaks. A rapid lift-off was vital and Tony called for more people to hold the basket down while he burned propane far longer than is normal after the balloon had been fully inflated to increase its buoyancy. When he said, "Stand back please, Gentlemen," we shot up at phenomenal speed, reaching one thousand feet in about ten seconds. We had planned to land in a field about a mile away and return before the end of the party but we were travelling much too fast. We radioed Southampton Airport to report that we were crossing their flight-path and flew along the River Itchen. As Tony had predicted, we encountered a sea breeze blowing up Southampton Water, all too obviously smelling of Fawley Oil Refinery. This carried us northwards over Ocean Village and the city, and then we changed course and turned south over the docks. Tony pointed to the two large fields on the west bank that he had shown me on the map as a likely landing area. "It's either there or over the New Forest, if we don't run out of gas," he said. The wind was now fresh and he warned of a 'hairy' landing. We approached the shore fifty feet above the water and directly along the line of a fence separating the two fields. It was made of old railway sleepers and we were flying *along* rather than *across* it. Fortunately the basket grounded a few feet to one side of the fence, tipped on its side and continued across the field towards a herd of cows, spinnakering like a sailing boat. I was lying on top of Tony but he extricated himself with difficulty, losing his shoes in the process, and managed to smother the balloon. We had been in touch with the retrieving vehicle throughout the flight and they had us in sight as they drove along the M27. We arrived home late in the evening long after the party had finished – and started another one.

As soon as I had succeeded in making the DSRU self-supporting I resigned my position as a Principal Medical Officer at the Department of Health. Recognition for sixteen years' service to the CSM and the Department was a short letter from a junior administrator (an 'Executive Officer') who thanked me on behalf of the Department — five years after I had left London. I could not help feeling slightly hurt that there had been no recognition for developing the national yellow card system from scratch, sorting out the thrombosis problem with the pill and the liver problem with halothane. The same indifference continued when I set up the DSRU and made PEM work on a national scale, confounding the gloomy predictions about the future of the Unit by those I left behind at the Department. In the eighties and early nineties, the severest critics of PEM and the DSRU were the new recruits to the CSM, the Medicines Control Agency and the Association of the British Pharmaceutical Industry (ABPI) who thought they should be responsible for developing post-marketing surveillance (PMS). In spite of all their puff and blow, however, none succeeded in getting a rival national scheme off the ground.

In 1988 I challenged a decision to remove the licence for a drug called mianserin that was used to treat depression. It had been marketed for nearly ten years but the MCA suddenly seemed to be concerned about a small number of cases with blood disorders. Over the years about one report had been received for every forty thousand prescriptions issued. The MCA's view ignored the fact that mianserin is a much safer drug when taken in suicidal overdose than many alternatives used to treat depression, such as amitriptyline. The officials could not agree that suicide is the greatest risk in depressive illness and that patients frequently overdose with the drugs that are most handy at the time, often those prescribed to treat their depression. It is possible that the officials were hamstrung by the wording of the Medicines Act that only permits consideration of problems arising during the *normal* use of drugs. Accidental or deliberate overdose was not included.

I decided that this was exactly the kind of problem that the DSRU was uniquely equipped to tackle. I chose a drug called amitriptyline for comparison with mianserin as it was the most frequently prescribed alternative. In neither of the two very large groups of patients that we investigated was there a single case of the severe and potentially fatal blood disorder that had been worrying the MCA. This did not mean that either drug was completely free from any such risk, but if cases did occur, they must be rare. The most striking difference, however, was between the subgroups of patients who had survived a suicide attempt. Not one of ninety survivors of mianserin overdose had required admission to an intensive care unit but among two hundred and forty survivors of amitriptyline overdose, fifty-six had been admitted to intensive care units. Seventeen of three hundred and ten survivors of attempts with other kinds of drug had also required intensive care. We had followed up a sample of prescriptions equivalent to about four per cent of one year's treatments for every patient in England and I estimated that as many as six thousand patients might overdose with mianserin each year, but hardly any of them would have needed intensive care. Similarly, about fourteen thousand would have overdosed with amitriptyline and about twelve hundred of them could have needed intensive care. Those interested in the cost of hospital treatment should not ignore this enormous difference. There was no doubt that mianserin is extremely safe in overdose. However, the authorities had already decided to ban its use by patients over sixty-five years of age. The manufacturers appealed to the Medicines Commission but their appeal was turned down. On February 17th 1989, Lord Justice Glidewell and Mr. Justice Pill ruled that I was right; safety in overdose was relevant and the Commission had been given incorrect legal advice. The Department continued to argue that under UK and EC legislation they could only consider 'normal' use of drugs.

In another rather similar situation I was told that I should mind my own business. I wondered what was so special about officials that only they may enter into a debate? As it happened, I had been responsible for handling the problem they were concerned about while working for the CSM in the same role as those who were now complaining. My opinion was exactly the same as it had been years earlier and it had been accepted by the CSM at the time, years before the MCA was started and while some of the officials were still in short pants. The drug was known as Halcion and was marketed in the United Kingdom as a sleeping tablet from 1979. It worked rapidly and left no hangover. In July the same year, the media in Holland reacted vigorously when a Dutch psychiatrist, Dr Cees van der Kroef, reported that he had treated eleven patients with Halcion and four of them had developed severe psychiatric symptoms not unlike a bad 'trip' on LSD. The Dutch licence was suspended for six months. I had found no evidence of a similar problem in the United Kingdom. We had received twenty-two reports of minor mental side effects and even if we assumed that only ten per cent had been reported, this was equivalent to about one for every ten thousand prescriptions dispensed. The doses prescribed in Holland, however, were usually four and sometimes eight or more times larger than those used in England and I advised the CSM that the most likely explanation was that this was a simple problem of dose. The Committee decided that no action was required, apart from a recommendation to prescribe fairly small quantities.

Subsequently the CSM continued to receive about one report for every million prescriptions written by GPs. In spite of this minuscule level of reporting adverse reactions, in December 1991, twelve years after the Dutch incident, the MCA suddenly decided to revoke the licence. This decision was astonishing since it seemed to have been based on data collected in one pre-marketing clinical trial in the United States twenty years earlier. The Upjohn Company had commissioned an experiment at a penitentiary in Jackson, Michigan. This was a maximum-security institution for violent psychopathic criminals and it is difficult to imagine a less suitable place to conduct a toxicity study of a sleeping tablet. As the clinician concerned pointed out to me many years later, any inmate who went to sleep was liable to wind up with a 'shiv' sticking in his back (as had several inmates and staff and a visiting lady psychologist). However, in those days it was normal for pharmaceutical companies to do trials in 'volunteers' in penitentiaries where the inmates could gain certain benefits by taking part in trials of new drugs. The MCA's contention was that the trial had been unsatisfactory and that a licence should not have been granted in 1978. How could an apparent defect in a trial performed so long ago have any realistic bearing on the safety of Halcion in 1991 in the absence of any new evidence to suggest otherwise? Moreover the drug had been reinstated in Holland and most other countries for use at a reduced dose.

The MCA's decision and the events that followed seemed to be a kite flying exercise, probably part of a campaign to reduce the size of the list of drugs supplied by the National Health Service. There was no suggestion that Halcion presented any new hazard at that time and the Upjohn Company appealed to the Medicine's Commission. Whoever started this affair seemed oblivious to the history of Halcion and once again forgot that those who ignore the mistakes of history are doomed to repeat them. As part of the appeals procedure, a more experienced member of the MCA's staff was appointed by the Medicines Commission to reappraise the original paper that had launched this particular kite and he concluded that there was insufficient evidence to justify withdrawal of Halcion.

I was one of a group who volunteered to participate in the appeal to the Medicines Commission. We were kept waiting for four hours in a hot stuffy office while the Commissioners finished their business and then had their lunch. When we finally got to the meeting several Commissioners shook hands or waved to me across the table although the civil servants avoided eye contact. The Medicines Commission recommended that Halcion could be used at a low (but still effective) dose for a maximum period of ten days, but the MCA refused to accept the Medicine Commission's recommendation. The Company then exercised its right to appeal to a second panel of experts appointed by the Commission. They in turn re-examined the evidence and came to exactly the same conclusion. Yet again the MCA refused to accept it. By this time there had been six separate assessments of Halcion. *'Halcion Days'* could have been set to music.

The officials of the MCA could not seriously believe that they were right and everybody else wrong. Clearly, the decision to ban the drug had already been made by the Minister's advisers long before the hearing and nothing was going to shift it. Why therefore subject everybody to hundreds of hours of unnecessary work and enormous expense consulting lawyers and outside experts and preparing the documentation for the hearings? The MCA could easily have published the reasons behind their decision to remove the drug and nobody would have held it against them. The losers in this affair were Upjohn who spent millions of dollars, and the officials managing the MCA who lost their credibility.

17

More Dirty Work at the Crossroads

Forty years after starting to develop the CSM's yellow card scheme, thirty years after first proving that low-dose oral contraceptives were the safest and twenty years after founding the DSRU, I still believe that my most important contribution to public safety was my campaign against promotional post-marketing studies. Ill-considered proposals by the CSM and active encouragement by the former management of the MCA and the ABPI, opened the floodgates for studies masquerading as research for which a minority of gullible and avaricious GPs were prepared to receive substantial payment from the industry. Since I retired it has at last become generally accepted that such trials are unethical and several of the measures that I proposed have now been put into practice. I believe that recent revelations about fraudulent research may have speeded up this process.

Many promotional studies are managed by company 'reps' or by contract organizations specializing in drug promotion. The GPs prescribe the new drugs on normal NHS prescription forms and send follow-up reports to the company. They are paid to register each patient and for each follow-up report. Representatives sometimes visited GPs with inducements that have ranged from golfing weekends overseas to electronic organizers, computers or equipment for the surgery and a trip on the Orient Express. A new drug may replace one that has a long and satisfactory safety record and may turn out to have unexpected side effects. The final irony is that while the doctor is paid handsomely by the drug company, the patient, unless in an exempt category, pays the prescription charge. Scientifically the studies are valueless.

Even before I qualified in 1956 I was aware that drug representatives regard immigrant doctors as soft targets for gifts and entertainment in return for promises to prescribe. I did not obtain hard evidence, however, until I started collecting information for PEM studies. Then it became obvious that a minority of doctors had some strange patterns of prescribing, especially with drugs used for chronic conditions such as arthritis or heart disease. It was unlikely, for example, that a doctor with a list of two thousand patients would be attending more than perhaps a dozen whose rheumatoid arthritis was in an active phase at any one time. It was even less likely that there would be a clinical need to change the treatment of all of them over a period of a few weeks. One of our early studies included twenty thousand patients who had received prescriptions for a new arthritis drug within a few weeks of its launch. The CSM had released it on the understanding that it was to be promoted only for the treatment of *active* rheumatoid arthritis. We found one GP who had prescribed the drug for two hundred and twenty-eight patients within a few weeks of its launch. Perhaps ten percent of all the patients in his practice had been prescribed an unnecessary drug in spite of the official recommendation. When I phoned the manufacturer, no secret was made of the fact that doctors were being paid a three-figure fee for each patient. The same GP was also the country's leading prescriber of a new heart drug that we were studying at the same time. He had prescribed it for one hundred and nine of the first three thousand four hundred patients ever to be prescribed it anywhere in England. I published this horrific story in *PEM News* and, in a press statement, I said:

> 'I hope the notion that doctors may be paid or offered substantial gifts as an inducement to prescribe new drugs or provide information for commercial purposes will prove to be as repugnant to them as it must be to their patients. I want the authorities to declare that it is unethical, immoral and dangerous to pay doctors to prescribe drugs'

The Association of the British Pharmaceutical Industry (ABPI) reacted strongly, declaring that the future for PMS lay in company studies.

> 'We believe that data generated by a doctor on behalf of an individual pharmaceutical company in connection with a specific product must be exclusive to the company concerned. That exclusivity should not exceed a period of, say, five years from the conclusion of the project, but is an exclusivity which a pharmaceutical company has a right to expect.'

The *Guardian* reported that the Marketing Director of VAMP (Value Added Medical Products), one of the companies that had distributed low-cost computers to GPs in return for post-marketing studies, had said that:

> "If VAMP, when sifting its data from GPs, discovers another potential Thalidomide or Opren, it will sell the life-saving information to the DHSS on a 'cost plus basis.' Nothing in business is free," said Mr.Collins.'

IMS International circulated a prospectus to clients in the drug industry who they hoped would use their services. Until we shortened it, the title of the DSRU had been the *Post-marketing Drug Surveillance Research Unit*. Our main activity was Prescription-Event Monitoring. IMS was now selling their *Post Marketing Surveillance Unit* and its main activity was said to be Drug Event Monitoring. The cost to a drug company of a ten thousand-patient study was £900,000, rising by 25-50% if comparisons were made with other drugs. Doctors were to receive a £5 registration fee for each patient and £5 for each follow-up report. If, for example, the trial of protocol involved five follow-up reports for each patient the doctor earned £30 per patient.

I have met most company medical directors over the years and have yet to encounter one who could look me in the eye and say that such studies are not promotional. I wrote:

'There are only two national, non-commercial schemes. Both report events which occur during normal day-to-day medical practice. Neither involves changing a patient's treatment deliberately. To do so in order to take part in a promotional study for which there is financial reward raises important scientific, ethical and legal questions which do not seem to have been adequately and publicly debated.'

The Medical Defence Union said that GPs should make sure that there was a responsible body of medical opinion in support of a new drug before changing a patient's treatment or *'they could find themselves in very hot water.'* My press statement was accurately reported. I had demanded that:

> 'All pseudo-scientific studies designed to promote sales should stop immediately.
>
> Drug firms should not start any more promotional studies.
>
> Drug Companies should publish a list of all commercial studies, whether promotional or not.
>
> All results, whether favourable or not, should be published.
>
> Doctors must obtain fully informed consent.
>
> No patient should take part in more than one study at a time.
>
> The number of patients in a trial should not exceed five or six, so that they may be properly monitored.
>
> Doctors involved in trials must continue to complete green forms for the DSRU.
>
> Doctors should seek evidence that the trial drug is more effective than any previous medication.
>
> Patients should ask doctors if the trial has any commercial link.

This skirmish and my 'Ten Commandments' had serious repercussions for the DSRU. By 1988 we had again outgrown our office space and I had started to look for funds to buy the old Children's Hospital at Bursledon, near Southampton. It had been used as a school for children with special needs and had housed some of the children who had been most seriously disabled by thalidomide. It suited the DSRU admirably, although more than £1 million would be required if a bid was likely to succeed. I had hoped that the six British-based companies might help, but ABPI, not noted for its altruism, advised all of them not to co-operate in view of my action against commercial PMS studies. The heads of the company medical departments apologised to me, but there was nothing they could do because the sales departments controlled the development budgets once drugs had been passed for marketing. A Southampton businessman, Bill Cox, had joined the Trust as a financial consultant and Bill and I set off for the United States to see if we could raise the necessary funds. A letter from ABPI to all companies at home and in the US preceded us:

> 'We understand that Professor WHW Inman, Director of the Drug Safety Research Unit (DSRU) at Southampton, UK, is currently visiting the United States of America, and whilst there is visiting a number of pharmaceutical companies. We wish to draw your attention to the text of part of the current edition of PEM News which is published by the DSRU, and which is circulated to all prescribing doctors in the United Kingdom. The text, which is attached, has been widely reported to the press here to the damage of both UK and US companies, many of whom are conducting effective post-marketing surveillance studies.'

Our legal advisers wrote to the Chairman of ABPI stating that "the letter was clearly designed to lower our clients in the estimation of those to whom it was published, and on that basis our clients are entitled to seek an apology and libel damages. That being said, our clients have no particular wish to proceed against you in this matter (although we do not confirm that they will not, and their rights to do so are strictly reserved) and may, if this is done promptly, be satisfied with a clarificatory circular to be sent out by you to those to whom the original letter was sent." I was hardly surprised that no apology was ever received and wonder if the public would have been better served if the Trustees had been sufficiently well funded to take action in the courts.

As it turned out, ABPI's letter caused so much offence in drug company circles in the US that it helped rather than hindered our quest and we raised more than £1 million fairly easily. Within weeks our bid for the Children's Hospital was successful.

Promotional PMS was taken up in a widely publicised programme on TV's Channel 4 programme, *Checkout,* in August 1991. The ABPI and the MCA declined invitations to participate. Stephen Dorrell, a Conservative Under-Secretary at the Department of Health, did grant a brief interview, saying that patients could be completely confident that their doctors could handle such matters. I emphasised that studies must be *non-interventional*, meaning that a doctor should not deliberately change or intervene in the patient's treatment in order to enter them in a study unless the latter was a fully informed volunteer. IMS did not appear on the programme although it was reported that they had denied that their studies were interventional and that doctors were participating in a 'study'. It was reported that they currently had fifteen 'non-studies', or whatever one was supposed to call them, in progress. Several doctors contributing to the programme described gifts such as video cameras and foreign holidays that had been offered to them to encourage them to participate. Dr. Joe Collier, the Editor of *Drug and Therapeutics Bulletin*, asked how the MCA could reasonably be expected to 'sponsor' the industry and protect patients at the same time.

A 'Newsletter' distributed to doctors by the Integrated Network for Computer Administration (INCA), finally blew the lid off the credibility of drug Company PMS.

> 'INCA has strong contacts with the Department of Health, with GP computer suppliers representing over 90% of computerised practices and with the leading authorities throughout all areas of healthcare computing. "Nor is it without significance" points out INCA's Joint Managing Director Garth Gunston, that "INCA is part of the giant pharmaceutical distribution Group AAH, a £1.5 billion Company which already has the most advanced health care on-line ordering network in Great Britain.'

> 'A recent survey suggests that a GP could earn up to £70 for half an hour's work by completing a batch of PMS forms in a single session ... A single report takes an average of three minutes and the fee payable is £7. On this basis, 10 reports completed in a single session would generate fee payments of £70.'

AAH is *Allied Anthracite Holdings*, a commercial holding company that should, perhaps, have stuck to its original role as coal merchants. AAH invited doctors to try out Glaxo's new migraine treatment, *Imigran* (sumatriptan). Incredibly it began:

> "Let INCA do your PMS reporting for you. If you are a Sumatriptan prescriber, but have no time for submitting PMS reports, INCA's Clinical Research Assistants will visit your practice... and still let you earn the £35 per patient allowed under the PMS Code."

Sumatriptan is a treatment for migraine, sold as *Imigran,* for use by self-injection or as tablets. The newsletter described an interview with a doctor who said he had no difficulty recruiting migraine patients. I wondered how his patients might have reacted if they had seen the newsletter first?

I decided we should undertake a massive survey of general practitioner prescribing. We could use the hundreds of thousands of prescriptions that we had processed over seven years to identify doctors and patients. Its purpose was to discover the extent to which over-prescribing by a minority of doctors was distorting the general pattern of prescribing of new drugs and how much it accounted for the thirty per cent of doctors who failed to return our PEM questionnaires. We needed to learn as much as possible about the prescribers themselves. Older doctors or females, for example, might be more cautious in their acceptance of new drugs.

More than half a million patients and twenty-seven drugs were included in our survey. The results were startling and I regard the publication in the *Lancet*, with my computer manager Gill Pearce, as one of my most important contributions to drug safety. Through our 'window' in their prescribing practice, we learned that excessively heavy prescribing was actually limited to a small number of GPs. Two hundred and fifty-one doctors out of about twenty-eight thousand GPs in the whole of England had each prescribed one or more of the drugs that we had studied by PEM for more than sixty patients within a few weeks of the drug's first appearance on the market. The drug companies no doubt regarded them as hotshot prescribers. Although only small in number, this group accounted for thirty-eight thousand treatments during the few weeks in which we had collected our samples of prescriptions. We found, against expectation, that younger doctors were more conservative in their use of new drugs than their older colleagues. The other finding, confirming the way drug companies target certain groups of doctors, was the correlation between heavy prescribing of new drugs and the country in which the doctor obtained his or her first qualification. Specifically, by far the largest group of heavy prescribers had qualified at medical schools in the Indian Subcontinent. There was no possibility that forty-two per cent of the need for the new drugs could be concentrated in ten per cent of the practices; patients do not vary to such an extent. We concluded:

> 'Irrespective of the underlying reasons for the very large variations we have found in the use of recently marketed

drugs (and variations in medical need cannot be one of them) there is no justification for expensive promotional studies that expose patients to the unforeseen hazards of new drugs in numbers that are far too large to be adequately monitored by individual doctors.'

We avoided headlines that might have led to 'ethnic' complications, but several Indian GPs congratulated me for having had the courage to draw attention to the problem caused by a minority of their compatriots. There were signs that some influential people were also beginning to come out in support. Sir William Asscher, who had recently retired as Chairman of the CSM, suggested in *The Independent* newspaper that company studies were often just a marketing exercise and the companies were not required to publish their findings. An Asian postgraduate tutor in general practice, phoned to congratulate the DSRU and then wrote at length:

'I have been targeted, but because of my basic beliefs I have not succumbed to the pressure. You may well ask why Asian doctors are susceptible to such pressures while the English doctors are not. In any society an individual accepts the mores of that society because he is part of that society and does not want to be alienated from it. An immigrant, whatever his attempts at integration, remains an outsider for reasons I need not go into. This is especially true if the immigrant is perceived to be a second-class citizen. If an immigrant is not integrated in a society then he does not feel bound to accept the mores of that society. He will break the accepted code of the society till he is in the grey area of behaviour which may be unethical but still legal. As we well know, those in high finance – the Maxwells of this world – do this every day. I am interested in this subject not only to reduce wastage in the NHS and provide better service to the patients, but also to maintain the reputation of a large majority of Asian GPs who try to give a good service but get tarred with the same brush.'

Our results were in line with those of Dr Paramjit Singh Gill and colleagues at the University of Leeds. They did a study that measured the number of prescriptions issued to patients from various ethnic groups. They found that patients from the Indian subcontinent were more likely to receive a prescription from their GP than were whites or those from the West Indies. For example, a Pakistani male aged between 45 and 64 was three and a half times more likely to receive a prescription than a white male in the same age group. This is because this group of patients would tend to be cared for by GPs from the same ethnic group that included a few of the heaviest prescribers [26].

The Minister of Health, Dr. Brian Mawhinney, visited the DSRU and I also had extensive correspondence with Jack Ashley who spoke in a debate on the Pharmaceutical Industry on April 28th, 1993:

> 'Some of the doctors ... are in danger of jeopardising the health of patients and even imperilling their lives. That is a scandalous situation which calls for urgent action by the government, the medical profession and the pharmaceutical industry. I am indebted for much of my information to Professor Bill Inman, who was the pioneer of the yellow card reporting system on adverse reactions and the originator of prescription event monitoring which is supported by four-fifths of Britain's GPs, many of whom do a great deal of work without payment.
>
> Some companies are carrying out their own drug surveillance, an idea put forward some eight years ago by a working party, and which at first sight seems very reasonable. What is wrong with people carrying out their own drugs surveillance? But what is unreasonable is the hidden agenda of some companies. The first urgent danger signals should be flying when we learn that patients do not have to be fully informed volunteers giving their written consent. Why should some doctors participate in

such potential malpractice? It is because they are offered inducements to take part in these commercial trials.'

Jack described the INCA letter as a blatant encouragement to doctors to supplement their incomes and said that the company trials were an outrage that should be stopped by the Government and by the medical profession.

In correspondence following his visit, Mawhinney reiterated his concern about over-prescribing but he still dodged the two most important issues. He failed to comment on whether or not patients should be fully informed volunteers or on the justification for changing existing effective treatment with drugs of proven safety and efficacy. He left the door open to doctors to prescribe a new (and often much more expensive) drug for patients who may not need it, who are not given any choice and are not aware that their doctor is being paid by a drug company to prescribe it.

In September 1993 our paper was published in *The Lancet*. It was at this time that Jack Ashley wrote to tell me that his second cochlea implant was beginning to be helpful. During telephone conversations with Jack, I had always been amazed at the speed with which he responded through his 'interpreter', presumably his wife Pauline or his daughter or secretary. If one had not been aware that he was totally deaf, it would be difficult to detect any pauses in the conversation. Jack arranged a meeting with Baroness Cumberlege, Parliamentary Under Secretary of State for Health in the House of Lords, for late October.

Shortly before our meeting, draft guidelines for company-sponsored *Safety Assessment of Marketed Medicines (SAMM)* were published. They had supposedly been formulated by a working party and a summary was published in the British Medical Journal on the 6th February 1988. The introduction stated that:

'They have been formulated and approved by the Association of the British Pharmaceutical Industry (ABPI), the British Medical Association, the Committee on Safety of Medicines, and the Royal College of General Practitioners.'

It was no surprise that the SAMM Guidelines were circulated by the ABPI rather than the non-commercial bodies or that the address for correspondence to the British Medical Journal was shown as Dr. Frank Wells, the ABPI's Director of Medical Affairs. The Medicines Control Agency had played a part in the formulation of the guidelines, but rather cleverly kept their name out of the BMJ statement. The ABPI is nothing more than a trade association that should not be involved in instructing doctors what they should or should not do in ethical matters. If proof were needed of the intimate and in my view unwholesome association between the drug industry and those who represent and guide the medical professions, here was proof.

One recommendation in the guidelines, however, was regarded by some of my supporters as a triumph for my campaign. For the first time it was admitted that it was *unethical to prescribe a new medicine when there was no medical reason for it*. Another clause stated that no patient should be entered simultaneously in more than one study. We had found patients who had been in up to four studies together or in rapid succession. The guidelines included no mention of the need for patients to be consulted before treatment was changed or for them to sign forms of consent. Predictably, the industry is now using 'SAMM studies' as a means of promoting their new products.

Baroness Cumberlege was a good listener and seemed to share my outrage about the disgusting INCA document. When she wrote a few days later in her official capacity, however, she was depressingly negative. She said that the Department was satisfied with the guidelines and that the *'Department of Health's view is that consent is not required'*. Finally she said *'I understand that patients' consent is not obtained for studies conducted by Professor Inman's Unit for example.'* Here she was merely passing on the lies of officials at the MCA. She had obviously not been told that there is no resemblance whatsoever between PEM studies by the DSRU and promotional trials run by drug companies. PEM is retrospective and non-interventional. Doctors are approached by the DSRU several months after starting to prescribe a new treatment for a patient. In complete contrast company studies are prospective and interventional and necessitate a deliberate change of treatment in response to a promise of payment by the company. The Department's response was dishonest and shameful; medical practice demands mutual trust between patient and doctor. Trust is compromised by the close affinity of some doctors to the industry and the Department of Health is not providing adequate safeguards. The only remedy seems to be for patients to insist that their doctors must be compelled to explain the reasons for any change of treatment. Doctors would do well to inform patients by means of notices in their offices and waiting rooms if the practice policy includes participation in drug-company studies.

In spite of the MCA's behaviour towards the DSRU, strong support for the work we were doing had come from the *House of Lords Select Committee on the European Communities*. In their 3rd Report for the 1991-1992 Session, they recommended that all member countries should adopt Prescription Event Monitoring (PEM) [28]. As our scheme was the only one singled out for detailed mention in their report I shall quote three paragraphs in full.

> (39) "We also received evidence of another system of pharmacovigilance in the United Kingdom, namely "Prescription Event Monitoring". It was set up by Professor William Inman initially in Southampton University's Medical School and now has independent charitable status. The Prescription Pricing Authority supplies a copy of every prescription written for each new drug during an evaluation period of 2-3 years. About 10-12 drugs are selected for evaluation at a time. About 22,000 doctors are involved; they report on every "significant event" in the patient's experience while taking

the drug. Once the data is transferred from questionnaire forms to a computer data bank it can be analysed by technically qualified assessors. A more detailed procedure is followed where patients have died during the study. The rate of response is said to be over 70 per cent, and claimed to be much higher than the United Kingdom's yellow card system. Professor Inman estimates that his system costs about £150,000 per drug, Modest when set against the estimated £80 million cost of the launch of a major new drug.

{See Drug Safety Research Unit PEM News No 7. August 1991. Pages 5-23}

(65) "Pharmacovigilance" was a major concern among our witnesses. Standards of post-marketing surveillance in this country are high. The success of the Community-wide system of rapid reporting of defective products has shown that such co-operation can work when all agree its value. We hope that a similar commitment will be forthcoming for effective pharmacovigilance of medicines in both human and veterinary use.

(66) In this context we recommend that the Commission considers the use of Prescription Event Monitoring throughout the Community. Its method of in-depth analysis of a carefully selected group of new products on the basis of data from a large random sample seems both effective and well adapted for Community policy."

A long list of European Council directives and a handful of government papers are quoted, but *"PEM News"* is the only independent literature reference shown in the report. John Butterfield and Bob Hunter were both members of the Sub-Committee comprising the fourteen Lords who conducted the enquiry. However, their recommendations for the European Community were never implemented and I have seen no evidence that PEM has been introduced during the last ten years in any country other than Japan!

I had become increasingly concerned about the industry's stealthily growing grip on the medical profession. This is not to deny the enormous benefits of modern drugs; many diseases that were formerly untreatable when I qualified as a doctor half a century ago have now been conquered. Average life expectancy has increased by ten years, much of it due to the successful control of chronic life-shortening diseases such as high blood pressure or acute infections such as pneumonia. The promotional techniques now being used are not new; drug 'reps' have been bribing doctors for fifty years. I myself had to steer a careful path through an ethical minefield to secure no-strings financial support to run the DSRU without signing contracts or submitting to political control by government officials. Most university departments of clinical pharmacology have to lean heavily on drug companies for financial support. These companies fund many postgraduate medical centres; they provide lunch for GPs attending meetings and set up stands advertising their products and distributing free samples and gifts. The drug industry plays an increasingly prominent role in medical education. This is not necessarily a bad thing because it is sometimes the only way that busy GPs can be kept informed of recent advances in treatment. I would guess that at least half of post-graduate education of GPs is paid for out of drug company profits. The Department of Health that should be responsible hides behind the tired old slogan that it is 'the responsibility of doctors to keep themselves up to date with the latest developments'. It is less clear how this is to be done and who pays for it.

Most of the profit from a new drug of the 'me-too' variety is made during the first two years of marketing and companies argue that if their freedom to use intensive promotional techniques were to be stripped away from them they would be unable to achieve the common goal that they share with the

NHS — improving the health of patients. The first two years is of course the period in which unexpected adverse reactions are most likely to occur and this is also the period during which properly organized intensive monitoring is most necessary.

When the Royal College of Physicians set up a Faculty of Pharmaceutical Medicine, I saw it as a way in which the College could help doctors working in the industry to strengthen their influence on its commercial activities. I was honoured to be elected a founder Fellow of the new Faculty. When, however, I saw that some of the people who had attempted to sabotage the expansion of the DSRU had been given prominent positions within the Faculty, I resigned immediately in protest. This hurt several colleagues and friends who had supported me over the years. My attack on promotional trials did bear fruit after I had retired. The Royal College came out strongly against drug promotion masquerading as research and declared such practice to be unethical.

One day I chanced on the following passage in Thomas Culpepper's *Complete Herbal* published 1653:

> 'The right worshipful, the College of Physicians of London in their New Dispensatory give you free leave to distil these common waters that follow, but *they never intend you should know what they are good for.*"

The list of potential remedies included 'Mouse ear... horsemints...English tobacco...hartshorn, and bullock's dung made in May'. It would seem that commercial interests could have influenced our revered Fellowship at least three and a half centuries ago.

In a keynote article in the BMJ, Professor Abraham of the University of Sussex noted that the national agencies are run as businesses and compete with one another for fees for regulatory work. In 1989 the MCA announced that in order to make its regulatory process "more efficient" it would now recoup all its running costs from licence fees instead of 60% as previously. Abraham reminded us that the MCA had recruited its Director,

Dr Keith Jones, from a US drug company and that "a concern to protect the commercial interests of the industry was enshrined within the agency's objectives." As evidence that the licensing procedure was indeed nowadays more efficient, the MCA's in-house processing time for licences was now 44 working days in 1998 compared with 154 in 1989. Is it possible that all the questions that should be asked and all the answers to them can be scrutinised within nine weeks of submission? And what measures can be taken to control the promotional activities of companies when the licences are granted for new drugs and post-marketing surveillance is supposed to commence? GP trials are very lucrative. Some startling information appeared in *Financial Pulse,* a 'throw-away' magazine distributed free to GPs.[32] It listed equipment obtained from trials in one practice that had included three ECG machines, one photocopier, nebulisers for asthma treatment, emergency portable oxygen equipment, cryoprobe equipment, audio-visual equipment for in-house education and piped music, a flip chart and overhead projector for trainee tutorials, substantial contribution to a semi-automatic defibrillator supplied by the British Heart Foundation and three quarters of the practice's first computer system. One practice delegated its research to a manager who ran it as a separate business with a turnover of up to £85,000, but complained that, since this included the manager's salary of £27,000 and other expenses, it left the GPs with "a miserable £3,000 profit". One practice was paid £150 for each of ninety patients who were prescribed a non-steroidal anti-inflammatory preparation to rub into their skin. The paper work had allegedly involved a nurse (200 hours at £8 per hour), a clerk (30 hours at £6) and a GP (30 hours at £60). The author pointed out that "if the FHSA finds out it may cut your reimbursement."[30] It is hard to accept all this nonsense in the light of complaints of understaffing and overwork in the health service.

As I have already mentioned, it was no surprise that the SAMM studies, dreamed up by the industry in collusion with the MCA, were used for promotion. For example, a marketing company called *IBRD Rostrum Global* that according to their web pages normally concentrates almost exclusively on the distribution of religious texts, wrote to me (by mistake, believing that I was a GP) on behalf of Bristol Myers-Squibb and Sanofi-Winthrop and tried to recruit me to take part in a SAMM study of two drugs used for hypertension. On 20th September they sent a 'PMS News Flash' that began:

> 'In our most recent SAMMs study, IBRD-ROSTRUM GLOBAL, in a record of 6 months, successfully completed enrolment of *7,500 patients nine months ahead of schedule.*
>
> IBRD-ROSTRUM GLOBAL can put your projects ahead of schedule using our unique and comprehensive, computer managed, paper based Post Marketing Surveillance (PMS) system. This highly efficient system has developed as a result of our considerable success and experience in conducting large-scale multicentre Phase IV studies. It has the flexibility to meet your specific requirements and complements any other method of PMS you may already be using.'

In 2002 I located GLOBAL ROSTRUM on the Internet but none of seventeen items had the remotest resemblance to anything connected to medicines or post-marketing research into drug safety. That the MCA, the BMA, the Royal College of General Practitioners, the Medicines Commission or the CSM should allow any drug company to involve innocent patients or gullible or avaricious general practitioners to be taken in by such methods of promotion beggars belief.

Shortly before I retired the Trustees of the DSRU invited the Chief Medical Officer, Sir Donald Acheson, to review the DSRU's progress and make recommendations that might be helpful in gaining more support from the Department of Health. Donald asked Professor Alasdair Breckenridge to spend some time with the Unit and write a report for the Department. Unfortunately a senior official of the MCA joined what the Trustees had anticipated would be a private, one-man delegation. Their report was circulated within the Department before being shown to the Trustees and contained comments on several topics not discussed with Breckenridge. They had clearly been inserted by certain officials within the Department who would have dearly loved to have seen the DSRU shut down. The report was so diminishing that the Trustees refused to pay for it.

18

Last Lap

The damage to my cervical spine several years earlier began to affect my life-style considerably during my last two years as Director of the DSRU. One morning I started to sign the cheques for the month's bills and realized that I could barely write my signature. Never my strongest hand since the accident, the muscles moving the thumb seemed to have seized up. The most likely explanation was nerve-entrapment in my neck. The Professor of orthopaedics had warned me that the scar tissue laid down in an area of bruising following a whiplash injury sometimes causes trouble years later. I telephoned my GP for advice; unfortunately he misinterpreted the severity of the situation suspecting that I might have had a stroke and, in spite of my protests, ordered an ambulance. He arrived seconds ahead of the ambulance and applied a blood pressure cuff to my right arm while I finished an important call from New York with my left. Still protesting that all this fuss was unnecessary, I was driven to the casualty department at Southampton General Hospital and deposited in a cubicle on a trolley. I could sense antipathy among the nurses who muttered audibly among themselves about my using an ambulance when it was clearly unnecessary and I lay on a trolley for two hours until a registrar sauntered in and gave me a cursory examination. Much later another junior doctor stuck pins from his lapel into me to the point where he drew blood. Both were agreed that I had not suffered a stroke (nor did I catch AIDS or hepatitis from the pins). I remained in A&E adding to the hostility of the nursing staff when I asked them to phone June, which they refused to do. Then I remembered that I had my briefcase with me and that it contained my mobile phone.

The partial loss of use in my right hand was permanent but it had one useful effect. It forced me to improve my computer skills. I had learned to type when I caught polio many years earlier. I hated my inability to shake hands convincingly but what should I do — pretend I really had suffered a stroke, shake with the wrong hand or both hands or kiss the man on both cheeks? I could no longer grip a fishing line between my finger and thumb. I had to learn to shoot at the rabbits that plagued our flowerbeds using my left index finger to pull the trigger. Unable to grip the hand-rim of my wheelchair, I became permanently dependent on an electric one. Yet another disaster overtook me when one of the two biceps tendons in my left arm snapped agonizingly as I was getting out of bed one morning.

I had to think even more seriously about retiring, but could not find an obvious successor. Fortunately the DSRU was now largely self-supporting, so I built a small extension onto our house (I call it my 'terminal care unit') and ran the DSRU from home, with one or two visits to the office each week. It was no longer possible to travel round the world giving lectures and fund-raising. The industry was beginning to contract as the flow of innovative new drugs diminished and there were numerous mergers of large companies. Funds for the Unit were drying up and I had the distressing task of making some employees redundant. At various times, Dr. Joan Clarke and Tom Lucas assisted me for short periods. Several post-graduate students worked on projects and one, Jane Andrew, wrote a valuable mini-thesis on the statistical aspects of PEM. Lynda Wilton, whose family was growing up, was now able to work full time. Gill Pearce, in charge of data processing, now had an assistant, Tim Leathers. Dr. Kiyoshi Kubota had also joined us. Kiyoshi revolutionised the arrangements for analysis of PEM data and eventually left to set up PEM studies in Japan and take a Chair in Tokyo.

For several years none of our advertisements had produced a successor who was prepared to join the Unit at a salary we could afford. The situation was partially resolved when Dr. Ron Mann suddenly became available. Ron had succeeded me several years previously at the Department of Health and more recently had become involved in post-marketing work with the 'VAMP' (Value Added Medical Products) organization. Although he was a year older he was prepared to take over until the Trustees could find a younger person of appropriate experience and seniority. Eventually one was appointed, Dr. Saad Shakir, who has made enormous progress in several areas that I did not have time or funds to develop.

I handed over the Unit in 1994, still a Trustee but determined not to breathe down the necks of those I left behind. I was now able to sit back and observe what was going on and particularly the ever expanding influence of the drug industry. I was increasingly suspicious of the relaxation of the tight controls that once applied to powerful drugs that formerly had to be prescribed by a doctor. Several are now advertised on television and sold directly to the public as 'over the counter' (OTC) products without the need for prior consultation with a doctor. Once a drug has been freed from prescription-only restriction it cannot be monitored by PEM because there are no prescriptions or medical records that would identify the patient. If a serious problem should arise, there is almost no way in which it could be investigated. Promotional post-marketing surveillance by drug companies was now more restricted, but it was obvious that deals had been made between the industry and the Medicines Control Agency which were clearly to the benefit of the former (though not, it is to be hoped, to the MCA). As a result of de-listing many OTC drugs could now be sold at a greatly increased price.

A good example is the group of potent drugs known as H_2-antagonists, mentioned in an earlier chapter, that are effective in the treatment of stomach and duodenal ulcers. During my years with the CSM and at the DSRU we had two reasons for being cautious about their long-term use. Firstly, we knew that they could mask the early symptoms of a serious disease such as cancer of the stomach and delay its diagnosis. Secondly, there was some suspicion that they might cause serious complications in the long term, even cancer of the large bowel. When we monitored the parent compound, Tagamet, in the early 80s I had arranged for a very large number of prescription forms to be stored for future possible use. Should the need have arisen, perhaps as much as twenty years later, it would have been possible to identify a large population of patients who had used Tagamet and find out how frequently a particular problem such as stomach cancer might have occurred. Tagamet and related products such as Zantac and Pepsid are now sold for minor gastric upsets such as heartburn. The cost to the patient when purchased 'over the counter' (OTC) is several times larger than the cost to the taxpayer when the same drug is prescribed. The drug companies no doubt delight in the relaxation of prescribing restrictions because they can now sell very much more of their product at a higher price. Whether they pay prescription charges or not, patients might do well to ask for a prescription because this gives their doctor an opportunity to consider if Zantac or one of the other similar drugs is an appropriate treatment for indigestion. If he does prescribe it, the patient will get a larger and more effective dose and will be asked to report back if the symptoms are not relieved so that the diagnosis may be reviewed and more appropriate treatment given if needed.

If a patient buys the 'over-the-counter' (OTC) equivalent of one of these products, he will be paying more. On a dose-for-dose basis, H_2-antagonists sold OTC for stomach upsets for example, cost up to three times as much as the prescribed item. An even more glaring example is the diarrhoea treatment, 'Imodium', extensively advertised on television. Purchased over-the-counter in fancy strip packs, eight 2mg capsules cost more than £3.60. When prescribed, the retail price of thirty 2mg capsules in a pharmacist's bottle is £1.22.[31,32] A lawyer might say, "I rest my case".

I find it difficult to believe that the members of the safety committees or the medical advisers employed in the Department will have willingly discarded the safeguards that prescribing, as distinct from OTC sale, affords to patients receiving potent drugs. Nor are they likely to be blind to the fact that release from prescription control reduces the patient's chance of future investigation of problems that may arise. The 'pharmaceuticalization' of medicine has trivialised some areas of patient care. I can't remember who invented this ugly word, but it describes what has happened quite well

Shortly after retiring I was honoured to receive the Distinguished Career Award for 1995 from the prestigious Drug Information Association (DIA). I was no longer mobile enough to travel to Paris to receive the award in person, so my address to the conference was recorded on video. It nevertheless gave me an opportunity to summarise the principles upon which I had developed both the independent UK monitoring schemes over thirty years.

The yellow card system and PEM have been criticised because they have not led to the *removal* of large numbers of drugs from the market. Withdrawal of a licence is often regarded as the benchmark of success, especially for people serving on government committees and civil servants. Anybody can take the easy decision to withdraw the licence for a drug but it demands courage and experience to permit a useful drug to remain on the market in spite of some risk. Critics forget that the primary objective of post-marketing surveillance is to confirm that drugs have an acceptable level of safety. It is almost as important to show that no serious hazard has been detected as it is to detect one.

I emphasised that perhaps the most important feature of both the yellow card scheme and PEM is their *independence*. The greatest mistake had been to position the yellow card system within the Licensing Authority, and the Medicines Control Agency that succeeded it. I recalled the doubts I had expressed to Sir Derrick Dunlop thirty years earlier. With the best will in the world it is not possible to serve two masters at the same time — to be loyal to a scientific committee on the one hand and the Minister-of-the-day on the other. However brilliant the scientists employed to advise and conduct research for the Department of Health, their credibility is almost always suspect when they are put on a public platform because they say what their political masters allow them to say and not necessarily what they believe to be the truth. The danger of allowing civil servants to take control was amply illustrated by the *Halcion* fiasco, the mishandling of problems with oral contraceptives, whooping cough vaccine and halothane and the failure to protect the public from covert price increases described above.

After thirty years in drug safety work I am convinced that the yellow card scheme and PEM should be brought under one roof and run independently from the Department. The two monitoring schemes are complementary. Signals raised by one method must be crosschecked with the other and both can then be used as starting points for more intensive clinical or epidemiological studies. They should be managed by a body such as the Medical Research Council and should be financed from public funds and not the drug industry. The management of the centre should report its findings directly to the MCA and to the relevant manufacturers when the centre considers that a new drug has either shown an acceptable level of safety or that it may have some unforeseen hazard that did not emerge before the licence was granted. The monitoring centre should be free to do its work and publish its findings without political interference or consideration of the possible effects of their decision on profitability or employment. Similarly the MCA should not be dependent on the industry for funding. The way in which the SAMM Guidelines were created is a symptom of the industry's influence on medical practice and practitioners at all levels.

I had learned the essential need for *transparency*. I looked back with affection to the days when the Industry co-operated because of enlightened self-interest and not because it was legally obliged to do so. After the passage of the Medicines Act, we moved into the dark ages of official 'Quangos' (quasi-autonomous governmental organizations) conducting their affairs in secret. Transparency is what I mean by freedom to communicate with professional colleagues and openness in dealing with the public and, for that matter, the politicians.

I reminded the DIA of the importance of comparing risks and benefits and that to do this it was essential to have *complete equations*. Comparison between relative risks is important (this is what PEM can do and the yellow card system cannot), but it is impossible to make sensible risk-management decisions without taking into account the *relative efficacy* (benefit) of the drugs whose risks are being compared. Only with complete equations for relative risk and the relative benefit can anybody be expected to decide if the risks are acceptable.

Finally, I repeated my intention to continue opposing promotional studies masquerading as post-marketing surveillance. They had introduced pseudo-science into an area in which it should never have been allowed to stray. Bribing doctors to change patients' treatments in order to expand a market for a new drug, especially when the patients were not volunteers, was demeaning to the profession and dangerous to patients. My greatest contribution was to uncover the covert abuse of patients that has been going on for so long. My campaign had made me unpopular with the ABPI, with some of the drug companies who adopt these unethical practices, with the Department of Health's MCA and with the secretariat of the Committee on Safety of Medicines. All of them had denied or ignored the necessity for patients to be *fully informed volunteers* when their doctors enter them into a commercial study and change their treatment. All of them knew that if patients had to give consent to such changes, promotional studies would stop because victims of adverse reactions would start to sue. I had tried to get the practice stopped through official channels. I continued to hope that the public would see that this was an abuse of their trust in doctors and would put a stop to it.

Two months after I retired, I saw a copy of a letter from ABPI addressed to my successor who had continued to request 'no-strings' support from the industry:

> 'The Medical Committee debated this at length, and the lack of development, the lack of clearly defined management succession, and of a proper business plan were all matters of concern. On balance, however, the Committee felt that the principle of supporting the DSRU should be encouraged, but not exclusively along the lines set out in your letter. It felt that support would be more likely to be forthcoming if we were able to influence the management of the Unit in some way, and it was suggested that a consultative committee might be established to bring this about. We had no confidence in the current structure and membership of your trustees.'

ABPI's Medical Director, Dr. Richard Tiner, is now one of the trustees of the Drug Safety Research Trust.

Prof Kiyoshi and Dr. Noriko Kubota

The smartest set of wheelchair ramps in the West End

19

Life in the Fast Lane

Aged sixty-five years I had completed many of the tasks that I had set myself. I had raised a family, developed both national monitoring systems, 'fathered' the mini-pill that probably saved (or rather extended) more lives than all other drug safety measures introduced over thirty years and unmasked a serious prescribing scandal that has yet to be dealt with. But I retired with three tasks uncompleted. Firstly, there is still no consensus about what risks are acceptable. Secondly, the criteria for granting a licence do not include essential data to show that there is a margin of greater efficacy of new products. Thirdly, trials without *written* consent are still permitted.

I had a lot of fun in spite of aggravation from those who had attempted to impede my work. After a long and fascinating working life it was time to write a bit, to develop old interests, to travel and to give more time to the garden and the family.... or so I planned.

I had carefully planned my retirement and the most productive way to spend my only really valuable residual asset — time itself. I chose the title for this chapter with some care. It would be life in the fast lane because time would pass too fast for comfort and there was much that I had hoped to do that would now be unattainable because of the frighteningly fast deterioration in my physical state. I had hoped to travel widely, especially in the British Isles, and to keep up-to-date with scientific discoveries outside the confines of medicine. I had not, however, anticipated the speed with which the long-term effects of nearly half a century in a wheelchair would overtake me, nor a financial disaster that has hit thousands of savers throughout the country. I began to sense the latter trouble when an elderly country gentleman in almost daily TV advertisements started telling his grandson that "it's an Equitable Life, Henry". Why, I thought, did one of Britain's oldest and most respected pension providers need to advertise for new clients on such a scale? If I had acted more promptly I could have saved half my pension fund. Now I can only grumble about the huge handouts to failed Equitable directors that I have helped to pay for; sums that are orders of magnitude larger than my whole pension fund.

June and I had to decide where to live. Our house was not ideal and the very beautiful garden increasingly difficult to maintain. On the other hand, a smaller house with exceptionally wide doors suitable for a large electric wheelchair, space for a custom-designed bathroom, a lift, storage for several wheelchairs and room for me to work would be hard to find and the only alternative would be to build. In the immediate neighbourhood we were protected from encroaching new building to a limited extent by our own three-acre field on one side, a railway embankment separated by a narrow strip of farmland on another side and established housing on the remaining sides. We were nevertheless concerned by the proliferation of superstores within a mile of our home, the approaching tidal wave of new houses, and the frequently gridlocked roads. I shall not live long enough to see the field-to-field development that will inevitably cover the whole South Coast area from Cornwall to Kent if no attempt is made to redistribute population. Why not, I dreamed, create an 'English Canberra' in the North-East, where Parliament, all government departments and all civil servants could be relocated, leaving local councils to find local solutions to local problems? The Houses of Parliament and palatial ministries could become major cultural centres. Dreams apart, we decided to stay put for the time being.

People have sometimes asked what I do to 'pass the time'. I have never passed the time; I have never been bored and have no intention of succumbing to boredom or to sit around waiting for the undertaker. I remember that several of my father's colleagues died within a year of retirement. Did they relax too much, or start activities that they were unfit for or could never hope to finish? I remember the quiet family supper on the evening my father left his office for the last time. It was interrupted by two phone calls. He politely but firmly turned down invitations to chair a Royal Commission and to head a United Nations enquiry. I was afraid he might relax too much, but he got the mixture right and lived happily for many years within the limitations imposed by the loss of most of his eyesight.

My own plans had to be drastically revised when I found that, in addition to damage to my neck from the earlier accident, I was losing mobility in several other ways. Top of the list of my problems was the Post-Polio Syndrome (PPS). My friends expect me to know a lot about the pathology of polio and seem amazed when I say that I have always been too busy to study the very disease that I was suffering from. I was therefore glad to be given what I saw as an opportunity to learn something about PPS. I was asked by the *British Medical Journal* to review '*A Summer Plague; Polio and its Survivors*' by Tony Gould.[37] Gould caught polio at the same age as I did while he was serving with the Ghurkhas in the Far East. He then went to Cambridge and became a successful author. He gave an excellent account of the history of polio and its conquest by vaccines. He also told the stories of some of the survivors including his own. Although Gould's book was detailed and well researched, I was disappointed to find little about PPS. Those of us who have survived forty or fifty years will probably all be stricken with it sooner or later. I had given little thought to the possibility that I would be faced with the certainty that much hard-won recovery of muscles paralysed during the initial attack would be lost. Five years after retiring I was slipping towards the helplessness that I had experienced for a few months after contracting polio in 1950. Little seemed to be known about PPS. Although there are post-polio clinics in most parts of the US (there is none that I am aware of in this country), there seems to be little incentive or funding for research into what may be thought of as an extinct disease. I wrote in my review that 'Nobody seems to know what to do about what has become a painful reality for us OPs ('old polios') when we become OAPs'.

Until a better explanation is found, I suspect some form of 'die-back' of the nerve fibres that had been spared in the initial attack. The effects are those of a progressive motor neurone disease, often first affecting those muscles that were the last to recover after the initial infection. Each muscle contains thousands of bundles of contractile fibres. Each bundle in turn is activated by signals from a nerve fibre called an axon. The axons have their origin in the spinal cord and are connected to the brain by other nerve cells. Let us suppose for a moment that 90% of all the bundles of contractile fibres in a particular muscle were lost and that recovery depended on the remaining 10% of the axons. Although there is some evidence that intact axons may grow new connections to inactive muscle bundles, there is no doubt that with physiotherapy and hard work the residual muscles can be strengthened considerably. By analogy with body-builders who 'pump iron' to increase the bulk and strength of their muscles, the remaining undamaged 10% of the bundles might be brought back to approach their original strength. The number of surviving bundles is not unlimited, however, and any significant further loss of axons will not be recovered. As each remaining axon ceases to function from whatever cause, the loss becomes relatively more serious. If I lose 1% of the original axons that are now doing the job of ten, I will lose 10% of my residual strength. Although electrical tests had confirmed that the sudden loss of strength in my right hand was probably a late result of the car accident, almost all movement had became restricted and I became entirely dependent on carers. I have one functioning, though weak, hand – my left hand – attached to an arm that I can no longer lift, and I am right-handed. I cannot hold a thin object such as a piece of paper between the finger and thumb of my right hand. I am no longer able to propel a manual wheelchair or lift myself even a fraction of an inch clear of a seat and have difficulty with buttons and laces.

In 1997 I voluntarily surrendered my driving licence and received a letter from the Motor Vehicle Licensing Authority thanking me and reminding me that I would no longer be permitted to drive a car! I realized that a time would come when I would no longer be able to control a car, although this was not yet my main problem. In some of my cars I pressed a switch operating a motor that pulled the passenger seat forwards under the dash. This was a procedure that always excited onlookers and would-be helpers. They are often in a dilemma when they see a disabled person or an elderly helper struggling with a wheelchair. They realize that their help is probably not needed but do not wish to appear uncaring. The disabled person on the other hand does not wish to appear ungrateful, but knows that it takes longer to explain how to dismantle a wheelchair and stow it in exactly the right position than to do the job himself. My method involved taking the right-hand wheel off my chair to reduce its width and then rolling it into the car on its left wheel. An unescorted disabled driver is usually able to handle a wheelchair without assistance. The best solution for a potential helper is a friendly wave and a "you OK?" and for the driver, when he sees someone hovering, a cheerful "Don't worry, I'm OK thanks." If the body signals fail to give the right message, he may have to accept help and possibly a delay in driving away.

Many years ago, seeing me struggling to lift a chair into the rear of the car, a lady rushed to my assistance. Ignoring my assurance that I could do it myself, she seized the folded chair and swung it through the door with such force that it wound up on the rear seat with the handles sticking through the fabric of the roof. I thanked her kindly and drove straight to the coach builders who replaced the torn roof and re-sprayed the car silver in place of its original light blue. It became an object of even more interest to bystanders in its sparkling new livery, although I kept an eye on potential Samaritans who looked fit enough to test their strength on the new fabric.

After giving up driving I bought a Renault *Kangoo* van. This is one of a number of converted vans in which the rear seats, fuel tank, spare wheel and various other features have been modified to provide access up a ramp at the rear of the vehicle. In some of the larger vans it is possible to drive from a wheelchair, but this is not possible in the Kangoo.

When I qualified as a doctor in 1956 I considered the possibility of useful employment at the spinal injuries centre at Stoke Mandeville. Sir Ludvig Guttman favoured the idea of a doctor in a wheelchair, but I was deterred by the thought that I might be used as an example of what might be achieved by a paraplegic rather than as a competitive member of his team. I tend to avoid other disabled people and have regarded my inability to walk as little more than an inconvenience. I dislike the patronising attitudes of some able-bodied who seem to regard anyone in a wheelchair as weak-minded. This often stemmed from the passive attitude of the disabled themselves. When June and I check into a hotel, the receptionist nearly always addresses June and ignores me. A waitress once asked June "Does he take sugar?" For a long time we thought this was unique until we read an article that used precisely these words as its title.

I avoid disabled people whose horizons have shrunk to arguments about their 'rights' or who make no effort to work to support themselves and wallow in the warm and comfortable environment in which everything is provided for them. Too few seemed to focus on how best to make use of such talents they may possess. Some do not share my compulsion to compete with all comers and support myself. I once started a public lecture by saying "The trouble with a lot of disabled people is that they don't pay enough tax". Jaws dropped and people in the audience looked at one another. Gradually it dawned on them that what I was saying was that the majority of disabled people do not earn enough to pay tax. As far as I am concerned, no disabled person should be satisfied until he or she is earning something to be proud of and, ideally, is able to put back into society more than has been taken out.

Because I was so busy shifting for myself, nearly fifty years passed before I became personally involved in a small way in care for the disabled rather than patients in general. I became the medical Vice-President of 'REMAP'. For those who have never heard of REMAP, I shall devote some of the remainder of this chapter to describing it. When I accepted I was not aware of REMAP's history. By a strange quirk of fate it took me back to my family background – ICI. REMAP is the acronym for *Rehabilitation Engineering Movement Advisory Panels*. It is a charity involving a large group of engineers and health care workers and I discovered that it had been started nearly fifty years ago at ICI Billingham by an engineer called Pat Johnson who had assembled a group of enthusiasts to design specialized equipment for the disabled. One of the leading lights and its first Chairman was the late Sir Geoffrey Gilbertson, at that time the Personnel Director at Billingham. Geoffrey contracted polio in the late nineteen forties. At that time my father, in addition to his work as Chairman of the Alkali Division in Cheshire, was a member of the Wilton Council, the body responsible for developing the huge new chemical complex adjacent to the factories at Billingham. He took me to meet Gilbertson in London in 1951 to seek advice about my own rehabilitation. Under Gilbertson's chairmanship REMAP had grown to incorporate sixty local panels by the time he retired in 1967. Gilbertson was succeeded by a former Deputy Chairman of ICI, Stanley Lyons, who increased the number of panels to one hundred. In 1967 REMAP merged with the British Council for Rehabilitation of the Disabled that later became part of the *Royal Association for Disability and Rehabilitation* (RADAR). As it continued to grow, however, REMAP separated from RADAR and became an independent charity in 1990. Because of differences in charity laws in Scotland a parallel organisation, REMAP (Scotland), was also formed.

REMAP's engineers work for nothing often using materials scrounged from engineering firms or scrap yards. They look for solutions to individual problems that cannot be satisfied by standard equipment purchased 'off the shelf'. REMAP is incredibly cost-effective. The notional annual value of REMAP equipment supplied free of charge to the disabled is nearly £2 million. About £1 is spent on administration and publicity for every £20's worth of end product supplied to a disabled person. About half of each panel of fifteen to twenty members are 'problem identifiers' such as occupational therapists, physiotherapists, or doctors. Half are 'problem solvers', mostly retired professional engineers and craftsmen and a few do-it-yourself enthusiasts. REMAP is a registered charity managed by a board of trustees. It has a small central office headed, until he retired recently, by John Wright, a salaried part-time National Organizer and professional engineer: John has been succeeded by Mary-Anne Mitchell. The other Vice-President, Professor Heinz Wolff, is well known for his work in bioengineering at Brunel University and for his appearances on TV in such programmes as *Young Scientist of the Year* and *Great Experiments which changed the World*. Among a number of messages that have impressed me when listening to Heinz is his theme 'tools for living'. He suggests that there is nothing very special about the word 'disabled'. A car driver caught out by a puncture in a rainstorm and who finds that someone has pinched the jack from the toolkit, is disabled. Physically disabled or not, what people need is simply *the tool for the job*.

REMAP projects have ranged from the construction of simple tools or utensils for clients with arm or hand defects, to elaborate toys and an endless variety of modifications to wheelchairs, beds, bathrooms and kitchens. REMAP provided a device for holding the bow of a one-handed violinist, a camera harness for an armless photographer and a device that enabled me to cast a trout fly and hold the line with the same hand. Unfortunately this particular gadget had only a short working life when my one good arm became too weak to cast. Much of the work of REMAP is aimed at improving the quality of life of disabled patients in their home environment. My special interest is the possibility that some of REMAP's 'clients' might be helped by equipment that could make the difference between employment and unemployment. Perhaps the most unusual example of a project in this category was a device made for a market gardener who dragged himself along the rows of plants sitting on a dinner tray. REMAP produced a three-wheeled trolley powered by a lawn-mower engine. The width of the machine corresponded exactly to the distance between the rows of plants.

In recent years, the Health and Safety Regulations have cast a shadow over the innovative work by REMAP. Sometimes they have become unnecessarily oppressive. No longer, for example, is it permitted for a wheelchair supplier to weld up a broken or cracked part. It is now a legal requirement that the part has to be replaced, sometimes at considerable expense to the customer. REMAP fitted an attachment to a wheelchair which enabled a woman to carry a baby or small child on a seat in front of her as she did her shopping This was deemed to be unsafe on the grounds that the wheelchair might tip. Of course there is always a small risk that a wheelchair will tip if mishandled. In my frustration I demanded to know what a disabled woman was supposed to do – leave the baby unattended and screaming in the car, let it wander around pulling goods off shelves or put it on a dog chain and tow it? Life is risky and would be very boring if it wasn't. Health and Safety has established thousands of 'jobs for the boys', but one must examine ludicrous recommendations such as the one that suggested that trapeze artists at the Moscow State Circus should wear crash helmets, presumably in case they miss the safety net.

I was once asked to comment on the arrangements that should be made to ensure that disabled passengers would be rescued from a sinking ship. Should the authorities insist, for example, that four members of the crew should be allocated to manhandle a wheelchair to a lifeboat? I am sure my comments were not expected or wanted. I pointed out that the paramount consideration is that other passengers must not be placed at risk because a disabled person is on board. A disabled person must recognize when he buys a ticket that, in an emergency, he will inevitably be at greater risk than an able-bodied passenger. If this is not acceptable, he should stay at home. I would hope that some kind person might wrap a lifebelt round me and toss me overboard to take my chances with the rest but I would not expect crew to be diverted from other duties in an emergency.

Once I had an argument on a Lufthanza plane bound for London. After I had been strapped into my seat and the attendants had left, the young Captain of the aircraft came into the cabin angrily complaining that he had an all-female crew and I must be disembarked and wait for another flight. "If we have an emergency you have no chance" he said. We both became heated and I said that I had been flying for years and had bought a ticket, and that in any case "with you flying, I probably have no chance anyhow, but I'm prepared to take the risk". Then we both calmed down, shook hands and I thanked him when we landed at Heathrow.

Is it reasonable for a disabled person, especially one in a wheelchair, to seriously inconvenience or endanger others purely in the pursuit of his own pleasure? I have seen a film of a bizarre struggle to haul a man in a wheelchair up a mountain in the Himalayas. I applauded the building of *Tenacious*, a full-rigged sailing ship providing facilities for the disabled, but I do not believe people in wheelchairs have any significant part to play as members of the crew of a tall ship. By all means let them experience the joys of sailing as a passenger but there is no way that a token pull on a rope or a hand on the wheel makes them crew members. During one of the early voyages of *Tenacious* there was a sudden squall and all the able-bodied crew were preoccupied securing wheelchairs on deck. Momentarily their attention was distracted and the ship nearly ran down a fishing boat that had appeared in the trough of a wave, dead ahead. I have enjoyed a number of potentially hazardous activities over the years; flying gliders, shooting, and fishing, all of them in a wheelchair and all well within my capabilities until I found that I could no longer do them safely or caused too much trouble to friends; then I gave up and found something equally interesting that I could do. Wheelchair ball games and races are fine but I draw the line at activities that put helpers at risk.

Like many retired folk enjoying time to read and reflect and keep up with current affairs I tend to fly kites and generally enjoy the role of 'Grumpy old Man'. For example, I object to the inappropriate use of language, words like 'cool', 'gay' and 'spin' and phrases starting with 'I have to say' or 'to be honest', although I suppose I should be thankful that they seem to have replaced 'sort of' and 'you know'. I am sick of 'Political Correctness'. For example, nobody can convince me that I could abandon a badly injured female soldier to the mercy of a mob during an essential tactical withdrawal from a battlefield, or expect a firewoman to carry me down a ladder. And what about the £3 million it cost to train a female pilot to fly a *Tornado*, and who immediately left the RAF to have a baby? I read about a well-run infant school that was threatened with immediate closure because an inspector examining the contents of a toy cupboard failed to find jigsaws and cloth books depicting black children (the infants at the school were all white or Asian). I delight in a glass or two of rich red wine, but I shall boycott the wines of Bordeaux until the supporters of *l'Union Nationale de defense des Chasses Tradissionelles* stop shooting migrating Turtle Doves and Song Thrushes. As an unrepentant woodpigeon shooter this may seem irrational but a significant agricultural pest cannot be compared with harmless and beautiful species that are slaughtered in thousands for the enjoyment of a small number of stupid people. The late President of the Royal Society for the Protection of Birds, Baroness Young, was sympathetic to my suggestion that, if more than a million members of the

Society were to buy their wine elsewhere, the wine growers of France might find other pastimes. Sadly, she told me that the RSPB was not able to indulge in political activities of this kind. I thought conservation *was* a matter for the attention of politicians.

Life in the fast lane has not been without incident. One day June mentioned that the Council had forgotten to distribute the liners for our dustbins that were due for emptying. She rang the Council and with astonishing speed a supply was delivered – by car! As it happened, I had just received a note from the Cabinet Office asking for suggestions for the award of 'Charter Marks', a scheme introduced by John Major to recognize good service to the public. With the bin-liners in mind and our experience of the efficiency and courtesy from the Council over the years, I proposed them for the award. Some months later, and to my intense surprise, I received an invitation from the Prime Minister to join him in Downing Street for the award ceremony! A magnificent set of metal ramps was set up on the steps of No.10, but wheelchair access to the garden, where the reception was held, involved partially dismantling my chair and descending unattended into the basement in the smallest passenger lift I have ever squeezed into and a winding journey through dusty cellars packed with cardboard boxes and bulging bundles of files tied with string. We were greeted charmingly by John Major who discussed Lord Snowdon's interest in wheelchair design that had taken me to the Royal College of Art more than twenty years earlier. Four large gin and tonics and a private viewing of the Cabinet Room completed a remarkable afternoon and June and I kept our secret that we were only there because of a packet of bin-liners.

All my life I have tried to pass on to colleagues and students the simple message that if something is worth doing it is bound to be fun. If something they were doing ceased to be fun for any reason I invited them to come and talk about it. There is a story about the physicist Albert Michelson, the first American to win a Nobel Prize and the first scientist to produce an accurate estimate of the speed of light. At the age of seventy-three he was asked why he bothered to continue experiments to obtain even more minutely accurate measurements. His reply was 'Because it is such good fun'. I know how he felt. I have had many problems but I too have had a great deal of fun over the years. I have worked and played hard. I have tried – I really have tried.

REFERENCES

1. *Oxford Dictionary of Music* 1994 2nd edition. Oxford University Press.

2. Reader, WJ. (1975) *Imperial Chemical Industries. Vol.2.The First Quarter-Century 1926-1952.* Oxford University Press.

3. Foot, MRD. (1984) *SOE An Outline History of the Special Operations Executive 1940-46.* BBC. London.

4. Hosking, EJ and Newberry, CW. (1944) *The Art of Bird Photography.* Country Life. London.

5. Knight, CWR.(1943) *All British Eagle.* Hodder & Stoughton. London.

6. Harrison, JM. (1942) *A Handlist of the Birds of the Sevenoaks or Western District of Kent.* HF & G. Witherby. London.

7. Dawkins, Richard (1989) *The Extended Phenotype.* Oxford University Press.

8. Inman of Knaresborough (1952) *No Going Back.* London. Williams & Norgate.

9. Cummins, CFA. (1961) The Flying Surgeon Service. *Medical Journal of Australia.* 341-344.

10. Willock, C. (1962) *Kenzie the Wild-Goose Man.* Andre Deutsch, London.

11. Sarkar, D.(1995) *A Few of the Many : Air war 1939-45.* Ramrod Publications.

12. Inman, WHW. (1999) *Don't Tell the Patient: Behind the Drug Safety Net.* Los Angeles.Ca. Highland Park Productions.

13. Medical Research Council (1967). Risk of Thromboembolic Disease in Women taking Oral Contraceptives. *British Medical Journal* 2, 355.

14. Inman, WHW, Adelstein, AM. (1969) The rise and fall of asthma mortality in England and Wales in relation to use of pressurised aerosols. *The Lancet* .2.279-85.

15. Inman, WHW and Mushin, WW. (1974) Jaundice after Repeated Exposure to Halothane: An Analysis of Reports to the Committee on Safety of Medicines. *British Medical Journal.* 1. 5-10.

16. Walton, B et al. (1976) Unexplained hepatitis following halothane. *British Medical Journal.* 1. 171-6.

17. National Academy of Sciences (1971). Report of the International Conference on Adverse Reactions Reporting Systems. October 22-23, 1970. Drug Research Board, National Academy of Sciences, Washington D.C.

18. Gent, M & Shigematsu, I. *Epidemiological issues in reported drug-induced illnesses.* McMaster University Library Press, Hamilton, Ontario.

19. Gross FH and Inman WHW. (1977). *Drug Monitoring.* Academic Press, London.

20. Inman WHW (ed) (1980) *Monitoring for Drug Safety.* MTP Press Ltd. Lancaster.

21. *Proceedings of the Kyoto International Conference Against Drug-Induced Sufferings.* Soda T. (ed) (1980) Excerpta Medica.

22. Inman WHW. (1981). Post-Marketing surveillance of adverse drug reactions in general practice. Part I. Search for new methods. Part II. Prescription-Event Monitoring at the University of Southampton. *British Medical Journal* 282. 1131-1132. Ibid. 1216-1217.

23. Johnson, C and Mellville A. (1982) Drugs under the Influence. *Guardian* August 2nd 1982.

24. Inman WHW. (1985) Risks of Medical Intervention, in Cooper MG.(ed) *Risk: Man-made hazards to Man.* Wolfson College 1984. Oxford University Press 1985.

25. Urquhart, J and Heilmann, K. (1984) *Risk Watch: The odds of life.* Facts in File Publications. New York NY and Bicester UK.

26. Gill, P, Scrivener, G, Lloyd, D and Dowel, A. (1995) The effect of patient ethnicity on prescribing rates. *Health Trends* 27,4,111-4.

27. Guidelines on postmarketing surveillance. Joint Committee of ABPI. BMA. CSM and RCGP.(1988). *British Medical Journal* 296,399-400.

28. House of Lords Select Committee on the European Communities (1991). *The European Medicines Agency and Future Marketing Authorisation.* Procedures. London. HMSO.

29. Abraham, J (2002). Making regulation responsive to commercial interests: streamlining drug industry watchdogs. *British Medical Journal* 325, 1164-7.

30. Knott, L. Clinical Trials: Boost Research and GP's Income. Grey, J. Planning your Profits. Dickson, J. The Trials in Real Life *Financial Pulse* October 1991.

31. Monthly Index of Medical Specialties (MIMMS) September 2000.

32. *OTC Directory 1998/99.*

33. Maslowski, HAM (1996). A new hypothesis for Sudden Infant Death Syndrome: the occlusion of vertebral arteries as a major cause. *J. Clin. Forensic Medicine.* 3. 93-98.

34. *Guidelines for Post Mortem Reports*. Royal College of Pathologists. August 1993. p.11.

35. Watkins SJ (2000) *British Medical Journal* 320, 2-3.

36. Meadow, R (2002) *British Medical Journal* 321, 41-43.

37. Gould, A. (1995) *A Summer Plague, Polio and its Survivors.* Yale University Press.

Glossary of Abbreviations

AAH	Allied Anthracite Holdings
AIDS	Acquired Immunity Deficiency Syndrome
ABPI	Association of the British Pharmaceutical Industry
ADRAC	Australian Adverse Drug Reactions Committee
ADR	Adverse drug reaction
ADROIT	Adverse Drug Reactions On-Line Information Tracking
AMAPI	Association of Medical Advisers to the Pharmaceutical Industry
APVDC	Association of Parents of Vaccine Damaged Children
ARE	Atomic Energy Research Establishment
ASLEF	Association of Locomotive Engineers and Firemen
BBC	British Broadcasting Corporation
BDC	British Dyestuffs Corporation
BGA	British Gliding Association
BMA	British Medical Association
BMJ	British Medical Journal
BNS	British Nylon Spinners
BrAPP	British Association of Pharmaceutical Physicians
BSI	British Standards Institute
CFC	Chlorofluorocarbon
CSD	Committee on Safety of Drugs
CSM	Committee on Safety of Medicines
DIA	Drug Information Association
DHSS	Department of Health and Social Security
DNA	Deoxyribose Nucleic Acid
DSRU	Drug Safety Research Unit
ECG	Electrocardiograph

EMS	Emergency Medical Services
FHSA	Family Health Service Authority
FAI	Fédération Aéronautique Internationale
FDA	Food & Drug Administration
GMC	General Medical Council
GMSC	General Medical Services Committee (of BMA)
GP	General Practitioner
GPI	General Paralysis of the Insane
GRO	General Registry Office
HAT	Handicapped Anglers Trust
HMS	Her Majesty's Ship
ICI	Imperial Chemical Industries
ICP	Imperial Chemical Pharmaceuticals
IMS	Intercontinental Medical Statistics Ltd
INCA	Integrated Network for Computer Administration
JCVI	Joint Committee for Vaccination and Immunization
JTC	Junior Training Corps
KICADIS	Kyoto International Conference Against Drug Induced Suffering
M&B	May & Baker
MCA	Medicines Control Agency (Now Medicines and Healthcare Products Regulatory Agency (MHRA))
MGC	Midland Gliding Club
MHRA	Medicines and Healthcare Products Regulatory Agency
MRC	Medical Research Council
NHS	National Health Service
NICE	National Centre for Clinical Excellence

OAP	Old Age Pensioner
OT	Occupational Therapist
OTC	Officer Training Corps
OTC	'Over the Counter' drug
PEM	Prescription-Event Monitoring
PIAT	Projector Infantry Anti-Tank
PMO	Principal Medical Officer
PMS	Post-Marketing Surveillance (of Drugs)
PPA	Prescription Pricing Authority
PPS	Post-polio syndrome
PQ	Parliamentary question
QC	Queen's Counsel
RAF	Royal Air Force
RCGP	Royal College of General Practitioners
REMAP	Rehabilitation Engineering Movement Advisory Panels
ROSPA	Royal Society for the Prevention of Accidents
RSM	Royal Society of Medicine
SAMM	Safety Assessment of Marketed Medicines
SARS	Severe Acute Respiratory Syndrome
SD	Steam Drifter
SMO	Senior Medical Officer
SMON	Subacute Myeloptic Neuropathy
SOE	Special Operations Executive
UAC	United Alkali Company
VAMP	Value Added Medical Products
WHO	World Health Organization

Index